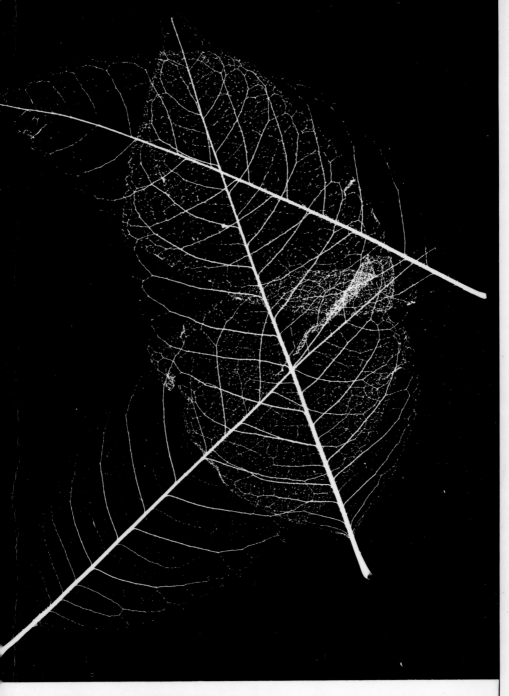

ONTEMPORARY BOUGHEY
READINGS IN
ECOLOGY

CONTEMPORARY
READINGS
IN
ECOLOGY

CONTEMPORARY READINGS IN ECOLOGY

ARTHUR S. BOUGHEY
UNIVERSITY OF
CALIFORNIA, IRVINE

DICKENSON PUBLISHING COMPANY, INC.
BELMONT, CALIFORNIA

CONTENTS

PREFACE

In the last decade, ecology may be considered to have finally come of age. While molecular biologists have been working brilliantly to unravel the genetic code, and biochemists and physiologists have been revealing the complex pathways of energy transfer in individual organisms, ecologists have at last succeeded in unifying into a single discipline the study of the three levels of biological organization beyond those of the cell and the individual organism: *population, community,* and *ecosystem.* The diverse and previously uncoordinated efforts of the taxonomist, the population geneticist, the population and physiological ecologists, the community and statistical ecologists, and the human ecologist have finally come to assume a common meaning and a single purpose. They emerge as different but related approaches to the study of the structure and function of the ecosystem, which is the very essence of modern ecology.

At the same time, the remaining tasks of ecology have also begun to emerge. The concept of the population must be critically reexamined and concisely defined. The nature of population regulation must be completely explained, as must that of the association between species populations, both as regards individual relationships, such parasitism and mutualism, and associations of populations, such as communities and continua. Productivity and cycling in ecosystems, especially terrestrial ones, remain only partially understood. So do the relationships among the populations encountered in these ecosystems. We are just beginning to reach for criteria and techniques that will provide us with information as to how social or *ethological* information, as well as genetical information, is circulated among these species populations, and how social characters adapt under changing selection pressures. Finally, we are now at last examining the population ecology of our own species and our interaction with the environment.

Ecology in its contemporary understanding has thus come to embrace a variety of fields commonly identified as physiological ecology, evolutionary ecology, population ecology, community ecology, human ecology, paleoecology, statistical ecology, ethology, taxonomy, and bioenergetics. As ecology integrates, so the distinctions among these several areas tend to disappear, and it becomes more difficult to work in one field without reference to the others. Nevertheless most workers, and therefore most research, are preforce confined to only a segment of this broad field.

This collection of readings has been grouped under four main headings— *Taxonomy, Evolutionary Ecology, Population Ecology,* and *Community Ecology.* This is not to imply that ecology should be, or currently is, divided up in a like manner. Some taxonomists, of course, would also describe themselves as working on problems of evolutionary ecology, and a number of population ecologists would relate their work also to community ecology. Nevertheless, if we regard contemporary ecology as dealing with the three higher levels of biological organization, the grouping of these readings under four sections becomes rational. Taxonomy deals with the circumscription and classification of the population level, evolutionary ecology with the development of each population entity, and population ecology in its broadest meaning with characteristics and behavior at this level. Community ecology relates to the association of populations at the two levels of organization of communities and ecosystems.

The twenty-two papers reproduced here are by no means an exclusive selection. It would be possible to arrive at a substantially different choice and still faithfully represent contemporary trends in ecology. However, each paper has been carefully selected as depicting a trend within the context of one of the four major areas previously mentioned. The ideas presented in each paper have helped to establish a new concept or to challenge an old one. The direction that ecology will take will be strongly influenced by the conclusions of these works, and an understanding of the challenges to which their authors are endeavoring to respond will provide the reader with an insight into the numerous and fundamental problems that still face this essentially new science of ecology.

A.S.B.

Irvine, California

1

Taxonomy

The basic unit of ecology is the species population. It is the entity that has been adapted by modification of its gene frequencies to a particular ecological niche, that interacts with other populations in the same habitat, and that plays a unique role, albeit of varying importance, in the processes of energy transfer in the ecosystems of that habitat.

By traditional taxonomic definition, species populations have been circumscribed solely on a morphological basis. Although this has long been recognized as quite inadequate, it is nevertheless the basis on which the great majority of the plant and animal species recognized today have been established. The continuing use of such taxonomic species would be unacceptable, were it not that in many cases the judgment of experienced taxonomists has selected as diagnostic criteria characters that in fact are determined by alleles represented in one population only. What traditional taxonomists have in fact generally achieved, although they did not set out to do so, is the demarcation of *genetical discontinuities* by the selection of a few key morphological characters.

Biosystematists have explored the breeding behavior and isolating mechanisms of numerous genetical species, and have even suggested a separate terminology, the *deme* system, for these populations. For the classical biosystematist, such genetical species are epitomized in the *biological species concept.* Askell Löve describes this concept in the first paper of this section. Dr. Löve is a biosystematist of very wide experience in boreal and arctic regions, who has published many papers dealing with the biosystematics and cytotaxonomy of the plants of these areas. Although he is essentially a botanist, the biological species concept as he describes it applies equally to animals. References in his paper to the work of such distinguished zoologists as T. Dobzhansky, J. Huxley, and E. Mayr underline the fact that any species concept should be applicable to all living organisms.

The paper by G. W. Gillett on *Phacelia sericea* has been included to illustrate the difficulties that may be encountered when applying the biological species concept to an interspecific variation pattern, and the impossibility of employing morphological diagnosis in some instances. When in hybrid populations the

1

many recombinants are subjected to selection over an extensive and varied mosaic of habitats, the results of adaptation defy classification.

The possibility of sorting such complex interrelationships by chemotaxonomy is discussed by D. Boulter, D. A. Thurman, and B. L. Turner, who based their discussion on work carried out in the Hartley Botanical Laboratories in Liverpool University, England. These authors consider that if polymorphism in respect of given enzymes or enzyme systems can be demonstrated in this way, such techniques can be used to detect hybridization and introgression in populations.

The fourth paper in this section is by the late R. E. Alston, who was long associated with studies of hybridization in the genus *Baptisia* by more traditional morphological and genetical methods. He concluded that eventually it should be possible to analyze such populational structure more effectively by chemical than by morphological criteria.

The last paper in this section is by R. R. Sokal and P. H. A. Sneath, who published jointly, in 1963, their text *Principles of Numerical Taxonomy,* which brought together for the first time the several trends that had been developing away from classical morphological taxonomy and toward a more rational system. Numerical taxonomy is an entirely new approach insofar as it insists on the circumscription of taxa by a complex of many characters of equal weighting. The selection of a few "good" characters is not permitted. In this insistence on a multitude of characters—morphological, cytological, chemical, and the like—numerical taxonomy is delimiting, in many instances, no more and no less than biological species populations as defined by Dr. Löve. However, numerical taxonomy does more than this. By utilizing the concept of the "phenon," which is a unit expressing taxonomic relationships of varying degrees of similarity, the difficulties inherent in the use of taxa such as species and genera are largely avoided. As Sokal and Sneath have expounded numerical taxonomy, they have made it possible to detect rapidly, using data processing methods, a discontinuity between populations that can be defined in terms of the nature of this discontinuity. It is the demonstration of discontinuities which will permit the construction of systematic classificatory systems. There is as already noted, a present tendency to refute the concept of the biological species, on the grounds that all such aggregates as so defined, when investigated, have been found to be freely interbreeding with other groups. Possibly with the development of numerical taxonomy we are finally nearing the achievement of the omega stage that Turrill some years ago envisaged as the ultimate taxonomy. In the important statement reproduced here, Sokal and Sneath look forward to the various effects that the extended use of numerical taxonomy will have on systematics, and therefore on ecology.

Askell Löve

The Biological Species Concept and Its Evolutionary Structure

Biology started as taxonomy, and it may well be said to be as old as human thought. In a sense taxonomy may perhaps be regarded as having originated with reacting organisms, since even the lowest of biota respond differently to a varied environment and effectively order their own world. It is but reasonable to expect that such an ancient and universal activity, vital to the most primitive tribes and the most advanced scientists alike, should have developed into a precise and undisputed technique. It may, therefore, be astonishing that it still is not uncommon for different students of the same material to arrive at altogether different classifications, and these may at times seem to be evaluated more by the reputations of their authors than on their approximation to reality. One of the reasons for this is probably the fact that even truly observational science has not yet reached more than a fraction of the biota of the world, and very many of those who work in the field of taxonomy are still confined to the basic ideas of pre-Darwinian thinking. Because of several seemingly unsurmountable difficulties, empirical studies still predominate with their inevitable tendency towards authoritarianism.

It must necessarily be realized that the method of approach to any scientific problem is of marked importance, and will have great effects on the type of discovery made. Or, to put the matter the other way round, the method of approach is itself largely ruled by the kind of answer one anticipates; it is, actually, also a kind of a question. In addition, time and the advance of knowledge in each particular field are likely to change the question in such a way that, when one method has provided the main crop of answers that it could be expected to yield, then it is time to ask another kind of question by adopting a new approach.

This is just what has happened in the field of taxonomy, where the original and basic approach is inevitably descriptive, because biologists set out to describe as fully and accurately as possible the variety of organisms and the phenomena which they display. This approach is designed to answer the question about what are the facts; though it needs categories as do all kinds of studies, these are arbitrarily chosen and hardly need to be more closely de-

Reprinted by permission of the author and publisher from *Taxon, 13:* 33–44, 1964.

fined. This long-lasting phase of biological science was initiated by the ancient Greeks; it was but natural that they based their classification of all objects on a single philosophical system, because they did not realize the difference in origin and development of living beings and dead materia. All natural objects were grouped by the distinctions of their morphological characters, which were regarded as unalterable entities distinguishable by complete and equally important discontinuities and characterized by qualities of similar significance, as are chemicals and stones. This concept was, thus, purely typological.

The descriptive approach must inevitably be supplemented by the comparative. This is first centered around the question of more advanced grouping or classification, because we need to know what pattern an aggregate of biota has in common, and what distinct types there are at various levels of characterization. This leads to classification of organisms in a hierarchical system of categories which have to be more or less clearly defined, although some degree of arbitrariness can easily be tolerated. The result of this approach in the field of biology was the acceptance of the so-called rational classifications, or systems closely connected with the object to be classified.

The basic categories to be used were, however, vaguely conceived and their circumscription was clearly based on the acceptance of the typological concept, or perhaps rather of its variant, the morphological concept, as is obvious in the works of Linnaeus and his successors. Nevertheless, it was the important work based on this approach and these concepts that led to the discovery and later acceptance of the theory of evolution.

Implicit in such a system is the idea of biological relationship. With the acceptance of the theory of evolution, this implicit postulate becomes explicit, and the question asked by the comparative method must become similarly altered, because behind common resemblances we must reach for common ancestry. The result of this is a phylogenetic classification, or a grouping intended to express evolutionary descent and relationships, and for this classification the definition and delimitation of at least the main categories is evidently important. When the great evolutionary significance of the category of species at last had been established, the replacement of the typological concept, which in the living world had become a misconception, and also of its variant, the purely morphological concept, might seem to have become a necessity, because an evolutionary approach requires an evolutionary concept. As a matter of fact, such a concept had already been defined by De Candolle (1813) when he claimed that a species is "la collection de tous les individus que se ressemblent plus entr'eux qu'ils ne resemblent à d'autres; qui peuvent, par une fécondation reciproque, produire des individus fertiles; et qui se reproduisent par la génération, de telle sorte qu'on peut par analogie les supposer tous sortis originairement d'un seul individu." Though this is a definition considering basic properties of the species in an evolutionary system, it has several disadvantages that are perhaps nowhere more evident than in the fact that it and numerous genetical species concepts proposed since have still not been able to extirpate the purely morphological idea as the basic concept of most taxonomists concerned with species description *per se*. Also, it is a confusion of the vaguely defined morphological concept and the theory of evolution that resulted in the absurd splitting of natural species into geographically defined taxa regarded to belong to this level by the followers of Wettstein and Komarov (cf. Juzepszuk, 1958), an idea which, if applied to the human species, would result in the splitting of mankind into even more "species" than the major races now recognized.

The comparative method in conjunction with the theory of evolution requires a new procedure, an approach which is best termed differential analysis. This seeks to clarify the major question about the causes of differences between the members of a related group and also between the related groups themselves. This, in fact, is the modern method of cytogenetics, making analyses after hybridization and studying the mechanism of cell division, and it forms one of the main pillars of what we term biosystematics. It is firmly associated with studies of the interrelationships and total pattern of each system of detectable components and the history of evolutionary divergence and its causes. It goes without saying that this treatment requires exact definition of its basic categories, since it sees in them important evolutionary steps that are repeated endlessly by all kinds of organisms. It is from this approach that we have been able to conclude not only that the category of species is a biological phenomenon of utmost significance, but also that the ability of this category to be sympatric to other related taxa of the same group without mixing coincides with the stage of evolution when a major genetical system becomes closed and loses its ability to interbreed and fuse with other such systems. It is true that good species are sometimes able to hybridize, but, if they are biologically sound, then their inherent reproductive barriers are likely to disturb the processes of interbreeding so radically that they effectively prevent miscibility. It is miscibility, not crossability, which is evolutionarily important. These genetical observations have added strength to the evolutionary ideas of classification below the generic level. As a result the idea of the species as the most important step in the evolution of barriers to genetical miscibility has been much clarified. However, by what looks like the irony of fate, at the same time the hope for a cytogenetical background for a phylogenetic system of plant classification including higher levels has faded away, because even cytological observations seem to be of a secondary and insecure value above the level of genus (cf. Constance, 1963; Löve, 1963); the scanty paleological evidence is still the only safe basis for general phylogenetic considerations. The idea of species, on the contrary, has been transformed into what we prefer to term the biological species concept. It emerged gradually and has been defined and redefined by many, whereas the most simple and clear definition was proposed by Mayr (1940) who regarded this species as "groups of actually or potentially interbreeding natural populations which are reproductively isolated from other such groups." The avoidance of all reference to morphological characters is significant.

It is an almost general claim by taxonomists who work on the basis of morphological or other quasi-typographical concepts, and also by cytogeneticists reluctant to escape the dominance of their education, which was based on these concepts, that species are of so many kinds that several definitions would not suffice (cf. Davis and Heywood, 1963). This is a misconception that proves the necessity of the biological species concept, and it seems to be caused by disregard of the fact that "to be a different species is not a matter of difference but of distinctness" (Mayr, 1963). The biological species concept is the only such definition that is universal and equally applicable to all biota, be they human, fishes or birds, mosses or angiosperms, or even bacteria, and, by proper inference from characters other than reproduction, even for taxa the sexuality of which has been replaced by apomixis (cf. Löve, 1960).

Another important discovery made by the aid of the cytogenetical approach is that races within a species—be they classified as subspecies, varieties, ecotypes, demes, or something else—are genetically open population systems with at least a potential ability for effective interbreeding that will certainly remove their distinctive identity by mixing whenever they can hybridize freely. They are Mendelian populations, which may differ in as little as a single gene, though more frequently they deviate in a number of hereditary traits, either visible and thus useful to the taxonomist, or invisible and determining physiological characters that can only be studied experimentally. Studies on numerous animals and plants have revealed that the differential traits of subspecific units are connected with all kinds of genetical distinctions, like a number of single gene mutations, multiple alleles and, perhaps most frequently, polygenes. The development of these subspecific or intraspecific traits has been shown to have progressed through the three basic processes of neo-Darwinian evolution: gene mutations, genetic recombination and natural selection. This discovery may seem to explain the futility of using morphological characters as a basis for definitions of species; but when such traits have become fixed by reproductive isolation and changed or added to by further evolution, they become most useful tools in distinguishing the genetically closed species systems.

It has been emphasized by Stebbins (1959) that gene mutations do not direct the course of evolution, nor do they provide the immediate source of variation on which natural selection acts. They rather replenish the gene pool, substitute for genes that are being lost by natural selection, and then become reshuffled into adaptive gene blocks by means of the processes of recombination.

The dynamism of the processes of subspeciation varies widely. They are thought to be highly effective in subtropical areas and especially in arid regions in the south (Stebbins, 1949). The so-called polymorphism in the more or less xeromorphic plants of New Zealand seems to be an example of wide subspeciation which may be breaking down again through hybridization, perhaps affected by ecological changes induced by human activities, as recently emphasized by Rattenbury (1962). The variations of the Mediterranean and southern North American taxa of *Platanus* and *Quercus* are apparently mainly subspecific, though jealous taxonomists have often split them into narrowly limited so-called species. These subspecific processes may also be responsible for the unwieldy variation in some groups of plants in tropical regions, particularly in the Pacific islands where geographical isolation and an equitable climate seem to favour vivid subspeciation, and they must inevitably aid in fixing certain traits within each isolate, especially in these climatically agreeable regions where diploidy is likely to be predominant among herbs. In the cold deserts of the northlands, however, subspeciation appears to be extremely limited and slow and, thus, even old and isolated islands here are not characterized by a high degree of endemic morphological traits. It is possible that this slowness of subspeciation in the Arctic may be caused by the fact that the effects of the genetical processes of evolution are markedly slowed down in perennial polyploids, in which these floras are particularly rich.

In some laboratory animals, and plants studied experimentally, distinct subspecific changes are observed after some generations of selective treatment. Cultivated plants and domesticated animals are good examples of relatively fast and drastic subspeciation. The human species itself, with its endless multitude of geographically more or less distinct variations at different subspecific and varietal levels, is also one of the best examples we know of rapid stabilization of various genetical traits by the aid of selection, isolation, and repeated hybridization. One of the many recently studied examples of rapid evolution in plants is an exception to the rule of the rarity of this kind of process in polyploid perennials of the northlands, since it comes from the Scandinavian-Icelandic species *Papaver nordhagenianum,* a decaploid and perennial alpine-arctic poppy with distinct morphological variations, studied mainly by Knaben (1959a, b) and somewhat by Löve (1955, 1962a, b). Within this species there are at least two distinct levels of subspeciation, one of which, classified as subspecies by the present writer, seems to have been formed not later than during the last Interglacial and possibly earlier, whereas within these taxa occur a number of different races, classified as varieties, which may have evolved in small isolates in the Scandinavian and Icelandic mountains during the perhaps 10,000 years that have elapsed since the last Pleistocene glaciers retreated.

Other species have evolved their morphological subspecific traits more slowly. There is a gentle gradation from the examples above to cases of no observable changes at all for 80 million years, as in the American *Opossum* (cf. Dobzhansky, 1951). Biogeographers know of numerous cases in plants, populations of which have been geographically isolated for perhaps millions of generations on islands, or even continents, without a conceivable morphological divergence. An example of this is the rare moss species *Bryoxiphium norvegicum* (Löve and Löve, 1953; Löve, 1964) known from scattered localities in high-arctic northeastern Greenland, Iceland, a limited unglaciated area mainly south of the Great Lakes in North America, Mexico, a locality on Mount Rainier, and two places in Alaska. In all these localities it shows so little variation that specialists cannot distinguish specimens with certainty without information about their origin, whereas Asiatic and Madeiran material differs somewhat af the subspecific level. In Iceland this species may even be a relic from the Tertiary-mesophytic flora which reached that region from the west about 60 million years ago (cf. Löve, 1963b, 1964). Another good example of a somewhat more recent isolation without any trace of subspeciation is *Carex scirpoidea,* which is widespread in North America but known only from a single locality in northern Norway where it has survived at least the last Pleistocene glaciation (Gjærevoll, 1963); and as a third one may quote the arctic circumpolar and very disjunct populations of the octoploid *Acetosella graminifolia* (Löve, 1943). One of the most significant cases of slow subspeciation seems to be the section *Cerastes* of the genus *Ceanothus,* recently studied by Nobs (1963), who showed that the taxa of this section usually classified as species on the basis of their morphological distinctness are in fact biological ecotypes, or races at some subspecific levels, which have been unable to create a reproductive barrier since the Miocene, or during at least 25 million years. To the same group of slowly evolving taxa without detectable reproductive barriers, other than geographical isolation, belong the two taxa of *Platanus* classified as species by Linnaeus and others, several of the European and American so-called species of some Amentiferae, and a number of other groups on both sides of the North Atlantic the distribution and close relationships of which seem strongly to support the hypothesis of continental drift.

The processes of subspeciation have been thoroughly studied in laboratories and experiments by geneticists, as amply reviewed in the classical works by Dobzhansky (1951) and Clausen (1951, 1959). From these studies "it cannot be emphasized too strongly that the population is ultimately the key to every evolutionary problem" (Mayr, 1963), since even the evolutionary opportunities of incipient species and taxa that later become isolated from older groups are based on the gene pool which was first combined and tried out in small populations. However, little has been done so far to find an explanation of the different speed and efficacy of subspecific processes. None of the explanations so far ventured seems to be biogeographically fully convincing. Since the methods of genecology used by Turesson, Gregor, Clausen, Keck and Hiesey, and others, and also the methods of population genetics as applied by Fisher and Sewall Wright and their schools, have satisfactorily clarified many of the problems of the rapidly evolving races, it is likely that concentrated efforts using similar methods will also solve the riddle of the apparently almost unbelievably slow morphological evolution of the extremely rigid species.

According to a still generally accepted view, the same processes as cause subspecific and morphological variability also lead to speciation and the evolution of genera and families. This would mean that subspecies are incipient species, as believed by Darwin, who postulated the gradual change of one species into another by aid of additive changes of populations into geographical varieties, through major geographical races up to the species level. Certainly, morphological differences between species have been formed by the same processes as produce subspecific variations, since gene mutations, genetic recombination, and natural selection continue to act within taxa at all levels.

However, there seem to be ample reasons to believe with Goldschmidt (1940) that the genically determined processes causing intraspecific variability do not necessarily lead to speciation, or to the reproductive isolation of the genetically closed systems we name species. They seem rather to be a kind of a blind alley carrying the species no further than to subspecific development and increased adaptation to diverse ecological conditions that ultimately may lead to extinction, though at the same time they form the paramount gene pool which determines the success of species and higher categories, if or when these are formed. As repeatedly pointed out by geneticists, most recently by Dobzhansky (1963) and Mayr (1963), a subspecies is an incipient species only insofar as an emergence of reproductive isolation between such genetic systems may give it a specific status, since reproductive isolation alone constitutes the effective closing of the breeding system at this level, actually or potentially. Our present knowledge does not exclude the possibility that such a barrier to reproduction could be formed by genetic changes of a similar kind and occurring parallel to those causing microevolution or subspeciation, if it affects some kinds of sterility genes, though we know of no safe example indicating that such genes have accumulated into a distinct and unsurmountable reproductive isolation. Even the case of the South American *Drosophila paulistorum* of the superhumid tropical forests, recently studied by Ehrman (1960, 1962), that Dobzhansky (1963) suggests may be "the missing link" in this chain, is still too obscure to be convincing, because it is still not impossible that the sterility genes observed in certain races of this species may prove to be comparable to the S-genes in plants and certain kinds of maternal effects resulting only in partial sterility of limited significance though perhaps subspecifically important. In all other cases so far studied there seems to be no observable correlation whatsoever between the processes of subspeciation, or the genetic changes which make races and species visibly and physiologically different, and the mechanisms which produce distinct reproductive isolation by means of hybrid sterility. This was originally demonstrated by Müntzing (1930) for *Galeopsis* and has later been substantiated by several others studying various genera of plants and animals (cf. Vickery, 1959). It is another matter that certain of the processes of speciation, like chromosomal rearrangements that result in partial sterility, begin already within the species and may proceed parallel to the subspeciation processes and even further them by the aid of partial sterility and the formation of irreversible gene blocks.

The processes leading to reproductive isolation are the processes of speciation in the strict sense. As defined by geneticists and especially by Mayr (1942, 1963), this term includes all those differences which prevent two populations from exchanging genes through the formation of fertile or, perhaps, partially sterile hybrids, actually or potentially. This kind of isolation ought not to be confused with isolation caused by marked differences in occurrence in space, in ecological preferences, in seasons of flowering, or in pollination mechanisms, since the latter are of a different nature and comparable to spatial or social isolation between human beings. Extensive cytotaxonomical research has shown that reproductive isolation is brought into being either by changes in the genetical arrangement within the chromosomes, or simply by changes in their number. The former process has fittingly been named gradual speciation by Huxley (1942) and Valentine (1949, 1963), whereas the latter has been termed abrupt speciation.

The processes of gradual speciation are complex and wear many guises, but they are always due to a variety of changes that lead to hybrid inviability, sterility and, finally, incompatibility, without affecting the chromosome number. As far as is known, they are caused by a number of inversions, segmental interchanges, and other chromosomal rearrangements, which prevent or interrupt chromosome pairing in hybrids. It is apparent from the extensive studies by Dobzhansky and his collaborators working with various species of *Drosophila*—the only organism which has so far been thoroughly studied from this point of view—that these changes tend to be additive. Inversions occur within every plant and animal species so far closely studied, sometimes even in considerable number, as has been reported though not yet thoroughly verified in *Paris quadrifolia* by Geitler (1937, 1938), and it looks, at least in some plants, as if many of these soon will be rejected because of selective inferiority. But if they survive and show a selective superiority or neutrality then they are slowly joined by aid of hybridization, whereas new alterations within the same chromosomes add to their effect on chromosome pairing until this has reached the degree of an effective barrier to genetic exchange. These changes are, naturally, irreversible at all stages. As pointed out by Dobzhansky (1963) for *Drosophila* and also clearly manifested in the diploid races of *Rumex* and dioecious *Acetosa* studied by the present writer (unpublished), natural selection seems to perfect the reproductive isolation of karyotype races more quickly in sympatric populations where hybridization is frequent than in allopatric races where exchange of chromosomes is prevented by geographical isolation. This seems also to have been the case in the evolution of *Clarkia franciscana* and some related species studied by Lewis and Raven (1958), who suggested that they may have originated "as a consequence of rapid reorganization of the chromosomes due to the presence, at some time, of a genotype conducive to extensive chromosome breakage". If these observations can be further substantiated from other organisms, they perhaps indicate that, though the effects of geographical isolation on the processes of subspeciation are considerable, its effects on the processes of speciation may be negligible, contrary to common belief. It goes without saying that geographical isolation, preventing genetic exchange and collecting and keeping independently produced chromosomal rearrangements, must inevitably, in the long run, result in speciation, as indicated by the floras of many islands that have been isolated for a long period of time. But the speed of this kind of evolution seems to be considerably slower than often surmised (cf. Skottsberg, 1938), and extinction of intermediates may be more effective in producing apparent distinction than the development of the real reproductive barriers themselves.

It is obvious that morphologically indistinguishable populations harbouring successful homozygotic combinations of a number of chromosomal recombinations of selective value may, in fact, have a better claim to be regarded as incipient species than have morphologically distinct subspecies without such chromosomal rearrangements. The limit between that kind of intraspecific sterility which is caused by chromosome changes and effective reproductive isolation is not sharp, and is often difficult to define; in some groups a few effective chromosomal rearrangements may result in a complete barrier to gene exchange, whereas in other groups, like the Onagraceae and *Paris,* many translocations and numerous inversions can apparently be tolerated without putting such a barrier into effect. Without going further into details of our still much too great ignorance of the development of this kind of isolation in plants, we can conclude that gradual and additive chromosomal rearrangements supported by hybridization and guided by natural selection seem to form by far the most important process by which reproductive isolation is being built up in most plant groups. Taxonomists have recognized this kind of isolation by means of morphological discontinuities, which are soon created by the ordinary processes of subspeciation and extinction of intermediates in such groups, and also by the fact that taxa having reached reproductive isolation are able to occur sympatrically without mixing, even when they do not reproduce by apomixis or autogamy. Nevertheless, it ought to be emphasized that gradual speciation is a slow and erratic process with irregular manifestation; it is in great need of considerably more attention by plant biosystematists having the ingenuity, patience and facilities to design and carry out suitable experiments with appropriate material.

The other process of speciation is the abrupt and instantaneous creation of a very effective barrier to reproductive miscibility by means of changes in the number of chromosomes. This may happen by alterations in the basic number through certain kinds of segmental interchanges or by a loss of a chromosome pair. In the families Cyperaceae and Juncaceae and in certain lower plants and insects this can also happen by the very special and still too little understood process of agmatoploidy, in which an increase in chromosome number occurs without an increase in chromosome matter, because the chromosomes are polycentric and can be broken into several pieces that still function. Most frequently, however, the abrupt creation of a reproductive barrier is connected with polyploidy, or the duplication of an entire chromosome set of an individual. This process is considerably less complex than gradual speciation and so it has been observed intensely and in greater detail.

Studies on chromosome numbers of at least the higher plants indicate that polyploidy is one of the major trends of evolution, though its frequency and importance varies considerably in different groups. It may even be claimed to be *the* major factor of evolution, if we consider that the protokaryotype is likely to have been based on a single chromosome pair and that even the higher plants started with only two chromosomes, as recently argued by Satô (1962). For practical considerations, however, it is convenient to limit the term to the cases in which differences in the chromosome numbers within a genus or a related group indicate that some of the species have been abruptly formed from the others. Recent estimates indicate that polyploidy occurs in about 30% of the dicotyledons, 50% of the monocotyledons, and more than 90% of the pteridophytes that now cover the earth, whereas some groups, like the Selaginellaceae, the gymnosperms, and the Annonaceae, have hardly any polyploids.

In this connection it may be appropriate to add a few words about the frequency of polyploids in different regions, since it has long been known that polyploids are more frequent in northern or alpine locations than they are in more moderate climates. When this was first pointed out, by Hagerup (1932), it was supposed to be caused by a higher frequency of formation of polyploids under extreme conditions. Phytogeographical observations, however, proved this to be a fallacy, since the distribution of most species of northern polyploids indicates that they are ancient and may have been well-established long before the formation of the climatical conditions under which they live at present. Several explanations of the increased frequency of polyploids with an increase in latitude or in the extremes of climate have been ventured in recent decades. An opinion expressed by Stebbins (1950) and supported by Reese (1961) and others, suggests that the increased frequency of polyploids towards the north is caused by the supposedly greater ability of polyploids than of diploids to invade areas newly laid bare, in this case the regions of northern Europe from which glaciers retreated some 10,000 years ago. This explanation seems, however, to be amply contradicted by the fact that the time since the ice retreated from northernmost Scandinavia is more than sufficient for the dispersal to that region and later stabilization of every species of higher plants met with in the unglaciated parts of Central Europe. It is also in conflict with the detailed studies of weeds recently made by Mulligan (1960), since he was unable to demonstrate any superiority of polyploids in invading open areas frequented by such plants. Above all, it is refuted by the fact that the frequency of polyploids in the northlands is highest on subarctic and arctic islands with a high percentage of glacial survivors, whereas recent invaders to these countries show a distinctly lower frequency of polyploids (cf. Löve and Löve, 1949, 1957, 1964; Löve, 1953, 1959). The only geobotanically and evolutionarily valid explanation of this phenomenon seems to be that of the selective superiority of polyploids based on their greater genetical variability, as proposed by Melchers (1946) and supported by Löve and Löve (1949) in connection with their critical review of the geobotanical significance of polyploidy. That explanation easily accounts for the apparently greater resistance to the environment shown in the occurrence of many polyploids in old floras that have had to survive the extreme conditions of the Pleistocene glaciations in the northlands, where only the selectively strongest could persist. It also explains the high frequency of polyploids among the now relic pteridophytes of which the diploids and lower polyploids seem to have been selectively weakest. And, finally, this is also the most plausible explanation of the recent finding by Mangenot and Mangenot

(1962) that the tropical African flora is characterized by a very high frequency of ancient polyploids, with $n = 11$ and 12, the diploid ancestors of which have long since succumbed to the rigid selection in these regions, where the species number is extremely high at the same time as each species is extremely infrequent (cf. Dobzhansky, 1950).

It has been understood for a long time that the abruptly formed barriers create a very effective reproductive isolation. In many cases a complete incompatibility is met with between diploids and tetraploids, whereas this barrier is usually weakened between higher levels of polyploidy and, thus, increases again the possibility of crossability (cf. Bernström, 1953). Since even such hybrids are more or less unable to give rise to strong and constant offspring, this kind of increased crossability does not impair the argument of polyploidy differences as a highly effective preventive to genetical miscibility.

It has been implied that abrupt speciation is the continuation of hybridization, since by far the highest number of successful polyploids undoubtedly have originated from hybrids. However, this is an argument to be taken with a grain of salt, because polyploids are most frequently formed by a duplication of the chromosome number of nonhybrid individuals of a normal population. Since such polyploids are, however, rarely successful, this does not invalidate the claim of the effect of hybridization on the survival ability of polyploids.

When polyploidy first became recognized as a speciation process, scientists were of the opinion that it in fact involved two typical and very different patterns, which were termed autopolyploidy and allopolyploidy by Kihara and Ono (1926). In the first instance, a single diploid population is visualized as giving rise to a taxon with the doubled chromosome number. This taxon is supposed to be very similar to the original population, though it is isolated from it reproductively and may have different adaptive properties caused by the difference in chromosome number alone. Formation of multivalents at meiosis was, and still is, regarded as a good indication of autoploidy, and even old and well established polyploids seem to be able to stand this disadvantage and compete successfully with other plants. Though the original polyploid was supposed to be morphologically very close to its diploid parental strain, further evolutionary divergence by aid of the subspeciation processes of gene mutations, recombination, and natural selection was assumed to take place to create morphological distinctions for the new species.

The alternative type of pattern is that of the rare and difficult hybridization between two species which are so widely distinct that their chromosomes are almost completely non-homologous and cannot pair, so that the hybrid is completely sterile. Its polyploid product, then, is a constant alloploid, combining the morphological and physiological characters of the parent species, and with essentially the meiotic properties of a diploid, no multivalent formation, and no sterility.

Studies of polyploids in the past two or three decades have revealed that situations intermediate between the two classical type patterns are considerably more frequent among successful natural polyploids. Therefore, polyploidy is certainly best understood as a single process more or less strongly connected with hybridization of taxa which are at different stages of gradual differentiation of their chromosome complements, and their success seems to be closely connected with how far this differentiation has advanced. Nevertheless it has been found practical to continue to speak about autoploids and alloploids, and even to divide each into two subgroups based on their origins (Löve and Löve, 1949). Typical alloploids, as described above, are then termed panalloploids, and typical autoploids are called panautoploids. In between these, without any distinct limit, are the hemialloploids, which are formed from not fully sterile species hybrids, and the hemiautoploids, which are produced either from more or less fertile intraspecific hybrids or by differentiation of the chromosome set of successful panautoploids. These two intermediate groups constitute the majority of known natural cases, of which the present writer has preliminarily scrutinized some 300 complexes that are reasonably well known (unpublished).

Panalloploids are extremely rare, whereas panautoploids have been observed in the frequency of 1–5 per thousand in most populations cytologically studied on a sufficiently large scale, even in species of *Picea* and *Pinus* and some other genera in which natural polyploidy is completely absent (cf. Löve and Löve, 1961). Because of their genetical and cytological handicaps, such panautoploids rarely survive more than a generation or two and become successful only in the extremely rare cases when they manage to produce seeds and adapt their chromosome homologies very rapidly towards those of the hemiautoploids. This they will probably do most easily if formed in populations with some structural hybridity so they will already at the start be on the limit to hemiautoploidy.

Because of the widespread confusion that still exists between the morphological and the biological species concepts, much ink has been wasted on discussions on the classification of polyploids, mainly by followers of the morphological concept. This hardly involves panalloploids, since they are almost invariably visibly distinct and, thus, recognized by all taxonomists as species of the same quality as good species of the gradually evolving group. The same is true for many hemialloploids, though some are morphologically less distinct, either because the parental species are closely related or, more frequently, because the polyploid may resemble one of its putative parents more closely than the other in characters regarded as taxonomically important from the morphological point of view.

The morphologically most critical group of natural polyploids are the hemiautoploids. Many cases are known in which classical taxonomists have recognized their discontinuities as compared to their diploid ancestors and, consequently, named them as species, whereas in other cases such taxa have been acknowledged as subspecies or varieties only. This acceptance is, however, not universal among morphological taxonomists, and it is not rare to see such taxa reduced to lower ranks or even ignored because of their close resemblance to the parental species in characters deemed more important than those in which they differ.

Hemiautoploids and hemialloploids are certainly as good biological species as are panalloploids. Therefore, their few differences rather than their perhaps many similarities ought to be strongly stressed, even or especially in cases when the perhaps most decisive character for the determination of some individuals or populations may still be their chromosome number. This was recently stated by Raven (1963) in a discussion of the critical species of western North American *Achillea,* and it has been repeatedly claimed by Löve and Löve, jointly and separately, during the past 20-odd years, in connection with studies of numerous species and genera of boreal plants. It is, indeed, difficult to comprehend how this taxonomical conclusion can be logically avoided except by rejecting the biological species concept. However, the reluctance to accept this without reservation, even by some prominent biosystematists, manifests the difficulty of emancipating from the classical procedures found even among those who know that such a rejection is not a slight but a very serious misconception of the basic principles of evolutionary biology.

In the case of the panautoploids the condition is different. As mentioned earlier, they are usually ephemeral phenomena of no evolutionary significance; thus, it is pointless to give them any taxonomic recognition. In the extremely rare cases when such polyploids manage to survive, they are, however, to be regarded as incipient or cryptic species which will require attention similar to that of hemiautoploids as soon as they have demonstrated their ability to reproduce and form an area of their own.

This carries us to a conclusion.

As implied at the beginning, taxonomy is the science of affinities, and its object is to invent a scheme of classification which mirrors not only the phylogenetic relations that unite different groups of organisms, but also the phylogenetic similarities at each taxonomical level. The system created by the classical method does this up to a certain degree, though its failure to define clearly the basic categories is inherent in its lack of appreciation of fundamental evolutionary processes. This has led to the constantly repeated statement that species are of so many kinds that several definitions would not suffice, an argument based on morphological observations but ignoring the discontinuities already observed by Ray and applied as a basis of species distinction by Linnaeus and De Candolle and their followers.

Biosystematists have shown that the real species, or perhaps rather the biological species as contrasted to the more or less artistic species of the ancient typologists and some more recent morphologists, is a natural and non-arbitrary unit of a genetically closed population system that has lost its ability to interbreed with other such systems. It usually coincides with the Linnaean species selected by aid of the reproductive gap. The genetical barrier has been found to be caused by cytological differences, and so it can be discovered and defined by aid of cytological methods. It cannot be emphasized too strongly that the biological species concept, even in the numerous cases where it has to be based on inference, usually permits the delimitation of a sounder and far more meaningful taxonomical species than does the often random aggregation of individuals based on the groping concepts of the classical avoidance of such a singular definition. Its general acceptance would soon change the ancient art of classification into the modern science of critical taxonomy.

When classifying subspecific taxa, we must realize that each species is a reproductive community, which interacts as an ecological unit with other such communities. It consists of populations, each of which is an expression of an integrated gene pool. Since their variations are formed by aid of the sub-speciation processes of gene mutations, recombination, and natural selection, but without participation of the speciation processes of reproductive isolation, evolution below the species level is characterized by a continuum of variations and not by a succession of distinct types, except when affected by some kind of successively formed geographical or other similar isolations. Subspecific variations may be very distinct due to geographical or other isolation; since they lack an internal barrier to gene exchange they are, however, only temporary advances that at any time can be reversed into the general gene pool of the main population of the species.

The biological species concept is the basic idea of biosystematics. It is perhaps likely that the classical ideas will long have to coexist with this concept, because the material requiring taxonomical studies still stretches over a complete range, in a gentle gradient, from the purely empirical art of classifying a single specimen representing the only knowledge of the living beings of a remote land, to the exact scientific evaluation of data and measurements from modern experiments with populations of well-known organisms. To require the same exactness of all taxonomical work is, thus, not possible and indeed illogical. But if all taxonomists aiming at an evolutionary classification would realize that the biological species concept is also applicable even at the levels of rudimentary knowledge because certain morphological character combinations may often be relatively safe indicators of reproductive principle, then this may perhaps shorten the way towards a universal and standard understanding of the biological species, which should be familiar to all scientists, steadily looked to, stubbornly struggled for and, even though perhaps never perfectly achieved for all groups of organisms, constantly approximated to, and thereby persistingly spreading and deepening its influence and augmenting our understanding of evolution in general and of speciation in particular. The only absolute demand that ought to be made of those working towards this goal of natural classification is that, whenever more advanced stages of information are reached for an animal or plant, then less exact classifications ought to be replaced by more advanced definitions and systems. This is the simple principle of progressive science. Only by adopting this ideal can we continue the successful improvement of our understanding of the phenomenon of the multiplicity of life and its endless variations that have interested mankind from time immemorial.

References

Bernström, P. 1953. Increased crossability in *Lamium* after chromosome doubling. Hereditas 39: 241–256.

Clausen, J. 1951. Stages in the evolution of plant species. Ithaca, N.Y.

—— 1959: Gene systems regulating characters of ecological races and subspecies. Proc. X. Intern. Congr. Genet. I: 434–443.

Constance, L. 1963. Chromosome numbers and classification in Hydrophyllaceae. Brittonia 15: 273–285.

Davis, P. H. and Heywood, V. H. 1963. Principles of angiosperm taxonomy. Edinburgh.

De Candolle, A. P. 1813. Théorie élémentaire de la botanique. Paris.

Dobzhansky, T. 1950. Evolution in the Tropics. Amer. Scientist 38: 209–221.

—— 1951: Genetics and the origin of species. Third edition, revised. New York.

—— 1963. Species in *Drosophila*. Proc. Linn. Soc. London, 174: 1–12.

Ehrman, L. 1960. The genetics of hybrid sterility in *Drosophila paulistorum*. Evolution 14: 212–223.

—— 1962: The transitional races of *Drosophila paulistorum*: A study of hybrid sterility. Proc. Natl. Acad. Sci. 48: 157–159.

Geitler, L. 1937. Cytogenetische Untersuchungen an natürlichen Populationen von *Paris quadrifolia*. Zeitschr. Vererb. 73: 182–197.

—— 1938: Weitere cytogenetische Untersuchungen an natürlichen Populationen von *Paris quadrifolia*. Zeitschr. Vererb. 75: 161–190.

Gjaerevoll, O. 1963. Survival of plants on nunataks in Norway during the Pleistocene glaciation. In: Löve, Á and Löve, D. (ed.): North Atlantic Biota and their History: 261–283.

Goldschmidt, R. 1940. The material basis of evolution. New Haven, Connecticut.

Hagerup, O. 1932. Über Polyploidie in Beziehung zu Klima, Ökologie und Phylogenie. Hereditas 16: 19–40.

Huxley, J. 1942. Evolution. The modern synthesis. London.

Juzepczuk, S. V. 1958. Komarovskaya kontseptsiya vida yeyo istoricheskoye razvitiye i otrazheniye vo "Flora SSSR". Problema vida v botanika 1: 130–204.

Kihara, H. and Ono, T. 1926. Chromosomenzahlen und systematische Gruppierung der *Rumex*-Arten. Zeitschr. Zellf. mikrosk. Anat. 4: 475–481.

Knaben, G. 1959a. On the evolution of the *radicatum*-group of the *Scapiflora* Papavers as studied in 70 and 56 chromosome species. Part. A. Cytotaxonomic aspects. Opera Botanica 2, 3: 1–74.

—— 1959b. On the evolution of the *radicatum*-group of the *Scapiflora* Papavers as studied in 70 and 56 chromosome species. Part. B. Experimental studies. Opera Botanica 3, 3: 1–96.

Lewis, H. and Raven, P. 1958. Rapid evolution in *Clarkia*. Evolution 12: 319–336.

Löve, Á. 1943. Cytogenetic studies in *Rumex* subgenus *Acetosella*. Hereditas 30: 1–136.

—— 1953. Subarctic polyploidy. Hereditas 39: 113–124.

—— 1955. Cytotaxonomical remarks on the Icelandic *Papaver*. Nytt Mag. Bot. 4: 5–18.

―――― 1959. Origin of the arctic flora. Publ. McGill Univ. Mus. 1: 82–95.

―――― 1960. Biosystematics and classification of apomicts. Feddes Repert. 62: 136–148.

―――― 1962a. Typification of *Papaver radicatum*—a nomenclatural detective story. Bot. Not. 115: 113–136.

―――― 1962b. Nomenclature of North Atlantic Papaver. Taxon 11: 132–138.

―――― 1963a. Cytotaxonomy and generic delimitation. Regnum Vegetabile 27: 45.

―――― 1963b. Conclusion. In: Löve, Á. and Löve, D. (ed.): North Atlantic Biota and Their History: 391–397.

―――― 1964. Sverdmosinn. Náttúrufr. 33: 113–122.

Löve, Á. and Löve, D. 1949. Geobotanical significance of polyploidy. I. Polyploidy and latitude. Portug. Acta Biol. (A), R. B. Goldschmidt. Vol.: 273–352.

―――― and ―――― 1953. Studies on *Bryoxiphium*. Bryol. 56: 73–94, 183–203.

―――― and ―――― 1957. Arctic polyploidy. Proc. Genet. Soc. Canada 2: 23–27.

―――― and ―――― 1961. Chromosome numbers of Central and Northwest European plant species. Opera Botanica 5: I–VIII, 1–581.

―――― and ―――― 1963. Útbreidsla og fjöllitni. Distribution and polyploidy. Flóra: Journ. of Icel. Bot. 1: 135–139.

Mangenot, S. and Mangenot, G. 1962. Enquête sur les nombres chromosomiques dans une collection d'espèces tropicales. Revue Cytol. Biol. Végét. 25: 411–447.

Mayr, E. 1940. Speciation phenomena in birds. Amer. Nat. 74: 249–278.

―――― 1942. Systematics and the origin of species. New York.

―――― 1963. Animal species and evolution. Cambridge, Mass.

Melchers, G. 1946. Die Ursachen für die bessere Anpassungsfähigkeit der Polyploiden. Zeitschr. f. Naturforsch. 1: 160–165.

Mulligan, G. A. 1960. Polyploidy in Canadian weeds. Canad. Journ. Genet. Cytol. 2: 150–161.

Müntzing, A. 1930. Outlines to a genetic monograph of the genus *Galeopsis*. Hereditas 13: 185–341.

Nobs, M. A. 1963. Experimental studies on species relationships in *Ceanothus*. Carnegie Inst. Wash. Publ. 623: 1–94.

Rattenbury, J. A. 1962. Cyclic hybridization as a survival mechanism in the New Zealand forest flora. Evolution 16: 348–363.

Raven, P. 1963. A flora of San Clemente Island, California. Aliso 5: 289–347.

Reese, G. 1961. Karyotype and plant geography. Rec. Adv. Bot.: 895–900.

Satô, D. 1962. Law of karyotype evolution with special reference to the protokaryotype. Sci. Papers Coll. Gen. Educ. Univ. Tokyo, 12: 173–210.

Skottsberg, C. 1938. Geographical isolation as a factor in species formation, and its relation to certain insular floras. Proc. Linn. Soc. London 150: 286–293.

Stebbins, G. L. 1949. Rates of evolution in plants. In: Jepsen, G. L., Mayr and Simpson, G. L. (ed.): Genetics, paleontology and evolution: 229–242.

―――― 1950. Variation and evolution in plants. New York.

―――― 1959. Genes, chromosomes, and evolution. Vistas in Botany I: 258–290.

Valentine, D. H. 1949. The units of experimental taxonomy. Acta Biotheoretica 9: 75–88.

Vickery, R. K. 1959. Barriers to gene exchange within *Mimulus guttatus* (Scrophulariaceae). Evolution 13: 300–310.

George W. Gillett

An Experimental Study of Variation in the Phacelia sericea Complex

The genus *Phacelia* (Hydrophyllaceae) is notorious for the degree to which intergrades occur between commonly recognized species. In the *P. Franklinii* group (Gillett, 1960b) such a pattern of variation extends between 2 perennial species, *Phacelia idahoensis* Henderson, and *Phacelia sericea* (Graham) A. Gray (Fig. 1). I have chosen to refer to the material included in this interspecific variation pattern as the *P. sericea* complex.

The variation of *Phacelia sericea* has had its impact on taxonomists to the extent that at least eight names have been used to refer to material of this species. Furthermore, in deference to the unknown limits of this extensive variation pattern, taxonomists have applied the name *Phacelia sericea* to plants of several other species, some of these applications having been made in floristic works. It seemed appropriate, therefore, to carry out an experimental study of the *P. sericea* complex using greenhouse cultures, experimental crosses, and cytogenetic techniques, and to coordinate these with the study of herbarium material.

Documents of experimental plants have been deposited in the herbaria of Michigan State University and the University of California (Berkeley).

Distribution

The distribution of *Phacelia sericea* subsp. *sericea* centers on the higher elevations of the Rocky Mountains, northern Cascade Range, and Olympic Range, occurring from 4500 ft. in the Canadian Rockies to 12,000 and 13,000 ft. in Idaho and Colorado (Fig. 6). Plants are often found on exposed roadcuts, and on open, unstabilized habitats such as talus slopes. This subspecies is common between the Jasper National Park region and southern Colorado on both sides of the Continental Divide.

Phacelia sericea subsp. *ciliosa* occurs on the upper reaches of isolated ranges in the northern Great Basin and in adjacent areas to the north and east. An

Reprinted by permission of the author and publisher from the *American Journal of Botany*, 48: 1–7, 1961. Research supported by Grant G–3886 from the National Science Foundation and All-University Research Grant 2493, Michigan State University.

isolated population occurs in the region of San Francisco Peaks, Arizona (Fig. 6).

Phacelia idahoensis is restricted to central Idaho where it occurs in a warmer climatic regime, between 2800 and 7000 ft. It is found on wet meadows, stream banks, and sites that are subject to light seasonal flooding. In general, plants of *P. idahoensis* grow on well-developed soils and are elements of the typically dense, wet-meadow vegetation in contrast to the propensity of *P. sericea* subsp. *sericea* for poorly developed, well-drained soils of unstabilized, open habitats of higher elevations.

Flower Structure and Breeding System

Plants of *Phacelia sericea* are self-compatible. The flowers have strongly exserted and mutually isolated styles and stamens (Fig. 4A, C). The young styles of *P. sericea* subsp. *sericea* are often bent at right angles to the stamen

Figure 1

Experimental plants of the *Phacelia sericea* complex × 1/5. (1) *P. idahoensis,* Donnelly, Valley Co., Idaho, *Gillett 1173* (UC); (2) Experimental F_1 hybrid of (1) × (3) *Gillett 1179* (UC); (3) *P. sericea* subsp. *sericea,* Sherman Mts., Albany Co., Wyoming, *Gillett 1169* (UC); and (4) *P. sericea* subsp. *sericea,* Glacier Park, Montana, *Gillett 1146–1* (UC).

filaments, making self-pollination less likely but promoting contact between the stigmas and the body of a nectar-gathering insect. The flower structure, therefore, would appear to favor out-crossing.

Plants of *Phacelia idahoensis* are also self-compatible. The flowers, however, have weakly exserted styles and stamens (Fig. 4D), and the style may be above, at the same elevation, or below the dehisced anthers. As the stigmas are often within a millimeter of the anthers, or below them, it would seem impossible for an insect such as a small bee to gain access to the nectaries without accomplishing self-pollination. The flower structure, therefore, would appear to promote a considerable amount of inbreeding.

Greenhouse Cultures

More than 275 plants were grown in greenhouse cultures established from seed obtained from wild plants. A total of 5 strains of seed were utilized, and these are listed below.

Phacelia sericea subsp. *sericea*

1. "Gore Pass." Newly graded road shoulder, highway #84, Routt Co., Colorado, 9.9 mi. west of Gore Pass. Elev. ca. 8000 ft. *Gillett 1145* (MSC).
2. "Sherman Mts." Eroded road shoulder, highway #30, ca. 14 mi. S. E. Laramie, Albany Co., Wyoming. Elev. ca. 8500 ft. *Gillett 1162* (MSC).
3. "Glacier Park." Gravel road shoulder 0.8 mi. west of Many Glacier Entrance Station, Glacier National Park, Glacier Co., Montana. Elev. 4800 ft. *Harry Robinson s.n.* [documented by *Gillett 616* (MSC)].
4. "Olympic." Hurricane Ridge, Olympic National Park, Callam Co., Washington. Elev. 5300 ft. *George Cornwell s.n.* (MSC).

Phacelia idahoensis

Moist bottomlands 2.9 mi. south of Donnelly, Valley Co., Idaho. Elev. 4800 ft. *James Hockaday s.n.* (MSC).

Experimental Crosses

In February, 1959, simultaneous flowering was accomplished in plants of the Sherman Mts. race of *Phacelia sericea* subsp. *sericea* and of *P. idahoensis*. Several cross-pollinations to the more easily emasculated flowers of *P. sericea* subsp. *sericea* produced a quantity of F_1 seed (a median of 15 seeds per capsule). By contrast, very little seed was produced by crosses to the *P. idahoensis* seed parent. Out of 20 flowers pollinated, only 3 set seed. Furthermore, of 10 *P. idahoensis* flowers pollinated later by an F_1 hybrid, none set seed. The failure of experimental crosses to the *P. idahoensis* seed parent could be due to a sterility factor, to an accidental injury to the ovary during emasculation, or to the failure to understand such less obvious details as the receptive period of the stigmas.

Experimental F_1 hybrids produced by crosses between *Phacelia idahoensis* and *P. sericea* subsp. *sericea* (Sherman Mts. seed parent) grew vigorously and, given low-temperature, "short-day" treatments, flowered 6½ mo. after germination (Gillett, 1960a). Selfed F_1 flowers produced numerous seeds and these F_2 seeds germinated to produce vigorous seedlings (Fig. 5). Additional interspecific F_1 hybrids were produced by crossing *P. idahoensis* to the Glacier Park seed parent. These germinated promptly and demonstrated vigorous early growth. The interfertility between *P. idahoensis* and *P. sericea* subsp. *sericea* is, therefore, generally strong.

Cytological Evidence

Both *Phacelia sericea* and *P. idahoensis* are diploids, each having 11 pairs of chromosomes. In the present investigation, the chromosomes of both species were studied in pollen mother cells by the acetocarmine squash technique. These were found to demonstrate consistently normal pairing. In pollen mother cells of experimental F_1 hybrids, no univalents, translocations, or inversions were detected. A close cytological relationship is indicated, therefore, between the 2 species (Fig. 5).

Variation Studies

The extensive variation demonstrated in the *Phacelia sericea* complex is quantitative, and involves at least 3 conspicuous morphological features. These are the design or cutting of the leaf blade; the pubescence of the herbage; and the shape of the corolla. The experimental cultures grown in this study indicate that all 3 of these characters are genetically controlled. The expression of these characters in greenhouse plants is summarized in Table 1.

Leaf Cutting

Plants of *Phacelia idahoensis* and of the Glacier Park strain of *P. sericea* subsp. *sericea* have very distinctive leaves (Fig. 2, A & D). Leaf design was sufficient for distinguishing 100 intermixed plants of the above, growing on the same greenhouse bench. In all strains grown of the *P. sericea* complex, the uppermost rosette leaves, formed as the inflorescence is developing, tend to have slightly narrower lobes. Leaf-shape comparisons were made between leaves of herbarium specimens and those of greenhouse cultures illustrated in Fig. 2. In the study of herbarium material, scoring on leaf cutting was limited to those specimens in which the leaf rosette was intact and well portrayed. The

Table 1

Leaf-blade, Pubescence and Corolla Shape in the Phacelia Sericea
Complex Under Greenhouse Conditions

	Character		
	Leaf cutting (Fig. 2)	Pubescence (Fig. 3)	Corolla shape (Fig. 4)
P. *idahoensis*	lobes broad	glabrate	urceolate
P. *sericea* subsp. *sericea*			
Gore Pass	lobes of intermediate width	dense-sericeous	campanulate
Sherman Mts.	lobes of intermediate width	dense-sericeous	campanulate
Glacier Park	lobes narrow	dense-sericeous	campanulate
Olympic	narrow to intermediate lobes	matted-sericeous	(not brought into flower)

specimens were scored in 3 classes, these graphically expressed by the length of the left-hand "ray" as portrayed by the symbols of Fig. 2.

The scoring symbols are those of Anderson (1953). In this paper, they are deployed on a map (Fig. 6), rather than in Anderson's conventional scatter diagram. By this method, the geographical distribution is portrayed for the quantitative expression of each character studied.

In general, the over-all variation in leaf cutting is such that no distinct classes are recognizable. Great uniformity in leaf cutting was demonstrated by cultures of *Phacelia idahoensis,* and by greenhouse plants of the Glacier Park race of *P. sericea* subsp. *sericea.* These mark the 2 extremes of the variation pattern. Numerous other races studied, including the Gore Pass and Sherman Mts. races of *P. sericea* subsp. *sericea,* demonstrated a gradual and imperceptible inter-gradation between these extremes.

Pubescence

The herbage of *Phacelia idahoensis* is a bright green, and at first glance would appear glabrous. A closer examination, however, reveals a vesture of short epidermal hairs (Fig. 3A). This pubescence type characterizes greenhouse plants and herbarium specimens of this species. On the other hand, the foliage of the Olympic race of *P. sericea* subsp. *sericea* (Fig. 3D) is nearly white, the vesture being of numerous, long, overlapping hairs, and termed matted-sericeous. These types mark the extremes of variation in pubescence. The dense sericeous pubescence of the Glacier Park and Sherman Mts. races

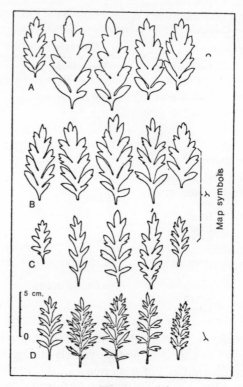

Figure 2

Leaf cutting in greenhouse plants. Each leaf repre-
sents the modal expression of a given plant. (A)
Phacelia idahoensis; (B) F₁ hybrids of (A) × (C);
(C) *P. sericea* subsp. *sericea,* Sherman Mts.; and (D)
P. sericea subsp. *sericea* Glacier Park.

Figure 3

Pubescence (upper epidermis of leaves) in greenhouse
plants of: (A) *Phacelia idahoensis;* (B) F₁ hybrid of
(A) × (C); (C) Sherman Mts. race of *P. sericea*
subsp. *sericea;* and (D) Olympia race of *P. sericea*
subsp. *sericea.*

of *P. sericea* subsp. *sericea* is composed of appressed, overlapping epidermal hairs, these giving a gray coloration to the foliage (Fig. 3C). The experimental F_1 hybrids (of *P. idahoensis* and the Sherman Mts. race of *P. sericea* subsp. *sericea*) have a gray-green foliage, with a pubescence of few overlapping hairs (Fig. 3B), termed light-sericeous. The illustrations of Fig. 3 and the leaves from which they were drawn were used in scoring herbarium specimens. The quantitative scoring is portrayed by the length of the vertical "ray" on the symbol at the lower right of each drawing.

The extensive series of intergradations in vesture portrayed by herbarium specimens would suggest that this character is regulated by a number of genes rather than by one or two. Leaf cutting and pubescence are loosely correlated in greenhouse plants and herbarium specimens. The more broadly lobed leaves usually have a lighter pubescence.

Flowers

There are several contrasting details in flowers of *Phacelia idahoensis* and of *P. sericea* subsp. *sericea* (Fig. 4). The scoring of corolla shape into 3 classes was based on the following criteria:

1. *Campanulate*—corollas with long petals, and non-gibbous tube.
2. *Intermediate*—corollas with long petals, and gibbous tube.
3. *Urceolate*—corollas with short petals, and gibbous tube.

Greenhouse plants and herbarium specimens of *Phacelia sericea* subsp. *sericea* demonstrate corollas of class 1 above, while those of *P. idahoensis* have corollas of class 3. Experimental F_1 hybrids and wild intergrades have corollas of class 2. Variation in wild material of the 2 subspecies of *P. sericea* is expressed as a continuous series of intergrading classes, ranging from material (*P. sericea* subsp. *ciliosa*) that is indistinguishable from experimental F_1 hybrids to the generally uniform campanulate form (*P. sericea* subsp. *sericea*) of the Rocky Mountains, Olympics, and Cascades.

The inheritance of leaf cutting, pubescence, and flower morphology was in each instance expressed by a continuous series of intergrades that made it difficult to score each character into as few as the 3 classes recognized. This continuous variation would suggest that each character is regulated by more than one or two and possibly by several genes. In their exhaustive study of *Potentilla glandulosa,* Clausen and Hiesey (1958) describe a similar type of variation for achene weight and leaf length and assign the genetic basis for these to no less than 6 gene pairs for the former and 10 for the latter.

The inheritance of leaf cutting, pubescence, and flower morphology in greenhouse plants is portrayed in the diagram of experimental crosses in Fig. 5.

Discussion

By mapping the information obtained from scored herbarium specimens (Fig. 6) a picture is gained of the overall variation in leaf cutting, pubescence,

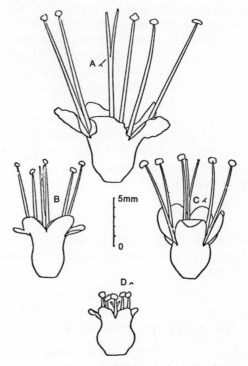

Figure 4

Flower shape in: (A) Sherman Mts. race of *Phacelia sericea* subsp. *sericea;* (B) experimental F_1 hybrid of (A) × (D); (C) *P. sericea* subsp. *ciliosa;* and (D) *P. idahoensis.* Scoring symbols to right of each letter. Drawings (A), (B), and (D) traced from photographs of living material. Drawing (C) made from herbarium specimen (*Macbride 901*, Owyhee Co., Idaho, CAS).

and flower shape in the *Phacelia sericea* complex. As these morphological features are genetically regulated, the map portrays the distribution and expression of gene systems operating in this complex. Significant information obtained from this distribution map includes evidence of wild populations that express leaf cutting, pubescence and corolla shape in the same degree portrayed by experimental F_1 hybrids. This morphological correlation does not involve scattered specimens here and there, but has regional and temporal continuity. In northeastern Nevada, specimens of 10 different collections demonstrate features of experimental F_1 hybrids. Similarly, in the Seven Devils Mountains of western Idaho, 17 specimens obtained in 4 different collections from the same locality (Heaven's Gate) are virtually indistinguishable from experimental hybrids. Putative hybrids occur from year to year in northern Carbon

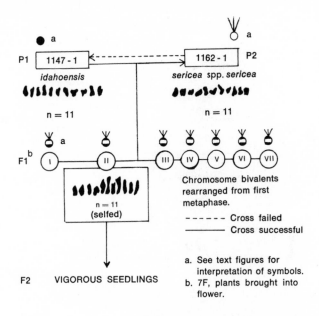

Figure 5

Diagram of the experimental cross between *Phacelia idahoensis* and *P. sericea* subsp. *sericea,* showing chromosome pairing. The inheritance of leaf cutting, vesture, and floral morphology is indicated by symbols explained in Figs. 2–4.

County, Wyoming; as well as in Lincoln and Sublette counties, Wyoming, where 19 specimens of 11 collections demonstrate the morphology of experimental hybrids.

At the present time, *Phacelia idahoensis* and *P. sericea* subsp. *sericea* are allopatric, though they are very nearly sympatric in Custer Co., Idaho. Locality data indicate that in the latter area these species are well-isolated geographically, the habitats of *P. sericea* subsp. *sericea* being from 1000 to 5000 ft. higher than those of *P. idahoensis.*

The geographical distribution and morphological expression of *Phacelia sericea* subsp. *sericea* merges with the distribution and expression of *P. idahoensis* through a series of intermediate populations recognized as *P. sericea* subsp. *ciliosa* (Fig. 6). These intermediate populations extend from Colorado and Wyoming to California, Oregon, and western Idaho. In *P. sericea,* variation is extensive where the distribution of the more northern subsp. *sericea* overlaps that of subsp. *ciliosa.* In each subspecies, there is less variability in regions distal to the distribution overlaps. Some populations in central Wyoming include material of both subspecies. This pattern of variation and the known interfertility in this complex suggest that the extensive intergradations between the sympatric subsp. *ciliosa* and subsp. *sericea* are products

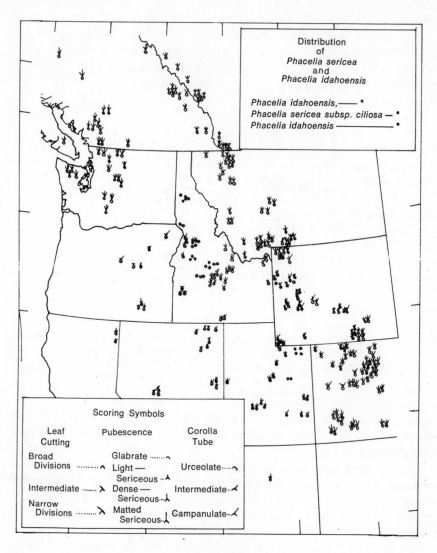

Figure 6

Geographical distribution of *Phacelia sericea* and
P. idahoensis.

of natural hybridizations (Stebbins, 1950). Taken as a whole, the loosely
correlated variation of differences between *Phacelia idahoensis* and *P. sericea*
subsp. *sericea* resembles that of experimental F_2 and backcross progeny in the
Whitlavia phacelias (Gillett, 1955), indicating that the spectrum of variability
could be the result of introgressive hybridization.

An alternative interpretation would be that the intermediate material

(*Phacelia sericea* subsp. *ciliosa*) represents ancestral stock from which both *P. idahoensis* and *P. sericea* subsp. *sericea* have evolved. The experimental evidence would then indicate that this "ancestral stock" has been synthesized by combining the genes of 2 derived lines (*P. idahoensis* and *P sericea* subsp. *sericea*). This would suggest that the "ancestral stock" has evolved a balanced complement of the same gene systems developed in each of the derived lines. While this may be possible, it appears excessively speculative.

The Pleistocene and post-Pleistocene shifts of *Phacelia sericea* subsp. *sericea* and of *P. idahoensis* were undoubtedly strongly related to the movements of the ice masses and permafrost. During the warm portion of the glacial cycle, the cooling effect of huge ice masses would have delayed the recession of cooler habitats while the warmer habitats encroached on the nearby outwash plain. Under these conditions, it would have been possible for *P. sericea* subsp. *sericea* to occur sufficiently close to the warmer habitat of *P. idahoensis* to permit natural hybridizations. (Such a juxtaposition of habitats involving the alpine *P. Lyallii* and the sub-alpine *P. sericea* subsp. *sericea* has been observed in Glacier National Park, Montana. In this region, both species occur on the moraine of Grinnell Glacier [*Hitchcock 1988* (NY) and *1989* (RM)]. On this moraine, the alpine *P. Lyallii* occurs 1000 ft. lower than at any other presently known locality.)

It is known that *Phacelia idahoensis* and *P. sericea* subsp. *sericea* have common flowering responses that would make natural hybridizations possible (Gillett, 1960a). Such hybridizations, including back-crosses into *P. sericea* subsp. *sericea,* would have involved the production of a wide assortment of recombination types, some of which could have been selected by the distinctive habitats developed concurrently in the Great Basin region through the drastic environmental changes known to have occurred there. There is evidence from the pattern of variation that extensive back-crossing occurred between the hybrids and populations of *P. sericea* subsp. *sericea.* This would be promoted by the open-pollination breeding system of *sericea*. In contrast, there is no evidence of similar gene infiltrations into the relatively uniform *P. idahoensis,* where the breeding system favors self-pollination. Thus, *P. idahoensis* would appear to have changed little through time, its inbreeding having conserved an adaptation possibly achieved long ago.

The vast array of intergrades selected from the out-crossing breeding system of *Phacelia sericea* would, therefore, seem best interpreted as recombination products of allopatric introgression (Anderson, 1953; Stebbins, 1959) between *P. idahoensis* and *P. sericea.* While the resulting intermediates have regional and morphological unity in the Great Basin area, this unity breaks down in the southern Rocky Mountain region to the extent that it is impossible to establish in that region a clear-cut morphological and geographical distinction between the Great Basin subspecies *ciliosa,* on the one hand, and the Rocky Mountain subspecies *sericea* on the other. When genetic materials undergo the shuffling and recombining characteristic of hybrid populations, and this is followed by the selection of many recombinations over a mosaic of habitats, the resultant productions stand in open defiance to a precise classification scheme.

Literature Cited

Anderson, E. 1953. Introgressive hybridization. Biol. Rev. 28: 280–307.

Clausen, J., and W. M. Hiesey. 1958. Experimental studies on the nature of species. IV. Genetic structure of ecological races. Carnegie Inst. Washington Publ. 615.

Gillett, G. W. 1955. Variation and genetic relationships in the Whitlavia and Gymnobythus phacelias. Univ. Calif. Publ. Bot. 28: 19–78.

―――. 1960a. Flowering responses in *Phacelia sericea* and *P. idahoensis*. Madrono 15: 245–249.

―――. 1960b. A systematic treatment of the *Phacelia Franklinii* group. Rhodora 62: 205–222.

Lanjouw, J., and F. A. Stafleu. 1959. Index Herbariorum. Part 1, 4th Ed. The herbaria of the world. Internat. Bur. Plant Tax. and Nomencl. Utrecht.

Stebbins, G. L. 1950. Variation and evolution in plants. Columbia Univ. Press, New York.

―――. 1959. The role of hybridization in evolution. Proc. Amer. Phil. Soc. 103: 231–251.

D. Boulter
D. A. Thurman
B. L. Turner

The Use of Disc Electrophoresis of Plant Proteins in Systematics

Introduction

Interest in plant chemotaxonomy has greatly expanded in the last five years as attested to by the number of articles appearing in biological journals (cf. Alston, 1966; Turner, 1966, for reviews), the appearance of several books (Alston and Turner, 1963; Hegnauer, 1962–65; Leone, 1964; Swain, 1963) and the fact that many of the papers delivered at national systematic meetings, especially in the United States, have dealt with some aspects of this subject.

With notably few exceptions most of the presentations have had to do with micromolecular approaches (i.e. working with small molecular weight compounds such as alkaloids, flavonoids, terpenes, etc.). Emphasis on the micromolecular has followed the development of chromatographic techniques which have made possible rapid and relatively easy surveys for such compounds. Indeed, many of the systematic papers have used mere spot-patterns or peaks (in the case of gas chromatography) to help resolve the problems at hand, a legitimate procedure *if* one assumes that molecular identity can be *reasonably* established by the techniques employed. Macromolecular data, with the important exception of serology, have been sparingly used in plant systematic investigations. The serological method utilizes injected rabbits (or other antibody producers) an an intermediary in the production of suitable test material. Because of this, and other problems inherent in the technique, most plant systematists have not attempted to undertake such studies. However, protein data may be obtained by techniques other than serological ones, since relatively easy electrophoretic techniques exist for their separation and detection. In fact, it is as easy to become familiar with the techniques for the acquisition of protein-band data as it is to perform paper chromatography for spot data.

That protein-band data have a high potential for plant systematic purposes especially in hybridization studies, can be surmised from the interesting data of Johnson and Hall (1965) (also confirmed in this laboratory), in which complex allopolyploids could be detected through the analysis of the protein-bands found in hybrids and their putative parents. Numerous other examples could be drawn from the literature in systematic zoology (cf. Leone, 1964).

Reprinted by permission of the authors and publisher from *Taxon, 15:* 135–143, 1966.

Recently Vaughan *et al.* (1965), in comparing protein-bands obtained by serological techniques (gel immunoelectrophoresis) against those obtained by the relatively simple gel acrylamide techniques outlined below, came to the conclusion that the latter was at least equal to the former in the resolution of protein-bands (the same protein sources were used in both sets of experiments). Similarly, Turner, Boulter and Thurman (unpublished) have found a unique protein-band pattern for at least one species of *Baptisia*, where, using the same protein sources, no such differences could be detected by the serological techniques of Lester, Alston and Turner (1965).

The systematic utility of protein data of the type outlined here is of small consequence when measured against the systematic implications to be expected from the knowledge of the sequential arrangements of the amino acids which comprise the proteins (Bryson and Vogel, 1965, for a recent symposium, especially the articles of Margoliash and Smith on cytochrome c). Unlocking this information with present techniques is time consuming and most plant systematists will be content to let the next generation cope with problems of this sort.

As indicated, however, recent powerful techniques have been developed which permit the isolation and separation of proteins, especially through the use of starch-gel and gel-acrylamide electrophoresis. Developments in this area have been rapid and, in spite of a recent major symposium (Whipple, 1964), held on the subject, it is likely that most plant systematists are unaware of the suitability of the technique as a taxonomic tool. The purpose of this paper then, is to introduce the approach at a nontechnical level, provide examples of its results, evaluate its potential and in general provide the systematist with a base from which to start his own explorations.

An Outline of the Disc Electrophoretic Method

The chemical knowledge needed for gel electrophoretic studies is slight, all that is required is familiarity with the use of a balance, centrifuge and pH meter. By following the instructions given below and in the paper of Davis (1964), it should be possible to obtain reliable data within three weeks of commencement.

In disc electrophoresis (the name is derived from dependence of the method on *disc*ontinuities in the electrophoretic materials used; Ornstein and Davis, [1962]), a protein-containing extract is placed onto the top of a polyacrylamide gel which is then placed in a voltage gradient. Conditions are arranged such that the proteins are first concentrated into a very narrow starting zone, which increases subsequent resolution, and then separated from one another due to size differences and differential mobility in the applied voltage gradient. Proteins move in a voltage gradient due to the presence in their makeup of certain amino acids which carry positive or negative charges depending upon the pH at which the electrophoresis is carried out. Electrophoretic separations described here take about thirty minutes, the gel is then removed from the voltage gradient and the separated proteins are located either with a general protein stain (Fig. 1) or stained for a particular enzyme (Fig. 2). For a comprehensive account of disc electrophoresis with theoretical considerations the reader is referred to the papers of Ornstein (1964) and Davis (1964), but since their

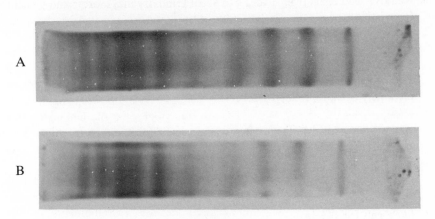

Figure 1

Albumins of A, *Phaseolus vulgaris;* B, *P. coccineus.*
Proteins located with amido-black.

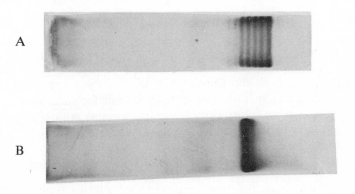

Figure 2

GDH isoenzyme patterns of the albumins extracted
from mature seeds of (A) *Vicia sativa* and (B) *Phaseolus vulgaris.*

accounts are necessarily somewhat technical we would like to emphasize the relative simplicity of the technique. The following will give some idea of the extraction and electrophoretic procedure, using legume seeds.

Extraction

1. Remove seed coats from 1 to 2 g of seed; grind dry in a mortar and pestal to form a flour.
2. Place 0.5 of flour in 5 ml. distilled water and stir in the cold room for 30 min.
3. Centrifuge the above slurry at about 3,000 r.p.m. for 15 min.
4. Take up supernatant (about 3 ml) add 1 g of sucrose—use this extract immediately or store in deep-freeze.

Gel Preparation and Electrophoresis

1. Prepare gels per instruction of Davis (1964)—takes about 1 hr.
2. Place about 0.1 ml. of protein extract on the top of each gel with a hypodermic syringe.
3. Electrophorise at 5 m.amp/gel for about ½ hr.
4. Stain gels for 1½ hr.
5. Destain gel by electrophoresis—2 hr., (gels may be stored in 3% acetic acid solution).

Ten to twenty samples can be processed in an eight-hour day using the apparatus shown in Fig. 3. More elaborate extraction procedures (described briefly below and in much greater detail in several of the references cited) can be tried, and since so little is known about the distribution of protein types in plants, the procedure that one settles for will be determined largely by trial and error. It should be emphasised, however, that the determination of the best extraction procedure for a given material can often be a major problem.

Apparatus

Disc electrophoretic apparatus together with suitable power supplies is commerically available from the Canalco Co. in the U.S.A., or from Shandon Scientific Instrument Co. Ltd., London. While costs for such equipment may be prohibitive to some, satisfactory apparatus together with a power supply can be easily constructed in the laboratory (estimated at about £ 15 or U.S. $40; see discussion below and Fig. 3).

Raymond (1962) has introduced another simple gel apparatus which can be used for protein-band resolution. It differs from the disc electrophoretic apparatus in that the protein extracts are applied directly to the gel slabs in a self-contained electrophoretic box. Commercial versions of the apparatus (E.C. Apparatus Corp., Philadelphia, U.S.A.) are available at a cost of about $300 (excluding power supply). Up to eight samples can be processed at the same time under comparable experimental conditions. Supplementary spectro-

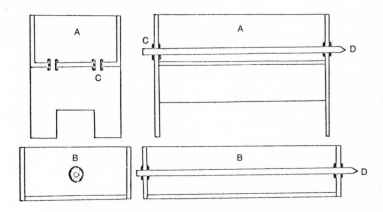

Figure 3

Electrophoresis apparatus—designed in conjunction with Dr. C. Rondle, Dept. of Bacteriology, University of Liverpool. The apparatus constructed of 1/8" perspex consists of an upper cathode chamber, (A), and a lower annode chamber (B). Two rows of 10 glass gel tubes each 6 × 0.5 cm. I.D. containing polyacrylamide gels complete the circuit between two compartments. Grommets (C) provide watertight seals round the tubes and the 1/4" diam. carbon rod electrodes (D).

photometric equipment for quantitative studies of protein bands can also be purchased and the E.C. company has recently marketed equipment for the elution of protein bands from gel slabs so that more detailed comparative studies might be made.

Extraction of Material

Different plant organs of the same individual may give different protein patterns on electrophoresis (see Fig. 4; and Steward, Lyndon and Barber, 1965); it is essential therefore, to work with comparable organs when making comparisons among species. In most of the work from this laboratory seeds have been used as a source of proteins. Seeds have many advantages as starting material. Dunnill and Fowden (1965) have pointed out that seed composition is unlikely to be affected by variation in nutritional or environmental factors during growth. Seeds lend themselves to ease of collection and storage and enable a population to be sampled quickly by pooling collections from different members. In addition their storage proteins are often concentrated and consequently good results can often be obtained from the extract of a single seed.

Crude extracts can be prepared as described above. If on electrophoresis band patterns of extracts are very faint, the extract should be concentrated before electrophoresis in one of three ways: (1) Place the extract into dialysis tubing, cover with polyethylene glycol (Mol. wt. 20,000), place between paper tissues and leave in the cold (0–4° C) until the appropriate volume reduction has taken place; (2) freeze-dry or, (3) saturate with ammonium sulphate, remove the precipitated proteins by centrifugation and redissolve them in a minimum volume of buffer; then dialyse the solution to remove ammonium sulphate. If the extract under examination contains large amounts of one or two proteins, minor components may be detected only after removal of the major proteins. Thus the albumins of legume seeds can be detected after most of the globulins have been removed by dialysis.

Results and Discussion

A. Comparison of Total Protein-Band Patterns on Polyacrylamide Gels

Stahmann (1963) has drawn attention to several factors which effect the stability of proteins present in extracts. However, it has been the experience of this laboratory over several years, and of others (Whipple, 1964) that reproducible band patterns are obtained provided that the proteins are extracted from comparable organs at the same developmental stage under standard conditions and electrophorised in a standard way. Thus protein-band patterns, prepared from different samples of the same batch of material, are found to be highly reproducible. Similarly it has been our experience that protein-band patterns of legume seeds obtained from different populations of the same species are also the same. However, polymorphism for certain protein types has been found to occur occasionally in animal species (Manwell and Baker, 1963; Frydenberg, et al., 1965 etc.), and similar variation can be anticipated in the proteins of plant species, both within and between populations.

It is important at this stage to enumerate some of the assumptions made when comparing band patterns. From band data alone one cannot be sure that bands having the same position on gels of different species are due to the same protein(s). Thus, even though the resolution of the technique is high, the initial extract may contain many hundreds of different proteins and hence a single band on the gel may be composed of more than one protein and, in different species, different proteins may run to the same position on the gel. One assumes therefore, that when two closely related species are being compared, the proteins running to the same position on the gel are identical; the further removed the two species are taxonomically, the greater the risk of this assumption being incorrect.

With the above discussion in mind one is led to ask at which taxonomic level will protein-band data prove most useful to the taxonomist. From results already obtained it appears that this will vary, it may be at the populational, specific, generic or yet some higher level. For instance, Vaughan et al. (1965)

have shown that different species of *Brassica* have different protein-band patterns, while Fox, Thurman and Boulter (1964) have indicated that protein-band patterns may be characteristic of certain tribal groupings in the Leguminosae.

B. Comparison of Major Organ-Specific Protein-Bands

Certain plant organs are characterised by an excess of a particular protein(s). Thus when the proteins of leaves are electrophorised the electrophoretogram is characterised by the so-called "fraction 1" of the chloroplast or, again, when the proteins of legume seeds are electrophorised the two major storage proteins (i.e. globulins) are readily detected (see Fig. 4). Future work

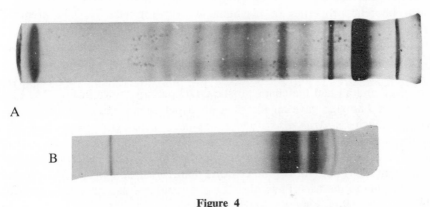

Figure 4

(A) Proteins extracted from leaves of *Vicia faba*, the major band represents the fraction 1 protein. (B) The major proteins occurring in the seeds of *Vicia faba*. Proteins located with amido-black.

may show that electrophoretograms of plant parts which contain an excess of a particular type of protein(s) may be highly suitable for comparative purposes since it is known that the same organ of different species will contain this type of protein(s). The major protein band(s) detected on gels therefore, will be this protein(s) and homology can be recognised in spite of any differences in electrophoretic mobilities.

C. Comparison of Enzyme-Band Patterns on Polyacrylamide Gels

The difficulty of comparing protein bands due to doubts about homology is to a large extent overcome by the use of a specific location reagent such as an enzyme stain. Many different enzymes can be detected on gels (Shaw, 1965) and the band patterns produced (zymograms) can be used for comparative purposes. In this method bands are presumed to be due to the activity of homologous enzyme or enzyme systems (isozymes), even though they run to different places on the gels. However, there is always the possibility that the enzymic activity is due to the products of analogous rather than homologous genes, but it would appear to be a valid assumption that, providing one keeps within a kingdom, the same enzyme is produced by homologous genes in different organisms.

Enzyme tests can be carried out with crude extracts. Many of the enzymes with which we have worked have been prepared from legume seeds. They occur in low concentrations as compared with the proteins giving the major amido-black patterns already referred to, thus a gel giving good resolution with respect to an enzyme stain will be many times overloaded when stained with a general protein stain and invariably the two cannot be compared.

As an instance of comparing enzyme band patterns, recent work on the electrophoretic properties of L-glutamate dehydrogenase (GDH) prepared from various members of the tribe Vicieae can be quoted. Enzyme preparations were made from seeds of the five genera which comprise the tribe and electrophorised as described; GDH was located using the tatrazolium procedure of Laycock, Thurman and Boulter (1965). Twelve species of *Vicia* were examined and all had the characteristic GDH pattern shown in Fig. 2A. Five species of *Lathyrus* gave an identical band pattern to that shown for *Vicia sativa*, though *Lathyrus roseus* and *L. nissolia* did not give this pattern. The GDH patterns of the *Pisum* and *Lens* species examined were also identical to that shown for *Vicia sativa*. However, *Cicer arietinum* is characterised by quite a different GDH pattern. It is noteworthy that *Abrus precatorius*, often treated as belonging to the tribe Phaseoleae or else separated as a monogenetic tribe (Hutchinson, 1964), gives a GDH pattern identical to that found for four of the five genera of the Vicieae. A comparison of the GDH patterns produced by four species of the tribe Phaseoleae, namely *Phaseolus vulgaris, P. coccineus, Rhynchosia phaseloides* and *Vigna catjang*, showed a GDH pattern different from that produced in the Vicieae. Figure 2B shows the GDH pattern for *Phaseolus coccineus* which is also found in the three other taxa mentioned.

It should be stressed that though these GDH patterns are easy to obtain, considerable effort is required to ensure that dye deposition is due to the initial activity of the enzyme under investigation and not due to nonspecific effects. The main difficulty in the interpretation of this data with regard to affinity is that only some of the changes in amino acid sequences will register as differences in electrophoretic mobility. Thus in relation to GDH mentioned above, assuming that the size and shape of the enzyme has remained constant, the only changes to be recorded will be substitutions in the polypeptide chain which effect the charge on the molecule. Thus one can envisage the situation where a single substitution of a charged amino acid by another of opposite charge would lead to a difference in mobility whereas say, a replacement of ten neutral amino acids by ten different neutral amino acids could remain undetected. In fact, since most amino acids are uncharged, it has been calculated that almost three fourths of all enzyme mutants in which a single amino acid might be affected will be electrophoretically undetectable (Shaw, 1965).

It will be obvious that comparative isozyme studies for systematic purposes will be considerably strengthened if a number of enzyme systems are compared in the different species rather than comparing a single system. We have made such a comparison for the four following enzymes: L-lactate dehydrogenase, L-malate dehydrogenase, L-glutamate dehydrogenase, alcohol dehydrogenase, plus the storage proteins, vicilin and legumin of the three species, *Vicia faba, Pisum sativum* and *Phaseolus vulgaris.* When any one of the above four enzymes or storage proteins was prepared from seeds of either *Vicia faba* or *Pisum sativum* it was found to have the same electrophoretic mobility and gave an identical enzyme band pattern. However, those of *Phaseolus vulgaris* differed considerably from these two taxa.

Shaw (1965) had reviewed the extensive literature dealing with enzymes and their variation, especially as related to the extent of polymorphism found among enzyme systems. His survey reveals that most studies have been made on cultivated or caged organisms and that among these ". . . it would seem that enzymes which vary are the rule rather than the exception." The extent of "polymorphism" found among the organisms for which reports are available is indeed impressive, yet "polymorphism" for enzyme systems, *per se,* does not mean that their distributional relationships in natural populations will prove polymorphic. For as Shaw correctly notes, "It is important to know whether the frequency of variation is relatively constant for homologous enzymes among different species. There are few data on this point." We favour the view that the selection of enzyme types will prove more effective under natural conditions. Thus, while expecting the occasional mutant forms that might affect almost any character of a large population, it is unlikely that polymorphism of enzymes will prove to be the rule. For example, Nyman (1965) reports that for freshwater fishes, "apart from the serum esterases the organ esterases seem to be rather constant within a species. The few intraspecific variations found in the serum esterases were with one exception due to developmental differences." Equally interesting is the study of Frydenberg *et al.* (1965) who report polymorphism for hemoglobin in Norwegian cod populations. From a study of 4,878 specimens from 35 populational samples they found that only three hemoglobin electrophoretic patterns (presumably determined by two allelic genes) were normally encountered. While intrapopulational polymorphism for these hemoglobin types was clearly established, it is noteworthy that only 28 aberrant patterns (all found in the more oceanic populations) were detected and that the gene frequencies controlling the three pattern types varied clinally from north to south.

Distributional studies for homologous enzymes in natural plant populations are badly needed. In fact, to our knowledge there has been no extensive study using the technique discussed here. If significant populational differences can be established for a given enzyme or enzyme system then these data can be used in the same way that microchemical data have been used by other workers to detect hybridization and/or introgression between species (Alston and Turner, 1963; Brehm and Ownbey, 1965, etc.).

Summary

A brief account of the gel acrylamide electrophoretic method for the detection of plant proteins is given, particularly as this might relate to systematic problems. Such methods do not entail immunoserological techniques, the usual approach associated with protein detection by taxonomists; in fact gel electrophoresis permits the acquisition of useful pattern data (protein bands) within hours of the direct extraction of protein types from plant materials. In the several comparative studies for which data are available, gel acrylamide techniques reveal as many protein bands, and often more, as are detected by immunoelectrophoretic techniques. Examples of such data, using legume seed proteins, are presented; consideration is also given to the systematic potential of comparative studies of isozymes in which presumably homologous enzyme systems are compared.

Literature Cited

Alston, R. E. and B. L. Turner. Biochemical Systematics. Prentice-Hall, Englewood Cliffs, New Jersey, 1963.

Alston, R. E. and B. L. Turner. Natural hybridization among four species of *Baptisia* (Leguminosae). Amer. Jour. Bot. 50: 159–173, 1963.

Alston, R. E. Comparisons of the importance of basic metabolites, secondary compounds and macromolecules in systematic studies. Lloydia (in press), 1966.

Brehm, B. G. and M. Ownbey. Variation in chromatographic patterns in the *Tragopogon dubius-pratensis-porrifolius complex* (Compositae). Amer. Jour. Bot. 52: 811–818, 1965.

Bryson, V. and H. J. Vogel (eds.). Rutgers Symposium on Evolving Genes and Proteins. Academic Press, New York, 1965.

Davis, B. J. Disc Electrophoresis—II. Ann. New York Acad. Sci. 121: 404–427, 1964.

Dunnill, P. and L. Fowden. The amino acids of seeds of the Cucurbitaceae. Phytochemistry 4: 933–944, 1965.

Fox, D. J., D. A. Thurman and D. Boulter. Studies on the protein of seeds of the Leguminosae—I. Albumins. Phytochemistry 3: 417–419, 1964.

Frydenberg, O., D. Møller, G. Naevdal and K. Sick. Haemoglobin polymorphism in Norwegian cod populations. Hereditas 53: 257–271, 1965.

Hegnauer, R. Chemotaxonomie der Pflanzen. Vol. 1–3. Birkhäuser Verlag, Basel, 1962–65.

Hutchinson, J. The Genera of Flowering Plants, I, Oxford, at the Clarendon Press, 1964.

Johnson, B. L. and O. Hall. Analysis of phylogenetic affinities in the Triticinae by protein electrophoresis. Amer. Journ. Bot. 52: 506–513, 1965.

Laycock, M. V., D. A. Thurman and D. Boulter. An improved method for the detection of dehydrogenases using tetrazolium salts. Clin. Chim. Acta 11: 98–100, 1965.

Leone, C. A. (ed.). Taxonomic Biochemistry and Serology. The Ronald Press Co., New York, 1964.

Lester, R. N., R. E. Alston and B. L. Turner. Serological studies in *Baptisia* and certain other genera of the Leguminosae. Amer. Journ. Bot. 52: 165–172, 1965.

Manwell, C. and C. M. A. Baker. A sibling species of sea cucumber discovered by starch gel electrophoresis. Comp. Biochem. Physiol. 10: 39–53, 1963.

Nyman, L. Species specific proteins in freshwater fishes and their suitability for a "protein taxonomy." Hereditas 53: 117–126, 1965.

Ornstein, L. and B. J. Davis. Disc Electrophoresis. Preprint by Distillation Product Industries (Eastman Kodak Co.), Rochester, N. Y., 1962.

Ornstein, L. Disc Electrophoresis. Ann. New York. Acad. Sci. 121: 321–349, 1964.

Raymond, S. Convenient Apparatus for gel electrophoresis. Clin. Chem. 8: 455–470, 1962.

Shaw, C. R. Electrophoretic variation in enzymes. Science 149: 936–943, 1965.

Stahmann, M. A. Plant Proteins. Ann. Rev. Pl. Physiol. 14: 137–158, 1963.

Steward, R. C., R. F. Lyndon, and J. T. Barber. Acrylamide gel electrophoresis of soluble plant proteins: A study on pea seedlings in relation to development. Amer. Journ. Bot. 52: 155–164, 1965.

Swain, T. Chemical Plant Taxonomy. Acad. Press, New York, 1963.

Turner, B. L. Plant chemosystematics: present and future applications. A symposium. New Trends in Taxonomy. Bull. Natn. Inst. Sci. India (in press), 1966.

Vaughan, J. G., A. Waite, D. Boulter and S. Waiters. Taxonomic investigation of several brassica species using serology and the separation of proteins by electrophoresis on gels. Nature. Vol. 208: 704, 1965.

Whipple, H. E. (ed.). Gel electrophoresis (A conference). Ann. N.Y. Acad. Sci. 121: 305–650, 1964.

Ralph E. Alston

Flavonoid Chemistry of Baptisia: A Current Evaluation of Chemical Methods in the Analysis of Interspecific Hybridization

In the last several years a rather large number of reports have been published in which chemical data have been applied to an analysis of interspecific hybrids. Some investigations were concerned with the composition of the hybrid as a means of establishing principles governing the inheritance of a number of species-specific phenolics (Williams, 1955). Other workers were primarily concerned with the techniques as means of documenting hybridization (Mirov, 1956; Pryor & Bryant, 1958; Turner and Alston, 1959). It is likely that the analyses of interspecific hybridization in *Baptisia* represent some of the most extensive uses of chemical criteria in the study of natural hybridization at this time. We now know that the success with such techniques in *Baptisia* depends upon the existence in this genus of unusually diversified flavonoid chemistry among taxa which hybridize readily. This is perhaps unfortunate for the general applicability of flavonoid chemistry to the study of interspecific hybridization. It will be helpful to review a few general principles pertinent to this work before proceeding further:

1. Flavonoid compounds similar to those found in *Baptisia* are genetically controlled, especially in their qualitative aspects. Mendelian dominance for specific flavonoid compounds is common. (Alston, 1964).

2. In *Baptisia* hybrids derived from parental species having quite complex assortments of flavonoids there is little evidence of epistasis, and the hybrid tends to approach a chemical pattern which is additive for the two parents. This result is seemingly in partial conflict with 1 above.

3. Since individual flavonoids appear to be reliable genetic markers, it is expected that in favorable situations such data will prove to be applicable to analyses of population dynamics or introgression.

In *Baptisia* the chemical data are superior to morphological data in individual instances although the reverse is true as well. For most morphological features which distinguish parental species, the hybrid is intermediate. This

Reprinted by permission of the author and publisher from *Taxon, 14:* 268–274, 1965.

intermediacy is not particularly troublesome in dihybrid populations, but in *Baptisia* many combinations of three actively hybridizing species may be sympatric, and one population of four hybridizing species has been analyzed (Alston and Turner, 1963). Here, morphological characters tend to blend in such a way as to introduce relative confusion into any attempt to designate the genomic origins of the various hybrid-type individuals.

Another advantage of the species-specific chemical markers, assuming their reliability, is that despite the fact that there may be some quantitative variation in the expression of a chemical character among different hybrids, and even within parental species, the presence of a chemical marker indicates the presence of a specific marker gene in the population. With many of the morphological characters one is presumably farther removed from the cause of the phenotypic attribute. While the ability to express a phenotypic character in chemical terms is not in itself the epitome of a perfect character, it is advantageous to know the chemical nature of a trait under investigation whenever possible.

We have been much impressed by the variation in exomorphic characters encountered among putative F_1 hybrids in the field. This question will be considered again below, but to simplify the problems facing one who may be studying population structure, he needs to know if possible, the percentage of F_1 plants; degree of selfing of hybrids; the relative extent of backcrossing to each parent, and many other facts. In *Baptisia* it is virtually impossible to obtain such data using exomorphic characters alone and to have confidence in a single interpretation. There seems to be a paradox in many *Baptisia* hybridizing populations; i.e., a near-continuum of morphological forms, from one parental type to another, exists in a population made up of *mostly* non-hybrids. An illustration of the degree of variability in exomorphic features is presented in Fig. 1. It is important to note that the leaves from the hybrid represent an ordered sequence of nodes from a single shoot. This gradual "conversion-like" alteration in form (Brink, 1962) is not typical of these *Baptisia* hybrids, but rather the individual leaf form seems in general to be only loosely correlated with its nodal position. One quite regular form transition occurs in the few individuals which we interpret as (*Baptisia tinctoria* x *B. perfoliata*) x *B. perfoliata* (Turner and Alston, 1965). This taxon, previously named *B. microphylla* (Larisey, 1940), tends to have its lower leaves simple but deeply trilobate while the upper leaves become trifoliate. The F_1 hybrid has petiolate, trifoliate, but stipulate, leaves. In any event, such variation in form is not accompanied in the same plant by significant differences in flavonoid chemistry. The degree of morphological variation is understandable when two genomes governing such different growth patterns are together, but it also serves as a warning to expect some increased tendency for variation elsewhere, indeed particularly in the best contrasting characters, for here the stress of one genome upon the other may be expressed maximally.

Before proceeding to describe certain selected examples from among the rather numerous *Baptisia* hybrids, some brief treatment of interspecific flavo-

Figure 1

Leaves taken from successive nodes of a single shoot of the hybrid, *Baptisia lanceolata x B. perfoliata:* (a) typical leaf of *B. perfoliata;* (b) typical leaf of *B. lanceolata;* (c–h) sequential series of leaves from a shoot from the hybrid. (From W. A. Jensen and L. G. Kavaljian, eds., *Plant Biology Today,* 2nd ed. Belmont, Calif.: Wadsworth Publishing Company.)

noid chemistry of a few other taxa will serve to place *Baptisia* in a better total perspective. Although the total number of flavonoids to be found among vascular plants is quite large (several hundred at least), certain of these compounds are of such widespread occurrence that they are apt to recur many times among unrelated species. In these instances, the compounds are of practically no systematic value in the larger taxonomic groupings, but they may still be quite valuable as intrageneric markers. A number of the major flavonoids of *Baptisia* fall into this category. Some of the common flavonoid types are illustrated in Fig. 2.

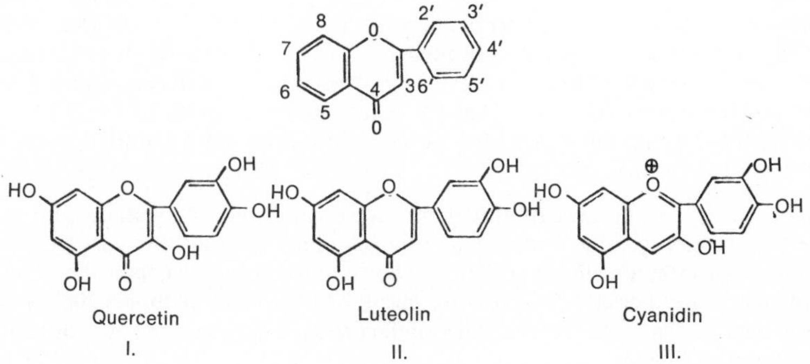

Figure 2

Common types of flavonoids.

Type I, flavonols, usually occur as 3-glycosides, 7-glycosides, 3-diglycosides, 3,7-diglycosides or as triglycosides.

Type II, flavones, usually occur as 7-monoglycosides or as 7-diglycosides.

Type III, anthocyanidins, usually occur as 3-glycosides or as 3,5-diglycosides.

Flavonoids of the Lemnaceae—this small family can be treated essentially as a genus although the 4 genera are readily separated from each other. Flavonoid chemistry of duckweeds is based on the three series shown in Fig. 2 plus a large number of "glycoflavonoids" having C-C sugar attachments at positions 6 and/or 8. McClure, who studied these compounds intensively in sterile cultures on defined media, found 47 different flavonoids among the 22 species in culture (McClure, 1964). Flavonoid chemistry of duckweeds is quite complex and these morphologically simple species are even more distinctive than are *Baptisia* species. This would be excellent material for genetic studies if interspecific hybridization can be effected.

Tragopogon—with extensive field investigations of natural hybridization completed by Ownbey, Brehm has now carried out parallel chromatographic studies (Brehm and Ownbey, 1965). The flavonoids are apparently chiefly flavones, and the species investigated so far have generally similar patterns with principally quantitative differences distinguishing the taxa. Hybrids can be recognized, however, on the basis of both morphology and chromatography. The ability to produce synthetic hybrids of chemically interesting individual plants represents a major advantage in this material.

From examination of data given of flavonoid analysis of parental strains and hybrids of *Vitis* species (Yap and Reichardt, 1964) this genus appears to be generally similar in its patterns of variation to *Tragopogon.*

Oenothera—despite the existence of a wealth of genetic material, made available by Dr. R. E. Cleland of Indiana University, this genus was not found to be suitable for flavonoid studies because of a lack of significant interspecific variability. Several flavonols and apparently aurones (a class having a five-membered oxygen containing ring) occur in the various species of *Oenothera* but in rather similar patterns.

Achimenes—with extensive hybridization occurring in this genus and numerous natural and synthetic hybrids supplied by Dr. H. E. Moore, Jr., of the Bailey Hortorium, Cornell University, it was hoped that *Achimenes* would prove to have interesting flavonoids. However, leaf extracts proved to have practically none of these compounds, and the flowers were apparently limited to anthocyanins among flavonoid components.

Psoralea—nearly 30 species of this genus were analyzed (Ockendon and Alston, 1965). Morphologically, *Psoralea* exhibits as much interspecific variation as does *Baptisia,* but interspecific hybridization apparently does not occur. The flavonoid chemistry is quite complex, involving many of the glycoflavonoids such as found in the duckweeds, plus O-glycosides of flavones, anthocyanins, and occasionally isoflavones (in which the phenyl ring is attached at carbon position 2 rather than at position 1). With a few exceptions (e.g., the isoflavones) species of *Psoralea* differ mainly only in the relative quantities of their various flavonoids.

It may be seen from the small sample discussed above that broad generalizations concerning flavonoid chemical patterns within a genus are difficult at best. We are still attempting to find suitable material to supplement *Baptisia* in genetic studies, so we would like to know of other instances of interspecific hybridization in which material is available in order to screen the material for flavonoids.

Even in *Baptisia* wherein some hybrids differ in a large number of flavonoids there are certain combinations of species in which hybridization can be validated only with great difficulty chromatographically. This has been discussed previously with respect to the combination *B. leucophaea* x *B. nuttalliana* (Alston and Turner, 1963). This hybrid is quite distinctive morphologically, however, having been named *B. intercalata* (Larisey, 1940). Other hybrid combinations in *Baptisia* which are difficult to validate independently by chromatography are *B. tinctoria* x *B. perfoliata,* and *B. leucantha* x *B. alba,* but because of a rather intensive study of the specific chemical components of these species, it is possible to confirm each of these combinations by special techniques *in theory.* In practice, we have found that all individual hybrids are not alike chemically, and when the criteria by which each species must be implicated in the origin of a particular hybrid involve minor components, it would be rash to guarantee success. In the genus *Baptisia* there are three so-called basic flavonoid patterns. These three patterns are arbitrary and may have no special phylogenetic significance, but it is a fact that each species can be immediately roughly classified in one of the three patterns. Pattern 1 includes the white-flowered species, and is characterized by 3-mono- and di-glycosides of flavonols plus isoflavones as the prominent components. Pattern 2, typical of *B. sphaerocarpa, B. tinctoria, B. perfoliata* and *B. hirsuta,* is characterized by flavone 7-diglycosides, often 7- or 3,7-glycosides of flavonols, and isoflavones. Pattern 3, typical of the remainder of the *Baptisia* species (plus all *Thermopsis* species tested so far) is characterized by flavone 7-mono-glycosides, few flavonols and a somewhat variable number of (among the species) isoflavones. Hybrids involving any two species from two different patterns are readily identified chromatographically (e.g., note the illustration of *B. leucantha* x *B. sphaerocarpa* [Alston and Hempel, 1964]), but among two species of the same pattern, it may or may not be easy to identify a particular hybrid. To risk a general statement, I have concluded that in the *recognition* of a particular hybrid combination, the chemical data are, in *Baptisia,* neither inferior nor superior to morphology. The important point is that when one type of evidence has been ineffective in *Baptisia* the other type has often proven to be effective, so that in combination the total effectiveness is greatly increased. We have been surprised at the ability to ascertain the typical hybrid flavonoid pattern from a single leaf taken from herbarium specimens. A number of specimens described as *B. sereneae* on herbarium sheets were found to be, chromatographically, hybrids of *B. alba* x *B. tinctoria.* We have found this hybrid on numerous occasions either growing alone or with only one of the parental species close by. Another instance of the value of combined morphological and chromatographic approaches to the study of natural hybridization is that of the complex population at Dayton, Texas, in which four species and six different hybrid combinations were obtained from one field (Alston and Turner, 1963).

A more provocative question is that of whether the chemical data are superior to other data in establishing introgression or in analyzing populational structure. In *Baptisia* when we have been specifically interested in the question of introgression, we have not obtained strong evidence supporting introgression. However, individual examples of what I judge to be introgression occur. For example, Mr. Karl Baetcke and I once collected a typical *Baptisia leucantha,* growing alone in a field in McCurtain County, Oklahoma. Four other species of *Baptisia* were collected in that county on that trip. This species is quite distinctive, with white flowers, and its hybrids always have pale-yellow flowers. The plant in question, having pure white flowers, was chromatographically a typical *B. leucantha* plus the addition of apigenin-7-monoglycoside, a compound found in at least three of the sympatric species, but never found in *B. leucantha.* I have given much thought to this situation and can only conclude that the apigenin-7-monoglycoside represents introgression from an unknown species.

Recently, McHale and Alston (1964) reported on a combined chemical and morphological analysis of hybridization between *B. leucantha* and *B.*

sphaerocarpa. Although the data were in good general agreement as to the composition of the group of plants collected, some individuals were classified as F_1 hybrids on chemical grounds while morphologically they were putative backcrosses either to *B. leucantha* or in other individuals, to *B. sphaerocarpa*. Since we believe that both the morphological and chemical data are valid, in that they are derived from accurate observations by reliable techniques, the academic question is, which type of characters are most variable in the hybrid, and secondly, can one even recognize a backcross type on the basis of its flavonoid chemistry? Although some plants were classified arbitrarily as backcross types by McHale and Alston there was really no way to prove the nature of these plants. Synthetic hybrids of *B. leucantha* x *B. sphaerocarpa,* now being grown, should at first clarify the point of F_1 chemical variation and eventually the appearances of various backcross types.

The following section will be devoted to a consideration of some of the advantages of specific chemical knowledge of the compounds. Obviously, some artifacts may be more effectively recognized if the compounds are known. For example, both flavones and flavonols tend to become hydrolyzed to some degree during the various stages leading to the completion of chromatographic analyses. If the hydrolytic products are counted, this will multiply the number of presumptive chemical differences but on a false basis.

Knowledge of the identities of the four hybrid-specific compounds of *B. leucantha* x *B. sphaerocarpa* leaves has proven to be of importance concerning the general question of enzyme specificity and the genetic regulation of secondary compounds. Although not all of the necessary data concerning the compounds #68, #69, #70, and #71 (these also appear in the hybrid, *Baptisia leucantha* x *B. tinctoria*) are available at this time, the following points appear to be firmly established. These four compounds are absent from *B. leucantha*. They are present in flowers of *B. sphaerocarpa* but absent in the leaves of this species. They are present in the flowers and in the leaves of hybrids of *B. leucantha* x *B. sphaerocarpa*. All of the compounds are flavonols having a 7-glycosidic linkage. *Baptisia leucantha* produces flavonols of the 3-monoglycosidic and 3-diglycosidic types, hence a mechanism for accumulating flavonols in the leaves already exists. This fact renders less convincing the argument that the appearance of the "hybrid spots" in leaves of this hybrid combination (and not in certain other hybrids) necessarily implies greater genetic differences between these two species (as opposed to those involved in other hybridizations with *B. sphaerocarpa*). Compound #70 is known to be quercetin 3,7 di-glucoside. Upon partial acid hydrolysis it yields #68 which must be quercetin 7-mono-glucoside. Upon enzymatic hydrolysis it yields quercetin. The glucose at C-7 is hydrolyzed off by acid less readily. Evidence now available indicates that compound #71 may be a quercetin triglycoside, but this is a highly tentative assumption. Only minute traces of 7-glycosides of the related flavonol, kaempferol, are present, although we know where this compound would appear on the chromatograms, and despite the fact that one parent, *B. leucantha,* produces large amounts of kaempferol

3-mono and 3-di-glycosides. Neither is there any evidence that a quercetin tetraglycoside occurs, although *B. leucantha* produces a large amount of rutin (quercetin 3-rhamnoglucoside). Since quercetin 3-rhamnoglucoside, 7-glucoside and quercetin-3-glucoside, 7-rhamnoglucoside would run in nearly identical positions on 2-dimensional chromatograms, more complex methods are required to establish the coexistence of these substances if they both occur in the hybrid. This work is now in progress. At this stage, however, it appears that when truly hybrid-type molecules can be predicted, theoretically, to occur in the hybrid, the compounds do not always occur, indicating a high degree of specificity in the enzymes involved in the synthesis of flavonoids in these species, or a highly regulated time and place of synthesis of the flavonoids by the two genetic systems. There are several pairs of southeastern species of *Baptisia* in which these or quite similar flavonols are involved. Analysis of these systems have progressed as far as the example cited above, and it is hoped that a complete analysis will be available soon. Also in hybrids of *B. leucophaea,* which forms apigenin-7-glucoside and *B. sphaerocarpa* which forms apigenin-7-diglycoside (probably rhamnoglucoside), both the mono- and di-glycosides occur, so there is no epistasis. This is true of several other hybrid combinations in which these two compounds are involved. It is surprising to find such a high degree of enzyme specificity existing in the synthesis of compounds of presumably little selective advantage to the plant. It remains to be seen whether or not this represents a general situation.

In summary, a comprehensive study of *Baptisia* flavonoid chemistry, though far from complete, has already contributed in several ways to comprehension of patterns of interspecific hybridization. When the chemical data are expressed eventually, as we hope, in terms of their genetic regulation, it should be possible to analyze populational structure mroe effectively by chemical than by morphological criteria. It is premature to attempt to predict how knowledge of flavonoid and other secondary chemistry may influence phylogenetic speculations about *Baptisia* species and possibly generic affinities though such data must be taken into account. Much more knowledge of the isoflavones, minor flavonoids and simpler phenolics are needed. The alkaloid chemistry, which has been under investigation by M. R. Cranmer, working with Dr. T. J. Mabry of our group, will be relevant to phylogenetic speculations. However, the topic is not within the scope of the present treatment.

References

Alston, R. E. and B. L. Turner. Natural hybridization among four species of *Baptisia* (Leguminosae). Amer. J. Bot. 50: 159–173, 1963.

Alston, R. E. The genetics of phenolic compounds. In "Biochemistry of Phenolic Compounds," J. B. Harborne (ed.), Academic Press, New York, pp. 171–204, 1964.

Alston, R. E. and B. L. Turner. Comparative chemistry of *Baptisia:* Problems of interspecific hybridization. In "Taxonomic Biochemistry and Serology," C. A. Leone (ed.), Ronald Press, New York, pp. 225–238, 1964.

Alston, R. E. and Karen Hempel. Chemical documentation of interspecific hybridization. Jour. Heredity. 55: 267–269, 1964.

Brehm, B. G. and Marion Ownby. Variation in chromatographic patterns in the *Tragopogon dubius-pratensis-porrifolius* complex. Amer. J. Bot. (in press), 1965.

Brink, R. A. Phase change in higher plants and somatic cell heredity. Quart. Rev. of Biol. 37: 1022, 1962.

Larisey, M. M. A monograph of the genus *Baptisia*. Ann. Mo. Bot. Gard. 27: 119–258, 1940.

McClure, J. W. Taxonomic significance of the flavonoid chemistry and the morphology of Lemnaceae in axenic culture. Ph. D. Dissertation, The University of Texas, Austin, 1964.

McHale, Janiece and R. E. Alston. Utilization of chemical patterns in the analysis of hybridization between *Baptisia leucantha* and *B. sphaerocarpa*. Evol. 18: 304–311, 1964.

Mirov, N. T. Composition of turpentine of lodgepole x jack pine hybrids. Can. J. Bot. 443–457, 1956.

Ockendon, David and R. E. Alston. The distributions of flavonoids in *Psoralea* species. (in preparation), 1965.

Pryor, L. D. and L. H. Bryant. Inheritance of oil characters in *Eucalyptus*. Proc. Lin. Soc. N. S. Wales 83: 55–64, 1958.

Turner, B. L. and R. E. Alston. Segregation and recombination of chemical constituents in a hybrid swarm of *Baptisia laevicaulis* x *B. viridis* and their taxonomic implications. Amer. J. Bot. 46: 678–686, 1959.

———— and ————. Unpublished observations, 1964.

Williams, A. H. Phenolic substances of apple-pear hybrids. Nature. 175: 213, 1955.

Yap, F. and A. Reichardt. Vergleichende Untersuchungen der Flavonoid und Oxyzimtsauren in den Blättern artreiner *Vitis*-Sorten und ihrer Bastarde. Züchter. 34: 143–156, 1964.

Robert R. Sokal
P. H. A. Sneath

Efficiency in Taxonomy

Introduction

The current literature reflects a period of considerable change in theory and practice ranging over the entire field of systematics. It is not our purpose to outline here the new theoretical framework being constructed for the field of systematics by various authors. This can be learned from numerous publications (see Davis and Heywood, 1963; Ehrlich and Holm, 1962; Gilmour, 1940; Michener, 1963, 1964; Sokal, 1962, 1964; Sokal and Sneath, 1963; Camin and Sokal, 1965; Sokal and Camin, 1965). The intellectual challenge resulting from these new ideas and approaches has on the whole been salutary for systematics, as is admitted even by their critics (Brown, 1965; Mayr, 1965; Rollins, 1965; Mackerras, 1963). We are witnessing reinterpretations of the nature of taxonomic relationships and of the concepts of phylogeny and homology. The usefulness and operationalism of other systematic concepts, such as the biological species concept, have been questioned. The desirability of binomial nomenclature is bieng challenged.

Some may deplore the upheaval and disorderliness of ideas and practices which necessarily accompany a period of transition. Yet there is little doubt that out of the current ferment a new theory of systematics will emerge, containing many of the proven elements of the classic theory, and assimilating those of the newer views which stand the test of time.

Much of the controversy has concerned numerical taxonomy, i.e., quantification of the classificatory process. However, portents of change are apparent in virtually every aspect of taxonomy. We shall try to assess these developments for the field as a whole. While we shall attempt to delineate the present and prospective roles of numerical taxonomy in systematics, much of our discussion below covers topics which are relevant regardless of the taxonomic philosophy adopted and thus should be of interest to taxonomists of every school. The subjects discussed will be largely procedural. It is our belief that the main reason taxonomy is currently facing such a major revolution, or even explosion as Simpson (1965) has put it, is because so much in taxonomy is procedure, and specifically, procedure concerned with the obtaining, recording, storing

Reprinted by permission of the authors and publisher from *Taxon, 15:* 1–21, 1966. The authors are indebted to J. H. Camin, V. H. Heywood, A. Löve, C. D. Michener, F. J. Rohlf, and A. M. Torres for their advice during the preparation of this article.

and retrieval of information. It is in these fields that science and technology have made tremendous strides in the last few years. This general field is called EDP, electronic data processing, and its advent is revolutionizing much of our civilization. In the next section we shall briefly review EDP and discuss how present and prospective EDP facilities relate to work in systematics.

Sokal (1965) has classified the various procedures in systematics into: (1) the analysis of infraspecific variation, including both intrapopulation and inter-population studies as well as the separation of the environmental effects upon the phenotype from genetically determined variation (this procedure is inti-mately connected with (2) which often rests on its results); (2) the definition and recognition of subspecies and of species; (3) classification at supraspecific levels; (4) the measure of evolutionary rates; (5) the study of cladogenesis and (6) biogeography. To these must be added the following practical taxonomic procedures: (7) description and identification of species; (8) definition and identification of supraspecific taxa; (9) nomenclature; (10) collection, storage and retrieval of information (in the form of specimens or recorded data).

In the sections that follow we shall examine some of these taxonomic proce-dures, and possibilities for improving their efficiency. Associated with this account will be the problem of storage and accessibility of study material in museums and information in the published taxonomic literature.

Electronic Data Processing

In recent years electronic computers and business machines with greatly improved performance have been developed. As their capabilities have in-creased, the cost per unit of work accomplished has diminished markedly. At the respective computer installations of both authors the cost per unit of work has decreased to 1/10 of what it was as recently as six years ago. With every improvement in a computer the cost per unit job decreases.

Computers can help the taxonomist in many ways. They rapidly compute similarity coefficients among taxa. They are able to generate classifications based on the representation of taxonomic structure by any of a number of definable principles and can present the output of such computations as dendro-grams or other schemes by a variety of graphic output devices. Computers can store information about single species, such as characters, collections and distribution records. This information may be searched at tremendous speeds and summaries or reports obtained on any group classified by any of a variety of criteria. Computers can store accession lists of museums and regularly update these in terms of loans and new accessions. They can prepare lists of materials available for study in a museum and search the lists of museum holdings for special material of interest to a given investigator. The usefulness of computers to taxonomists can be greatly increased by connected auxiliary devices. Machines which record printed information optically and convert it into input for computers are still in their infancy, but already optical scanners (which convert information on photographs, microscope slides, or pen and ink drawings into digital output) are being marketed. This will result in a drastic change in the methods and rates of data acquisition in taxonomic biology. The preparation and presentation of taxonomic reports and information can also become quite automated. Not only dendrograms of various sorts, but faunal and floral lists, distribution and geographic variation maps and eventually even drawings of morphological structures can be done by computer through graphic output devices which are currently available in many models.

The use of computers becomes ever simpler. The various automatic coding languages grow more powerful, and are also simpler to learn, as they become more and more similar to English or ordinary algebra. Recent years have seen the widespread acceptance of FORTRAN (and similar languages such as ALGOL, QUICKTRAN or PL/I) in scientific circles, and programming in one of these languages is now routinely taught to graduate students in many biological sciences departments. The importance of such languages lies not only in enabling scientific workers to solve problems on the computer without having to master the intricacies of computer machine language, but also in having these problems stated in a simple, near-algebraic format that can be employed on most computers so that programs developed in one center can be used at another center. An ever increasing advantage (see Watt, 1964) is that FORTRAN programs state mathematical and logical operation in a simple universally understood language which often permits formulation and solution of problems that defy conventional mathematical methodology. Thus from a mere convenience, these languages are developing into a heuristic tool and a major aid to research for a variety of biological problems.

As computers have become bigger and computation centers more elaborate, closed shop procedures have been instituted. This means that the data and programs are presented (usually as cards) at a reception window in the computation center and the output is subsequently returned to the researcher. No longer must the mechanics of actual computer operations be learned by the investigator. This is an important development which will help break down the psychological barrier between the systematist and the computer, a barrier that currently is an impediment to the acceptance of EDP in taxonomy. Even when convinced of the value of computer techniques, most taxonomists will hesitate before becoming involved with these machines. The complexities of the involvement are rapidly diminishing.

The most revolutionary aspect of data processing involves time sharing, so-called, and on-line devices. By time sharing is meant the simultaneous use of a big computer by numerous persons whose programs are being processed simultaneously. In such a system users are generally connected to the central processor (computer) by on-line terminals. These are direct lines from their laboratories or offices to the computation center which may be hundreds of miles away. The advantages of on-line devices are immediately apparent. No longer must a user take two trips to the computation center to process his data, or wait while punched cards are shipped back and forth by mail. Immediate response to the user's inquiry establishes a new phase of man-computer inter-action which permits continuous interrogation of evidence such as would apply when working through a taxonomic key. Such a 'conversational mode' of computer use was previously impossible. On-line devices are frequently supplied with a cathode ray display tube, similar to a television tube, in which numerical and graphic information is visually presented to the user. There are ways in which this information can be corrected by the user at the console and the record updated in the memory of the computer. The first on-line devices are currently being installed in various universities and the next two or three years will see a rapid proliferation of this type of computer installation.

Time sharing is an important development especially for smaller and more isolated institutions. A separate powerful computation center for such an institution may be financially impossible. However, a line into a computation center located elsewhere may be economically feasible, comprising only rental of a telephone line or other communications device as well as the cost of a terminal installation at the institution. Subsequent charges would only be for computation time as used. Computer developments are rapidly moving toward 'the time when a computer facility will be very much like a public utility from which time is bought and paid for as used. As soon as this is generally avail-able, every institution or department (and even individuals) should be able to obtain ready access to computing facilities. Another advantage of time sharing is also that any one user has a much bigger and faster machine at his disposal than he could afford if each department were to have its own computer.

The Taxonomic Process

As taxonomic EDP systems are designed we have to decide whether auto-mation shall only be applied to the traditional taxonomic process or whether the taxonomic process itself shall be reevaluated. If we are to design a system, which Swanson (1964) has defined ". . . loosely as a collection of people and machines organized for a purpose," we must clearly formulate what the taxonomic purposes are. We need to know what types of procedures should constitute the future taxonomic process, rather than take it for granted that taxonomy should continue to comprise the very same procedures in the future that it did in the past. A proper formulation of operational principles and pro-cedures in taxonomy is therefore essential.

It may be useful to consider the separate types of operations which a tax-onomist undertakes in his work. Of course, not all of these are carried out in any one taxonomic task, but in the course of his career he is likely to encoun-ter most of these operations. The question is, can he make his decisions ob-jective and his procedures efficient? Objectivity has been adequately discussed in the numerical taxonomic literature. The quest for objectivity is intimately tied up with operationalism in taxonomic research as detailed by Sokal and Camin (1965).

The need for efficiency in taxonomic research is more controversial. Some would maintain that scientific research can never be efficient in the same sense that an office operation or an industrial process can be efficient. Yet such criteria do come into the day-to-day processes of research. Much of taxonomy consists of certain routine, repetitive operations which can be made more efficient. For specialized aspects of taxonomic work efficiency has risen throughout the development of taxonomy. There has in fact been continual improvement in methods of preparing specimens for study. There have also been better techniques of examining specimens and recording findings and isolated efforts at better catalogues and filing systems. However, on the whole there has been little concerted effort at increasing the efficiency of taxonomic procedures.

Before we proceed further we shall have to define our measure of efficiency. Efficiency could be measured simply as time taken to complete a process, but it is probably better to measure the efficiency of a taxonomic procedure as the cost of achieving a given taxonomic task. Through this avenue time enters the equation. Let us compare the relative efficiencies of three hypothetical taxonomic procedures. For completion of task X, procedure 1 would require the services for ½ year of a Ph.D.-level taxonomist whose salary is $8,000 per year—net cost $4,000. Procedure 2 would employ a technician for one year at a salary of $4,000 per year—net cost also $4,000. Procedure 3 involves a Ph.D.-level taxonomist 1 month, and a technician 2 months, and requires 5 hours computer time (the latter at $150 per hour)—net cost $2,083. In this fictitious example it is clear that procedure 3 would be more efficient than the first two methods. For reasons not entirely of efficiency, we might argue that method 2 is preferable to 1 because it would free the Ph.D.-level worker for more intellectually challenging tasks. In such a cold-blooded measure of efficiency there are not entered intangible personal factors such as the satisfaction the Ph.D.-level taxonomist may get out of carrying out this particular job, or conversely his joy at being freed from such a job. On the whole one may expect that any job that a machine or technician can do equally well should not be done by higher level personnel, who might confine their activities to those tasks requiring their talents.

This leads us directly into the problem of time-costing with relation to taxonomic work, especially in taxonomic institutions such as museums and herbaria where efficiency levels may generally be poor. A justified retort would be that budgets of many such institutions are equally low, but we would maintain that for any given expenditure level it should be possible to obtain more taxonomic output by mechanization and modernization of procedures.

It is important to estimate the relative efficiencies of various taxonomic procedures when alternative procedures are available. For instance, it has been argued by Michener (1963) that conventional taxonomy is of value for describing little-known forms by processing taxonomic information rapidly. This is brought to the attention of the taxonomist until sufficient data have been accumulated for numerical taxonomic study. Assuming for the moment that the results of the conventional and numerical approaches were equivalent, i.e., of equal scientific value, then a decision between them becomes simply a matter of relative efficiency. It has never been established whether a conventional classification takes more or less time in terms of actual hours of work than a numerical classification starting from various degrees of absolute ignorance of the material. The study by the "intelligent ignoramus" referred to elsewhere in this paper will give us some evidence on this. However, many more such comparisons are needed and it therefore seems to us to be imperative that agencies concerned with taxonomic work should fund pilot studies to compare various numerical with conventional approaches to determine the economics of the various alternatives.

There are many countries, especially in the tropics, where taxonomic work on animals and plants of economic importance is urgently needed. Insect pests, for example, may cause heavy loss of crops, so that their ready identification is important. Land use surveys may rely heavily on the accurate identification of thousands of plant specimens. In such situations the most pressing need is for diagnostic keys and not for monographs. Even though monographs are better than keys they may take too long to produce. It is therefore an urgent matter to find out whether savings of time and money can be made by using numerical taxonomy. The methods would need adapting to the primary aim of making useful keys, and since the motives would be economic, results that were not ideal scientifically might nevertheless be useful.

In actual experience Funk (personal communication) has shown that in a relatively unknown group, numerical taxonomy is indeed of value when applied initially. In a study of 25 species of euzerconid mites, only one of which had been described previously, Funk found numerical taxonomy to be an effective tool in grouping the species, which groups in turn directed his attention to the generic characters. This had been very difficult to do by conventional procedures. Numerical taxonomic procedures also called his attention to a new species which had not been recognized before. Similar experiences are common in applying numerical taxonomy to bacteria (Sneath, 1964a). It may therefore be of value to describe characters immediately in some detail and store this information on cards until such time as enough characters and OTU's (operational taxonomic units of any rank; Sokal and Sneath, 1963) have been described to produce a numerical taxonomy.

We have as yet little evidence on comparative costs except in the field of bacteriology, where numerical taxonomy and semiautomated techniques are now commonly employed. Even here accurate figures are not yet available, but the following remarks are ones which we think would be generally accepted by bacteriologists.

Substantial saving of time and effort can result from the planned approach of numerical taxonomy. The savings come under two heads: the organization of the systematic work; and the taxonomic analysis itself.

The need for a planned approach facilitates efficient organization of the work. The bacterial taxonomist can specify a wide range of tests which can be carried out largely by laboratory assistants (though under supervision). He himself can then give more time to the selection of tests and bacteria, and he can concentrate on the many technical problems which arise in this field. A number of advances have recently been made in automating the tests, a trend which is becoming more rapid and paying increasing dividends. It is true that economies under this head are not restricted to the practice of numerical taxonomy, but they are not so attractive when attempting conventional classifications. The traditional method was too often based on a patchwork of data, collected haphazardly, too seldom under standard conditions, much missing, much held only in the memory and insufficiently tabulated. While good work was done by these methods they cannot have been very efficient. Numerical taxonomy makes imperative demands on the worker to fill in as completely as possible the table of characters versus organisms. This is itself a major step in improving the quality and efficiency of taxonomy. Automation and numerical analysis have here each encouraged the development of the other. It may be noted that even in a field which is relatively orderly in its methods, angiosperm taxonomy, the descriptions are very frequently incomplete and not readily comparable. Again, a planned approach can surely increase efficiency.

In bacterial taxonomy it also seems clear that numerical taxonomy is much more efficient than attempts to sort the bacteria into taxa by relying on the memory or by inspecting tables of test results. A computer is faster than mulling over the data. Also the numerical results are easier to check; an unsatisfactory analysis (though uncommon with bacteria) is at least presented in detail for criticism, while the alternative intuitive classifications, some plausible, others less so, are harder to get down on paper and criticize. If a computer analysis and an expert intuitive analysis did yield virtually the same result, it seems clear that computer analysis is today quicker, simpler and cheaper (except possibly in the very simplest cases, such as two homogeneous and easily recognized phenons). Again it seems safe to say that this must also be true for many other groups of organisms besides bacteria. It is not just that most characters in bacteria are non-morphological, for Stearn (1964) points out that numerical taxonomy is useful in plant material in which there are too many character correlations to remember or the detail is minute and so not easy to compare between specimens.

The trend in bacteriology is thus toward automation and numerical analysis. A similar pattern of development, though different in detail, can be expected with many other groups of organisms.

Logically first among the activities of the taxonomists is the collection of specimens. This is a most difficult aspect of the taxonomic process to mechanize or automate. There are, of course, a number of automatic devices for collecting certain groups of organisms. There are automatic light traps, collecting large numbers of flying insects, semiautomatic devices such as Berlese funnels for soil-dwelling arthropods or mass washing techniques of hosts for parasites, and so forth. Perhaps the farthest strides in this direction have been taken by the oceanographers, who in recent years have developed a variety of automatic collection equipment for sampling marine organisms. Success of these methods has forced them to look further for automatic methods of sorting and cataloguing their catches which are beginning to overwhelm them. In special studies, e.g., vegetational classification, devices such as areial photography may be of great value.

Sorting specimens is still a tedious task, difficult to automate except in special cases. The greatest hope for this type of work is in microscopy where electronic devices exist for scanning microscopic structure such as blood cells or chromosomes that count as well as classify these structures. The next logical step is the storing of specimens which, however, will be discussed in a subsequent section on The New Museum.

Finding characters would seem to be an essential function of the taxonomist, who has to compare individuals to get species sorted out, to determine the amount of intraspecific variation and to recognize what characters seem to be of value to distinguish among species. Numerical taxonomy has done much to deemphasize the presumed importance of certain characters. Any features differing from one OTU to the other would be acceptable. It is generally thought that it takes the experience of a specialist in the field to recognize some of the characters and to eliminate those that are obviously unsatisfactory. However, experiments testing these beliefs are currently under way. These are variations of the experiment of the "intelligent ignoramus" in which an unexperienced worker is attempting to classify a group from characters he can observe in a relatively limited period of time. In a small study using hypothetical creatures it has been shown (Sneath, 1946b) that a child of seven could choose characters from diagrams of heraldic beasts to give a dendrogram by numerical taxonomy; there can be little doubt that the dendrogram makes good sense, as can be seen from Fig. 5 in the paper cited. Should these experiments yield satisfactory results much of the emphasis on experience in the recording of characters cannot be justified. From here it is only a relatively small philosophical step, although a major technical advance, to automatic data recording devices whose development should be one of the highlights of the decade to come. Optical scanners are now coming on the market which, like a television camera, scan photographs, film, microscope slides and similar objects and convert these to input for the computer. The computer could then define characters of the organisms according to logically set rules. Under favorable circumstances classifications could be produced for organisms whose characters and measurements are entirely automatically recorded. Similar techniques are being developed for larger structures, especially photogrammetry for vertebrate skulls. There already exist machines for the automatic analysis of biochemical differences, such as animo acid analyzers which "fingerprint" organisms automatically. Such fingerprints might subsequently be used as input for numerical taxonomic work.

Far simpler than definition by the computer of optically scanned characters is the random delineation of characters. Masks with random patterns of holes are placed over the output of the scanner and images of different OTU's are compared by their patterns visible through these masks. This technique deliberately removes all biological judgment from the taxonomic process and would not, on face value, appear to be a promising approach. Yet, as this paper goes to press Rohlf and Sokal (1966) have just completed a pilot study of this method on two groups of organisms (mosquitoes and the hypothetical "Caminalcules"), which yielded surprisingly good phenetic classifications. If this approach continues to be successful, its simplicity would make optical scanning of organisms feasible much earlier than if characters have to be defined by the taxonomist or the computer.

As long as characters are manually recorded, their efficient transformation to a form suitable for EDP handling is important. The numerical or plus and minus coding of qualitative characters as well as the numerical recording of quantitative characters are conventional. It is customary to record characters on specially prepared sheets already in the format in which they are to be punched on cards for input to the computer. If there is any advantage in permitting input of qualitative information (such as word descriptions) into the computer this can also be arranged. Programs could be written which would automatically convert terms such as LARGE, or SMALL, or RED and GREEN into numerical codes.

It is our belief (Sokal and Sneath, 1963; Sokal and Camin, 1965) that the emerging new theory of taxonomy will be largely empirical. It should lead to important advances in our understanding of evolution, while maintaining a formal separation between evolutionary studies and classification based on phenetics (for a contrary view see Mayr, 1965, as well as Sokal *et al,* 1965 for a discussion of the points raised by Mayr). Much systematic work will be numerical and statistical in the wider sense, although the actual techniques of numerical taxonomy as we know them today may be considerably modified. The recent incorporation into numerical taxonomy of objective and operational techniques for estimating cladogenies (Camin and Sokal, 1965) is reconciling some of our more hesitant colleagues to the numerical philosophy.

Studies of infraspecific variation will be basically statistical in nature. Suitable statistical procedures should be used for these studies and computer aids employed whenever possible to cut down computational load as well as to enable the investigator to carry out appropriately complex computations rather than simple ones which do not really answer the questions involved. For further discussion of these procedures see Sokal (1965). The study of geographic variation is specially suited to automation by means of computers. The necessary multivariate computations can only be efficiently carried out on computers; however, various computations related to mapping the variation, such as trend surface fitting (Krumbein, 1955) or multidimensional representation (Jolicoeur, 1959; Thomas, 1965) are also done by machine, as is the preparation and copying o the maps themselves.

The definition and recognition of species is currently a controversial subject aggravated by the use of the term species in different senses. If phenetic species are sought, the methods of numerical taxonomy can effectively find them. If, on the other hand, biological species are sought, we are not yet in a position to discuss their efficiency since we believe that the criteria for definition of the so-called biological species category are usually nonoperational. The description of similiarities among species and higher taxa and their assignment to higher categories can be more adequately and efficiently done by numerical taxonomy than by any other method currently available.

Work in numerical taxonomy during the last decade has demonstrated that similarities among taxonomic units can be efficiently estimated by computer techniques. The computations for the analysis of the *Hoplitis* complex by Michener and Sokal (1957) which originally took several months to carry out, can now be handled in two minutes on an IBM 7094, including the drawing of the dendrograms. The cost of 10 to 20 dollars includes the keypunching of the data. Reviewing this amount of data (122 characters for 97 species) by conventional methods would take prohibitively long even if it were feasible.

The assumptions and practices of numerical taxonomy are still undergoing revision at the present time. We are still gaining information on how many characters we need for a reliable study. We are learning whether there really is an asymptote of information as more and more characters are added to a study. We need to learn more about confidence limits of the various statistics employed. There is considerable doubt whether the coefficients of similarity proposed so far are the best possible, and methods of representation of taxonomic structure are currently undergoing revision. Some of these changes we have been able to forecast as early as three or four years ago. Stability of concepts and practices will be reached sooner as more systematists investigate the methodologies and collaborate in the development of new ones. We may hope that institutions whose major function is the study of taxonomy will also stimulate and sponsor research in the theory and practice of taxonomy in general, in addition to research on specific animal and plant groups.

The remarks made above also apply to the finding of taxonomic structure. While new clustering methods are constantly being developed for defining and describing taxonomic structure, it is already obvious that these techniques will be computerized and that conventional computer output (or output by means of plotters) will be used to represent the taxonomic relationships and arrive at classifications.

In the recently developed numerical phylogenies (Camin and Sokal, 1965) computers assist us in the phylogenetic evaluation of characters and the deduction of cladistic sequences, as well as their graphic representation. Only with computers can the many alternative hypotheses be evaluated and decisions be made on the most probable course of evolution.

Keys

Having established a classification by some operational method, the construction of the relevant keys to identify specimens can clearly be done by computers. Some of the errors which are occasionally committed in setting up dichotomous keys would be avoided by logical and consistent computer programs. For purposes of taxonomic keys and identification of specimens, weighting of characters must be introduced to emphasize those characters which are most effective in distinguishing between previously established taxa. Weight must not only be statistical in the sense of providing an efficient criterion for differentiation, but must also take into account the ease of observing or measuring a given character, the probability of its being present in the specimen that is likely to be studied, the chance of it being damaged or confused, etc. Alternative structures must be provided for identification in case the preferred structure is unavailable.

Although the logic of key-making may change little, their physical form can be adapted to EDP and a variety of forms may prove useful in different circumstances. However, non-divisive keys are very suitable for EDP; in these the unknown is matched against a table of chosen characters to find the taxon that shows the best fit. Such tables have the shortcoming that some characters are redundant in any given task of identification. Too large a table is therefore inefficient, and it will be better to use several small ones successively. Both for these and for the usual divisive (dichotomous) keys it will often be advantageous to have punched cards with the key characters printed on them, while for taxa that are rarely required it would be simple to have a printed mask under which a card could be slipped for marking or punching. Such developments will raise in an acute form the problem of standardizing descriptive terms. Considering the difficulty of reaching wide agreement on these it may well be more effective to substitute nontechnical descriptions of the characters (perhaps with diagrams) and thus widen the range of users. Although computers will be of major assistance in preparing the data for all keys, they will not necessarily be required to operate them; all steps from the usual keys in books to EDP machines will have their place. Several attempts are now being made to develop simple, portable devices for use in bacteriology.

The more sophisticated keys will usually be probabilistic, that is they will give (on assumptions reasonable in the light of current knowledge) the likelihood that the identification of a given specimen is correct. Other possible alternatives and their probabilities will also be given. This type of key is unnecessary at higher taxonomic ranks, where the phenetic groupings are sharply distinct, but at low ranks such keys may be of great value. Besides assessing the reliability of the identifications, they also pinpoint intermediates if they occur and draw attention to deficiencies in the identification system.

The advent of on-line computing will make possible a new interaction between taxonomists and computers for the identification of specimens (see also Jahn, 1961, 1962). Taxonomic keys can be stored in the computer and keys can be presented in the form of a dialogue between the taxonomist and the computer. The taxonomist could type in a message: I HAVE AN ANIMAL, and the computer would reply at once by asking questions corresponding to the couplets in a taxonomic key (i.e., HOW MANY LEGS HAS IT?). The taxonomist replies to these questions and is posed further questions by the computer. A much more intricate logic could be built into a taxonomic identification program than is customary in the conventional taxonomic keys. Branching to other keys, checks against "false turns" and graphic displays of pictures of the animal or its parts are possible. When the automatic recording of morphological or biochemical characters becomes commonplace, the identification can be carried out routinely with minimum intervention by the investigator. We visualize that another ten years or so should see the development of machinery which will automatically carry out the biochemical analysis of an insect (or other organism) submitted to an agency for identification. The results of such an analysis would be automatically fed into the computer, compared with previous data and identification issued unless the specimen matches nothing in the memory of the computer (in which case its biochemical characteristics could be listed).

Finally, entire descriptions of new species and higher taxa could be stored in memory banks of various sorts. These descriptions could be of the conventional verbal kind or more likely would be abbreviated using some system of coding that would also permit numerical taxonomy to be carried out in these organisms. A variety of information storage and retrieval devices are now being manufactured, marketed and developed in connection with automation of libraries. These devices, which include the storing of verbal as well as pictorial information, would be ideal for recording species descriptions. The ability to sort through material of this sort and extract the pertinent information on certain queries would be an important advantage of computerized species descriptions over the conventional printed form. We shall further elaborate on this aspect of automation in taxonomy in the section on the International Taxonomic Center.

Nomenclature

Any change in taxonomic procedure inevitably will involve a change in nomenclature. Although it can be done in a formal way the subject of nomenclature cannot in practice be dissociated from taxonomy per se. As long as we are going to study and group organisms (by whatever criteria), we will want names or labels to refer to them. Berio (1953), Cain (1959) and Michener (1963) have been among the recent critics of the present system of naming organisms. Sokal and Sneath (1963) have pointed out that the present system of nomenclature does not adequately fulfill the various functions expected of it. Change is also necessary because of the inevitable adoption of EDP for the processing of taxonomic information, whatever the fate of numerical taxonomy. We have pointed out elsewhere that as new methods of processing taxonomic information are developed taxonomic procedures should be modernized. Conversely, any new nomenclatural system must clearly be EDP oriented. Michener (1963) believes that current classifications are not as natural as they could be, partly because of the tradition of mutually exclusive taxa, reinforced by the system of nomenclature by which the genus name is part of the classification and at the same time part of the name of the organism being classified. He would therefore institute a system of uninominal nomenclature visualizing advantages such as simplicity of rules and relatively great stability in addition to freeing classification from the restrictions of nomenclature. He proposes that present generic and specific names be united or hyphenated to form stabilized uninominals. Genera and higher categories would then become relatively informal groupings. A system of nomenclature is tentatively suggested and is illustrated in a subsequent paper (Michener, 1964). Michener also proposes a double system of numbering species by a registration, or serial number which we will call a reference number below. Such numbers would be consecutive and have no taxonomic implication. The other part of the system is the classification number whose separate digits would represent the position of the species in the system of nature (as suggested by Gould, 1958).

Any nomenclatural system developed today should allow for automated information storage and retrieval, otherwise we will be in the position of a newly organized, major corporation equipping their bookkeeping department with simple adding machines. We have to free ourselves from the notion that a name can fulfill a multiplicity of functions. What are these functions? Most obviously one function is that of a label for a group of organisms, so that when we mention the name others will know what we are talking about. However, that is already an imprecise statement. In what way will they know what is being talked about? Will they know what the creatures look like? This is true in relatively few cases only. Almost everyone knows *Canis familiaris* or *Musca domestica*. However, there are very few people who will have any idea of *Pemphigus populi-transversus*.

Is the name to serve as a proper name for a group of organisms which the other person can look up in various reference works? In that case, a number will do as well as a name for this and it is probably easier to look up and find.

Should the name of an organism have mnemonic value? In some cases, yes. When we speak of *Ulmus americanus,* most of us would know that we are referring to the American elm. It would be much more difficult to refer to 73264 and know that this number refers to an American elm, although numbers are probably more easily memorized than people are willing to admit. This is a controversial point, witness the present controversy in the United States about changing telephone exchange numbers from alphabetical prefixes to numerical ones. Trivial names have long lost the descriptive value they had in the early days of binominal nomenclature.

Should we know from the name what the systematic position of an organism is? There is much to be said in favor of this and it was one of the important reasons behind the development of the binominal system. However, with the successive splitting of genera, and the great multiplication of generic names, the usefulness of the old genus names has largely vanished. Perhaps there are as many as 100,000 names of genera. It is not possible for anyone to remember the names of more than a minute fraction of this number. For indicating systematic position of a taxon a numerical system would be superior to a verbal one. Such a number for our organism should be clearly distinguished from a reference or registration number which is just an arbitrary sequential listing (let us call the sequential listing the *reference number* and the new number which explains the classificatory position of the organism the *classification number*). Such a classification number would enable a trained taxonomist to tell immediately the phylum, class, order, family and genus of any given species.

Beyond that we need a common reference name for those organisms that are frequent subjects of research or common knowledge. A uninominal system contracting the present genus name with the species name has many advantages. The name in the most recent revision of the group should be accepted; author names would be unnecessary. For new species the prefix could be taken from the most phenetically similar organism. For ordinary faunal lists, the reference number would be sufficient, although names could be given if desired; the arrangement of these numbers could be in numerical or in systematic order. Another approach might be the completely automatic renaming of all taxa for which a name is desired. This is already being done by computer for newly developed drugs.

An important consideration of a nomenclatorial system is the question of how information about the organism is to be retrieved. Among the problems of document retrieval being discussed currently is the following: What is the optimum system of classification for a series of documents so that in a large organization a document can be retrieved with a minimum of searches? Any given document must be indexed under those headings which will most frequently be employed. Storage should be arranged so that access to more frequently required documents is easier than to those less often needed. These problems have clear relevance to taxonomy. Research in this field is urgently needed.

Finally, let us take up the problem of changing classifications and Michener's problem of overlapping taxa. As regards changes in affinities, this can be done easily by changing the proper digit in the classification number. The reference number would remain sacrosanct, except in the case of the splitting or uniting of species. One or two digits might be reserved in that number for allowing for derivative taxa in the case of splitting, although this is unnecessary because a note could be made that taxon 173456, prior to such and such a date was included with taxon 122570. Since higher taxa would have numbers as well as names, the fact that a given form may have given its name to a higher taxon and later was removed from it, is not particularly important.

We are not yet convinced of the necessity of overlapping taxa since we believe that the relationships for which Michener (1963) feels this device necessary can somehow be described both through a series of separate relationships of a given OTU to other taxa or perhaps by the use of intersecting sets in a hyperspace. One way might be by the establishment of an undefined subtaxon in a given higher taxon such as in the *Clarkia* case discussed by

Michener (1963). We could consider that intergeneric hybrid to be a species in an undefined taxon located in the same family as the genus *Clarkia* and the genus *Exus*. Alternatively it could be regarded as a new genus. Probably a not inconsiderable number of what are now genera of flowering plants arose as intergeneric hybrids, i.e., from crosses between species considered to be in different genera.

The New Museum

Methods of housing and storing of specimens have undergone rapid changes during the last few decades. In entomological collections the adoption of movable trays permitting easy rearrangement of groups of specimens is a major time-saving device. Steps to break up named collections left to an institution as a legacy and integrating these with the research collection by some systematic arrangement also help make research collections more functional.

Ehrlich (1964) in a recent paper has asked some rather fundamental questions about the scientific purposes of natural history collections apart from their value as hobbies and for esthetic reasons. Is it necessary to continue collecting ad infinitum or should only certain representative samples of nature be represented in collections? Certainly it is not axiomatic that all of nature must be collected and stored.

The arrangement of the specimens in museum collections and herbaria should be such that those used most frequently should be most accessible, those used less frequently less accessible. This might be more important from the point of view of efficiency in a museum than arranging the collection by some systematic catalogue.

We cannot anticipate all uses to which specimens will eventually be put and therefore they should be preserved in as general a way as possible, permitting future study of various organ systems, their biochemistry, etc. Thus the traditional methods of storing specimens, such as skins of birds or pinned butterflies, may be unsatisfactory from a scientific point of view.

Another function of the museum of the future may be as a repository for records of the detailed structures revealed by molecular biology, as well as a source of specimens for such study. Some attempts have already been made to exploit the information in the amino acid sequences of proteins (e.g., Margoliash, 1963; Buettner-Janusch and Hill, 1965). Sackin and Sneath (1965) have described a computer method for comparing protein chains and estimating the overall similarity between them that can also detect deletions, reduplications and inversions. It may one day be possible to read molecular detail by the electron microscope. If so, well-preserved specimens may be a valuable source of data. This would open a vast new field in which museum and herbarium specimens could be exploited to yield new knowledge. Of course we do not yet know how closely phenetic difference in fine structure (as revealed in proteins, for example) parallels phenetic difference estimated from conventional characters. But if the parallel is close it may well be that far more information of taxonomic value than we anticipate will come from molecular biology. This is illustrated by the two proteins of the bacterium *Pseudomonas fluorescens* whose structures are known, cytochrome C and azurin (Ambler, 1963; Ambler and Brown, 1964): the amino acid sequences of these, 210 in all, must represent a sizeable fraction of all the information available on this bacterium from all sources. Certainly the potential information is vast, so that EDP will be essential to handling it, and the only feasible way of using it for systematics will be by numerical taxonomy. In addition such information will be of enormous interest to other branches of biology.

Automatic data processing of museum catalogues will profoundly affect museum science. Most of the cataloguing procedures as now practiced in various museums around the world are inefficient in terms of manpower as well as budget. Collections of vertebrates and fossils are generally supplied with an accession number. The vertebrates have labels attached to them, fossils are recorded in catalogues and are numbered correspondingly. Entomologists have always shied away from accession numbers and generally would find it impractical to list each individual insect. Thus collection records, identifications and any other pertinent information are stored on the pin together with the insect. Similar information is recorded on the herbarium sheets on which plant specimens are generally mounted. Efforts to use an accession number system (with information recorded in ledger books) have often been made, but have generally resulted in bad experiences, with ledger books being mislaid or destroyed and the accession numbers becoming meaningless.

Even with the simplest types of data-handling machines (such as a keypunch, a sorter, and a tabulating machine) a very efficient card catalogue of the holdings of a museum could be prepared. However, the development of modern computer systems makes storage on magnetic tapes or disks more efficient. The detailed system for cataloguing a museum's holding would have to be devised by a committee of experts. We understand that moves in this direction are under way at several institutions. Some of the properties of such a system may be mentioned. Each individual accession item would have the minimum information now contained on museum labels, i.e., the scientific name and author name, the collection locality and date, the collector's name, possibly the donor's name. Since more information could be handled in an EDP system we could add several higher category levels for a specimen such as family, order, class; various geographic categories such as county, country, continent; ecological information, the accession date, the sex and condition of the specimen. The location of the specimen must also be indicated since it is unlikely to be stored in museum cases sequentially by accession number. Assuming no more than 160 digits of alphabetical, numerical or special symbols, the above information on one specimen could be coded onto three IBM cards and stored in less than 1,000 bits of memory.

Once committed to the memory a file of information of this sort could be used to prepare printed catalogues of various sorts: one ordered numerically by accession number, a second ordered in conventional taxonomic sequence, a third arranged alphabetically based on species names. These catalogues could be produced from high speed printers producing several thousand lines of type a minute and multiple copies of certain catalogues could be prepared by photo-offset from the computer output or by sending output tape to one of the establishments specializing in offset printing from computer tapes. To avoid the aforementioned danger of mislaying a catalogue, several copies would be available in different places in the museum and others would be located at libraries in other institutions to make the holdings of the museum widely known. This would avoid much of the current tedious correspondence inquiring about the availability of specimens at a given institution.

A master file and multiple reproduction of catalogues from it should clearly lay to rest any fears about loss of the file containing the information corresponding to accession numbers. There is some danger of the accession number being lost from the specimen but that is no different from the present danger of a label being lost. If for some reason curators would still prefer to have the entire written record attached to the specimen this could be produced by various devices. Photo-offset of the computer output reduced in size would be one solution, another would be punched paper tape which could actuate a linotype machine setting miniature type, while a third would be microfilm produced by the computer. An interesting possibility might be the development of labels containing small sections of magnetic surface strips to contain the same information as is recorded in the master file. Similar records are now on the backs of the statements of many banks.

However, not only can such general catalogues be prepared but also special catalogues in response to special requests. Examples are lists of the following for a given museum: All the Diptera from Kenya, all the undamaged specimens of a given species of crane fly from western North America, all the insects donated or collected by a given person, all bees recorded as feeding on a given species of host plant and so on and so forth. As Gould (1958) has pointed out, a wide variety of information would be obtainable at relatively small cost, information that is essentially unavailable today, because the work which it would take to answer these questions in prohibitive. When out of the spirit of scientific collegiality curators do answer questions, such as "how many specimens of XYZ do you have in your collection that you could lend me?," this takes a substantial proportion of their time which could be much more valuably spent on other endeavours. In this connection some of the remarks made earlier on time-costing are especially appropriate. Once the initial investment in creating the file is made, the actual expenses for maintaining and undating it and preparing the catalogues would be relatively minor. However, expenses for maintaining such a file are likely to be higher than anticipated on the basis of the *present* demand for information, since once such a file exists, it will receive many new questions, which now are never posed. Frequently, because of the limited time of curatorial staff, graduate students working on theses, as well as mature investigators, have to make trips to visit a collection, not so much for a study of the material itself, which could be sent by mail, but for an examination of the collection to find out what it contains of interest to them. The periodic updating of collection records is an important positive feature of an EDP museum system. If the computer is located away from the museum and on-line computing is not yet available, the updating has to be carried on at relatively infrequent intervals, possibly once a month. At this time new cards are sent to the computer center indicating any new accessions, loans and status changes in present holdings. Updating for small and middle sized collections would require going through the entire file once. Large files should be substructured. For very large collections, if the updating is not extensive, an external catalogue would provide indications, which file needs to be entered for the updating. The most logical arrangement for a museum file would be taxonomic, irrespective of the sequence of the accession numbers. Thus a search of material on Miocene horses would not require searching through the information on Recent Coleoptera, simply because it would be so unlikely that any single query would cover two widely different taxa, while (for example) arrangement alphabetically by generic name would involve searching almost all the files.

The queries to the system could be carried out at the same time that the updating is done or in a pass through the updated file immediately subsequent to the updating. Even monthly queries to the system would be of great usefulness and interest since curators frequently wait far longer than one month to reply to certain time-consuming questions. However, biweekly or weekly passes through the file may be quite feasible both as regards time and cost. As soon as on-line facilities are available and the museum's business warrants it, the total museum accessions could be on a slow access memory file and could be questioned and updated continuously. As new material is accessioned this could be communicated to the computer via teletype.

Speed and costs might be of interest here. We estimate that a one hundred thousand specimen file could be adequately maintained on a single roll of tape if 160 alphanumerical characters are sufficient for one record. Such a file could be reviewed, searched and updated by a medium speed computer in less than three minutes at a cost in computer time of $9 or less. Many queries could be answered simultaneously in a single pass through the computer. Costs would mount for a more extensive collection but only if all of it had to be processed or kept on-line continuously. For the typical museum, departmentalized by taxonomic units, it is likely that the file (although handled by a central processor) would be taxonomically structured into subfiles. Thus the various rolls of tape could be mounted in succession and only be requested if updating or queries are required of them, keeping costs down considerably even for a one or two million specimen museum. However, in a relatively short time tapes will be outdated for a data storage task of such dimensions and will be replaced by disks. For all practical purposes disks have unlimited storage capacity. They can usually be directly accessed through the computer and their cost per unit storage is decreasing rapidly. On-line inquiries to the system, not involving searches of the entire file, would be quite inexpensive. Inquiries from the outside may well be charged a fee for the information. A person who on request receives a printed record of all the holdings of species X in the museum, complete with dates, collection records, etc., may expect to pay for the cost of obtaining this information in the same way as for a microfilm of a research report. At the moment such costs are absorbed by the museum (as they are sometimes absorbed by libraries) and since museum budgets for technical assistance are limited, inquiries are answered at the expense of the curator's research time.

The duties of museum curators also need reconsidering. A substantial proportion of their time is taken up with tedious repetitive tasks, which could be performed by lower level personnel and in many cases by a machine. Labeling, cataloguing, searching and rearranging of collections are among these tasks. They are frequently carried out by curators with Ph.D. degrees at the expense of time devoted to taxonomic research. There are a number of reasons for this, which are not always easy to disentangle. Partly it is due to tradition; certain routines are part of the accepted work load of the profession. It takes a substantial revolution in outlook to change such attitudes on the part of curators and museum administrators.

Secondly, funds for help have not been available. Museums are on notoriously slim budgets. Museum curators everywhere would doubtless agree with us on this point, and would join us in a request for more funds for museums, and especially for semiskilled staff to do some of the repetitive tasks. Indeed, shortage of such staff was perhaps the biggest complaint found by Beaman (1965) in a study of questionnaires to herbarium curators. Museum curators should define more clearly than in the past the nature of their functions. Increased emphasis on their scientific and research roles may well result in increased budgets and status as reflected in the pay scale of professional museum personnel. If taxonomy is to become a science whose rate of progress and intellectual status is to be comparable to those of other biological disciplines, the amount of time taxonomists devote to it rather than to the pinning of bugs or shipping of specimens would have to be greatly increased. Automation of the museum is clearly not the whole answer to this problem, but it is certainly a step in the right direction. We quote from a relevant, recent discussion on automation in libraries (Swanson, 1964): "In my view, therefore, automation is far more likely to upgrade the profession of librarianship than to replace it. Automation upgrades it by permitting a sharper and clearer identification of that which is really of professional character in librarianship. Those librarians who have some kind of irrational antipathy toward mechanization *per se* (not just toward some engineers who have inappropriately oversold mechanization) I regard with some suspicion, because I think they do not have sufficient respect for their profession. They may be afraid that librarianship is going to be exposed as being intellectually vacuous, which I don't think is so. Even in a completely mechanized library there would still be need for skilled reference librarians, bibliographers, cataloguers, acquisition specialists, administrators, and others. Those librarians in the future who regard mechanization, not with suspicion, but as a subject to be mastered will be those who will plan our future libraries and who will plan the things that machines are going to do. There will be no doubt of their professional status." Replace "librarian" by "taxonomist", "library" by "museum" and "librarianship" by "taxonomy" and the comment is very much to the point in the present context.

The International Taxonomic Center

Many of the changes advocated in the previous sections can be undertaken by individual institutions and some of them by individual scientists. If the latter are not associated with a university equipped with a computation center they may have difficulty automating their taxonomic procedures. But this is not insuperable as long as data processing can be done by mail and eventually by telephone lines. Cataloguing and accession EDP systems for museums might well be worked out at one museum and then adapted to other, similar institutions to avoid waste of time and effort. However, some of the procedures require taxonomic, phylogenetic and nomenclatorial decisions made by international agreement. Centralization of these procedures will therefore be necessary in the same way that international agreement has to be obtained for the present international codes of nomenclature. We visualize the functions of a national or international taxonomic center as follows.

It stores names and numbers of organisms as the basic record of a vast filing system. Stored together with these names and numbers (or accessible through them) is a large amount of bibliographic and other information on each species —as many characteristics as have been recorded by different observers, ecological facts, distribution records and the like. The organization of such a file is a challenging task. Should these data per species merely be a bibliographic extract of where the information is to be found, without any indication as to what the information is? Or, at the other extreme, should all information about the species be stored verbatim in the memory (a prodigious feat, probably beyond the capacity of present-day computer systems, although not necessarily so five or ten years from now)? Or should the system of storing be somewhere in between these extremes (most reasonable, but most probably least economical of time in terms of preparing the file)? Much thought will have to be expended on such problems and they will have to be attacked in small pilot studies first, to check the feasibility of the suggested procedures on a relatively small group. A total file for all organisms would clearly have to be prepared over a large period of time and by different groups of people for different fields.

If the data can be stored in such a way as to be available for subsequent numerical taxonomic work much time will eventually be saved. Data could, of course, be coded in such a way that they can be used directly for numerical taxonomic computations. However, a standard format of verbal description of characters (as is quite conventional in a number of taxonomic fields) may also be used. For each taxonomic group descriptive terms would have to be closely defined. It may be that description in not too highly technical language, using a fairly limited vocabulary, may be better suited to this purpose. It is quite possible for the computer to store this information either in verbal form and automatically code it numerically when a numerical taxonomy is undertaken; or the verbal format familiar to the taxonomist can be automatically coded and stored numerically in the memory of the computer and subsequently used for numerical taxonomic work.

One of the functions of the center will be the preparation, in collaboration with the taxonomists who use its services, of classifications of various groups from the information available in memory. These will be general taxonomies for general use (natural *sensu* Gilmour). Special classifications for various special interests and purposes will continue to be made as needed. These will include numerically constructed cladograms. It may well be convenient to have the taxonomic center prepare these on demand from data abstracted from the central records, the center functioning as a sort of general taxonomic utility. It is expected that numerical taxonomy will produce stable classifications when based on an adequate number of characters. Nevertheless, additional information both as regards new characters and new taxa will occur regularly and will require the periodical updating and revision of classifications. This can be done automatically by the computer, and if new insights on taxonomic relationships result these can be communicated to those interested.

Taxonomic lists of all known species in any genus or family can easily be prepared by the center and would be available for checking to interested investigators and for deposit in libraries. The preparation of general taxonomic keys and of special faunal keys could also be automated (as discussed in the previous section) and these could be obtained from the center either in printed booklet form or in the form of a computer program permitting a man-machine on-line interaction (conversational mode) for identification of organisms.

A very important function of the international center would be the storage of descriptions of new species. New species would have to be assigned only new reference numbers under a "numericlatural" scheme (Little, 1964), and both reference numbers and names under a nomenclatural scheme (Michener, 1963, 1964). In the latter case there must be a search to find whether the name is preoccupied. This can be done by the computer. If a mononominal system is adopted the computer may actually assign a name to the species similar to current practices in the drug industry where computers after searching their memories for preoccupied trade names construct euphonious names for new products.

Sufficient information will be needed to describe the species, to distinguish it from all other known similar species and to permit its incorporation into the taxonomic system by numerical taxonomy. This will require some standardization of species descriptions within taxonomic groups. New descriptions would have to meet standards established by a committee of the international taxonomic center. If the new organism described were indistinguishable from one described previously, or if insufficient distinguishing characteristics for a critical evaluation of its taxonomic status were provided by the investigator, the new description would not be accepted by the center. Taxonomists, who so far have had few restrictions on publishing information (and misinformation), may find such regulations, and the possibility of a taxonomic "censorship board," irksome. However, we feel that an information-screening committee, functioning properly, fairly, and equitably, would be salutary for systematics. Similar review boards function well in other fields of science. Taxonomic legislation so far has been largely regulative rather than restrictive, meaning that only after damage has been done by a misidentification or a wrong name or false placement in a taxonomic group will this be corrected in a subsequent publication. The waste of time and effort resulting from these activities should be curbed.

The automatic search for homonyms and synonyms is another benefit of committing taxonomic information to an EDP system. We should point out that while the computerized taxonomic system could handle many aspects of these problems, to the extent even of suggesting new unused names for species carrying homonyms, *the purpose of such a new system should be not to repeat procedural mistakes of previous generations more efficiently, but to devise a system in which such occurrences are either impossible or at least far less likely.*

It is obvious that many different catalogues can be provided from the information stored at the center. These would include faunal or floral catalogues for given areas, possibly restricted to certain taxonomic groups, ecological catalogues, and catalogues of special types of characters such as morphological or biochemical. Catalogues of museum holdings abstracted from the information for each species could be prepared independently at the center simply from sorting through the information on a taxonomic group for locations where specimens of a given species are preserved.

One of the most important aspects of an international taxonomic center, however, would be its bibliographic potential. One of the great difficulties in any scientific field is keeping up with the literature. The taxonomist working on a special group wishes to know much or all of the information that is being published about it. Especially does he wish to be informed of any new species described in the group and of any recent revision of the group. Such information could be obtained through the international taxonomic center. Persons who are interested in special groups could have subscriptions to the bibliographic series of the center which would not only provide references to papers having information about species in these groups, but which would also provide the interested person with descriptions of new species as well as revisions of higher ranking taxa. At the moment this information is distributed in a very inefficient fashion. At present one has to publish a paper, usually in a journal, in order to describe a new species or to revise a taxonomic group. These papers take up a tremendous amount of shelf space in libraries, but very frequently are of interest to only a very few specialists in the world. Yet they take up general journal space which should contain material of much wider interest. How much better would it be to have this information centrally stored and available on demand, yet not cluttering up bookshelves in numerous libraries all over the world quite uselessly? The time is at hand when the flood of taxonomic literature will have to be channelled more productively and economically to the persons who really need to have this information. There are numerous graphic output devices which would permit the reproduction of line drawings (and even photographs). Clearly there should be centers in different countries, and certainly on different continents, where all of this information is readily accessible.

The Training of Systematists

The changes in procedure discussed in the previous section will require levels of training among taxonomists far greater than those still largely prevalent (Sokal, 1964). Students must be taught not only the legalities of nomenclatural rules but they must also obtain a thorough grounding in the principles, philosophy and history of taxonomy. They need to know what they are attempting to do and whether their practices will achieve their goals. Taxonomists need to have a thorough understanding of current evolutionary theory. They must be familiar with modern ideas on speciation and evolution with population genetics and ecology. Depending on their field of research, they should have an understanding of principles and techniques of such fields as cytology or behavior. A knowledge of biochemistry and of techniques for investigating biochemical differences in organisms is equally necessary.

Of the ancillary fields of systematics the most important is clearly statistics. The application of this field to systematics has recently been reviewed (Sokal, 1965). Even present-day practices in systematics require a thorough knowledge of statistics for their proper execution. The prospects for the future are that this trend will continue at an ever accelerating pace. The requisite knowledge of statistics for a taxonomist is not limited to the rudiments of the subject (i.e., mean, standard errors and t-tests) but requires a thorough understanding of analysis of variance, correlation and regression techniques and several of the multivariate techniques currently being applied.

Those taxonomists concerned with information storage and retrieval in organisms (e.g., museum and herbarium curators) will need to become familiar with principles and practices of electronic data processing. Courses in the fields mentioned above should become required of all persons aiming to specialize in systematics in graduate school.

Recommendations on the training of systematists in Britain have been recently made by a committee of the Systematics Association (Anonymous, 1964), and some of these would also be appropriate to conditions in other countries. In particular taxonomy should be taught wherever possible as a unified subject, and not compartmentalized between botany, zoology, paleontology, etc. Taxonomy is often not taught as such, and students are expected to acquire its rudiments during other courses of instruction. Yet even undergraduate teaching in taxonomy should enable a student to negotiate with reasonable success almost any group of organisms without being a specialist in them, and with a minimum of help from specialists. The basic principles of taxonomy are applicable (with some modification) to all groups of organisms. There is also a tendency for some institutions, particularly museums, to become cut off from the mainstream of systematics. If so, closer contacts with university departments are one answer, but another is to set up within the institutions research groups which do not have heavy routine commitments.

Summary and Recommendations

We would like to summarize our thoughts on preparing taxonomy for the decades ahead by means of the following recommendations to taxonomists and to institutions responsible for taxonomic work.

Museum authorities should give considerable thought to the application of electronic data processing to cataloguing and bookkeeping of their collections and to other repetitive work by the museum curators. A number of efforts should be made to automate relatively small collections to determine the problems faced by taxonomists in automating this aspect of their work; to seek improvements; and finally to develop general systems applicable to most museum collections. It will also be necessary to investigate what differences in such systems are needed because of the different nature of various collections (e.g., insects, plants, birds). At least one if not more of the scientific staff members of a museum should be familiar in depth with problems and procedures in EDP as it relates to museum work.

Responsible national and international agencies should take steps to examine how the present rules of nomenclature should be amended to permit automation of nomenclature and cataloguing of all organisms. Any subsequent changes in the international rules of nomenclature should take requirements of electronic data processing into consideration.

Moreover, serious deliberation should take place whether the entire system of Linnean nomenclature should not be changed so as to make it meet more nearly the requirements of modern biology as well as those of electronic data processing.

These developments are likely to come about eventually, regardless of whether steps are currently taken by organizations concerned with taxonomic work. It would, however, be much to the benefit of the science if these measures could be taken in an orderly deliberate fashion, rather than as decisions made by EDP specialists unfamiliar with the biological necessities and requirements.

In this connection funding agencies, both governmental and private foundations concerned with scientific research, should give serious attention to seeding various pilot projects that will develop procedures of the sort discussed in this paper in order to effect an orderly transition from conventional to automated data handling in taxonomy. By an active interaction between taxonomists and EDP specialists we may also begin to see the development of systems (software) as well as the hardware specially designed to meet the needs of taxonomy. To the extent that government scientific bodies guide national research policy, movements that encourage the automation of taxonomic procedures should be encouraged and sponsored.

References

Ambler, R. P. (1963) The amino acid sequence of *Pseudomonas* cytochrome C-551. Biochem. J. 89: 349–378.

Ambler, R. P. and L. H. Brown. (1964) The amino acid sequence of *Pseudomonas fluorescens* azurin. J. Mol. Biol. 9: 825–828.

Anonymous. (1964) Development and support of systematics in Britain. Nature 203: 358–359.

Beaman, J. H. (1965) The present status and operational aspects of university herbaria. Taxon 14: 127–133.

Berio, E. (1953) The rule of priority in zoological nomenclature. Bull. Zool. Nomenclature 8: 30–40.

Brown, W. L. Jr. (1965) Numerical taxonomy; Convergence and evolutionary reduction. Systematic Zool. 14: 101–109.

Buettner-Janusch, J. and R. L. Hill. (1965) Molecules and monkeys. Science 147: 836–842.

Cain, A. J. (1959) The post-Linnean development of taxonomy. Proc. Linn. Soc. London, 170 Session (1957–58): 234–244.

Camin, J. H. and R. R. Sokal. (1965) A method for deducing branching sequences in phylogeny. Evolution 19: 311–326.

Davis, P. H. and V. H. Heywood. (1963) Principles of Angiosperm taxonomy. D. Van Nostrand, Princeton and New York. 556 pp.

Ehrlich, P. R. (1964) Some axioms of taxonomy. Systematic Zool. 13: 109–123.

Ehrlich, P. R. and R. W. Holm. (1962) Patterns and populations. Science 137: 652–657.

Gilmour, J. S. L. (1940) Taxonomy and philosophy, pp. 461–478. *In* J. S. Huxley [ed.] The new systematics. Clarendon Press, Oxford. 583 pp.

Gould, S. W. (1958) Punched cards, binomial names and numbers. Am. J. Botany 45: 331–339.

Jahn, T. L. (1961) Man versus machine: a future problem in protozoan taxonomy. Systematic Zool. 10: 179–192.

Jahn, T. L. (1962) The use of computers in systematics. J. Parasitol. 48: 656–663.

Jolicoeur, P. (1959) Multivariate geographical variation in the wolf *Canis lupus* L. Evolution 13: 283–299.

Krumbein, W. C. (1955) The statistical analysis of facies maps. J. Geol. 63: 452–470.

Little, F. J., Jr. (1964) The need for a uniform system of biological numericlature. Systematic Zool. 13: 191–194.

Mackerras, I. M. (1963) The classification of animals. Proc. Linn. Soc. New South Wales 88: 324–335.

Margoliash, E. (1963) Primary structure and evolution of cytochrome C. Proc. Nat. Acad. Sci. 50: 672–679.

Mayr, E. (1965) Numerical phenetics and taxonomic theory. Systematic Zool. 14: 73–97.

Michener, C. D. (1963) Some future developments in taxonomy. Systematic Zool. 12: 151–172.

Michener, C. D. (1964) The possible use of uninominal nomenclature to increase the stability of names in biology. Systematic Zool. 13: 182–190.

Michener, C. D. and R. R. Sokal. (1957) A quantitative approach to a problem in classification. Evolution 11: 130–162.

Rohlf, F. J. and R. R. Sokal. (1966) Taxonomic structure from randomly obtained characters. (M.S. in preparation.)

Rollins, R. C. (1965) On the bases of biological classification. Taxon 14: 1–6.

Sackin, M. J. and P. H. A. Sneath. (1965) Amino acid sequences in proteins: a computer study. Biochem. J. 96: 70P–71P.

Simpson, G. G. (1965) Current issues in taxonomic theory. Science 148: 1078.

Sneath, P. H. A. (1964a) New approaches to bacterial taxonomy: use of computers. Ann. Rev. Microbiol. 18: 335–346. .

Sneath, P. H. A. (1964b) Computers in bacterial classification. Advancement of Science 20: 572–582.

Sokal, R. R. (1962) Typology and empiricism in taxonomy. J. Theoret. Biol. 3: 230–267.

Sokal, R. R. (1964) The future systematics, p. 33–48. In C. A. Leone [ed.] Taxonomic biochemistry and serology. The Ronald Press, New York, 728 pp.

Sokal, R. R. (1965) Statistical methods in systematics. Biol. Rev. (Cambridge) 40: 337–391.

Sokal, R. R. and J. H. Camin (1965) The two taxonomies: areas of agreement and of conflict. Systematic Zool. 14: 176–195.

Sokal, R. R., J. H. Camin, F. J. Rohlf and P. H. A. Sneath. (1965) Numerical taxonomy: some points of view. Systematic Zool. 14: 237–243.

Sokal, R. R. and P. H. A. Sneath. (1963) Principles of numerical taxonomy. W. H. Freeman & Co., San Francisco and London. 359 pp.

Stearn, W. T. (1964) Problems of character selection and weighting: Introduction, p. 83–86. In V. H. Heywood and J. McNeill [eds.] Phenetic and phylogenetic classification. Syst. Assoc. Publ. No. 6, London. 164 pp.

Swanson, D. R. (1964) Design requirements for a future library, p. 11–21. In B. E. Markuson [ed.] Libraries and automation. Library of Congress, Washington, D.C. 268 pp.

Thomas, P. A. (1965) Geographic variation in the rabbit tick, *Haemaphysalis leporispalustris*. Ph.D. Thesis, University of Kansas.

Watt, K. E. F. (1964) Computers and the evaluation of resource management strategies. Am. Scientist 52: 408–418.

2

Evolutionary Ecology

The species populations that the taxonomist must circumscribe and the population ecologist characterize develop by interactions with the environment in time and in space. The function of the evolutionary ecologist is to determine the nature of the variation that has permitted this selection and adaptation, and the manner in which the several environmental influences involved have modified gene frequencies.

The first paper in this section is by P. R. Ehrlich and R. W. Holm, both of whom have made major contributions to contemporary evolutionary ecology. In this paper, they emphasize the essential unity of ecology, and link the subject material of all four sections of this book—from taxonomy to community ecology. They emphasize the need for conceptual frameworks and a dissolution of disciplinary boundaries in ecology. They also challenge the validity of a number of common basic ideas.

In the second paper, F. B. Livingstone considers the significance in human ecology of the abnormal hemoglobin genes. Dr. Livingstone, who is a leading worker in this field, points out that these genes are the first genetic system in man to which genetic theory may be applied in detail, and that they also provide evidence of the intimate relationships between cultural and biological evolution in our species. Dr. Livingstone further concludes that the extensive use of subspecies as major evolutionary units may be, as Mayr has recently maintained, essentially artificial.

The possibilities for the establishment of local populations within species is discussed in terms of gene flow and environment by R. Levins, who has been concerned with the application of mathematical models to genetical situations. In this particular paper, he examines the problem of why local speciation does not occur on a much larger scale, and why widespread species are rather numerous. He concludes that the adaptive significance of gene flow arises from its damping of short-term environmental changes while permitting selective responses to extensive long-term ones.

The ability of a population to adjust to a changing environment is further examined in this section's last paper by A. M. Brues. The question of the "cost of natural selection" was first raised by the late British geneticist J. B. S. Haldane some ten years ago, and later considered by Mayr. The particular significance of Dr. Brues' work is that it illustrates how computer modeling can be introduced to such considerations of gene flow and gene substitution.

Paul R. Ehrlich
Richard W. Holm

Patterns and Populations

An important and rapidly developing area of biological science is the study of aggregations of organisms. This field, which we call population biology, may be defined as including all aspects of groupings of organisms and organisms in groups. Often, however, it is considered to comprise only ecology in a relatively narrow sense, or even population genetics alone. We feel that there is much to be gained from taking a broad view in the study of populations, in which emphasis is on the many similarities in the phenomena studied by the taxonomist, the ecologist, the geneticist, the behaviorist, the economist, and perhaps the mathematician as well. Despite the apparent heterogeneity of this assemblage it seems to us that there are many basic problems common to these diverse disciplines. Often these areas of mutual interest have not been recognized, even though many workers have urged broad interdisciplinary approaches. Perhaps the time has come to dissolve disciplinary boundaries. Such a unification will require a careful study of techniques and procedures, in addition to an anlysis of the language and the conceptual frameworks involved, with particular attention to the Whorfean hypothesis [1]. Conceivably, a new mathematics must be developed in order to handle the problems of population biology. The mathematics of information theory [2] and game theory [3] already are being shown to have possible applications in this field, but so few biologists are versed in these mathematics that their importance and utility are only beginning to be investigated. A general mathematical theory of population biology may be formulated eventually, but a great deal of intellectual brush-clearing must necessarily precede even preliminary groping for overall principles. In the discussion which follows it may seem that we have restricted ourselves largely to destructive criticism, demonstrating the disadvantages of established procedures and modes of thought. But these must be pointed out before it is possible to develop improvements. Although we have not always discussed possible improvements in detail, these often are presented in the works cited. In science it frequently is necessary to criticize existing theoretical structures to clear the way for new ideas.

Reprinted by permission of the authors and publisher from *Science, 137:* 652–657, 1962. Copyright 1962 by the American Association for the Advancement of Science.

Facts and Concepts

The thinking concerning many problems in population biology has been colored strongly by the terms invented to deal with them. People are inclined to confuse concepts with established facts and then consider it.unnecessary to investigate the facts further. Often terminology differs with different disciplines, and thus areas of study are isolated and relationships are obscured. For example, it is difficult to find a neutral term for "more than one organism" which has not already been used in a restrictive sense in one or more disciplines. Whereas earlier we used the word *aggregations* to refer merely to a plurality of organisms, it has several different meanings in ecology. The fact that semantic problems of this sort cause serious difficulty throughout all human endeavor should not deter us from attempting to correct the situation.

Many concepts in population biology have low information content and little or no operational meaning. In this category we would place such concepts as "competition," "niche," "community," "climax," "species," "population fitness," and to some extent "population" itself. Dissatisfaction with the concepts of population biology is widespread. Ecologists recently have attempted to develop an operational definition of "niche"—that is, to specify the set of physical operations which would assign to every niche a unique value, such as the coordinates of an n-dimensional hypervolume [4]. The language of ecology has been analyzed [5] with the aim of eliminating semantic confusion; the idea of natural selection as an ecological concept has been investigated [6]. The concept of population fitness, one of the most difficult problems in population genetics, has received a great deal of attention recently [3, 7]. Boulding [8] has discussed conceptual problems as they relate to economics, and the behavioral literature is filled with discussions of the value of such ideas as "instinct," "releaser," "displacement activity," and "learning."

Any attempt to avoid this confusion of concepts and facts would seem to entail changing our approach to the entire "population" level of biological organizations. Perhaps the best way to start is by asking questions in a manner which is divorced as much as possible from our present conceptual framework. For example, three very broad and basic questions in population biology which are of particular interest to us are the following: (i) What are the patterns of variation which may be observed in nature? (ii) How can we evaluate the reality of the observed patterns? (iii) What hypotheses can be advanced to account for the observed patterns?

The reality of such concepts as "fish," "bird," "mammal," "conifer," and "grass" is rarely questioned; it seems obvious that they represent major clusters in patterns of variation. That peoples of other cultures order natural phenomena differently bothers most of us very little (for example, Eskimos have no generic term for water but have a detailed and useful terminology describing the various kinds of frozen water; gauchos have some 200 terms for horse colors, but they divide the vegetable world into four species: *pasta*, fodder; *paja*, bedding; *cardo*, woody materials; and *yuyos*, all other plants [9]. It also seems to bother biologists very little that other scientists—for example, physicists—take a rather disturbingly different view of what is real and what is unreal, what is fact and what is construct. For instance, the Newtonian concept of absolute time is not employed by modern physicists because no phenomenon with the postulated properties of absolute time has been found experimentally. As we shall demonstrate, the concept of genetic (or "biological") species, the idea of the community as a unit, and many other concepts current in subdisciplines of population biology have much in common with the idea of absolute time.

The New Taxonomy

Traditions and force of habit have influenced present-day workers in taxonomy more than they have influenced workers in most other disciplines. For nearly 200 years taxonomists have followed Linnaeus in arranging organisms in "natural groups." Darwin supplied a rationale for the existence of such groups, and in the minds of many workers the existence of groups and their probable cause have become inseparable. This has led to the so-called phylogenetic approach to taxonomy, in which, in the absence of satisfactory fossil records, taxonomic systems often are used as the basis for constructing phylogenetic trees. Unfortunately, these trees sometimes are then employed to alter the original taxonomic system. This circular procedure produces systems with some predictive value and information content, although the process of creating these systems through repeated revision is time-consuming and relatively inefficient.

About 5 years ago in the United States and England, taxonomists began to investigate multivariate methods of assaying similarities among organisms [10]. The newer methods have methodological and philosophical advantages over older methods of multivariate analysis [11], and there is the additional advantage that data may be handled by modern automatic data processing equipment. Several different techniques have been developed which give similar and repeatable results. The systems of logical relationship obtained in this manner have relatively high information content. They supply a base for phylogenetic speculation, but the speculation is not involved in establishing the base.

This general approach thus seems to provide a means of answering the first question posed above, and it presents a possible basis for answering the second question as well. The genetic relationships among a group of organisms (that is, the pattern of similarities or differences among genotypes) might be considered a parameter which one could estimate by taking samples of the genetic information for each individual and then calculating the matrix of similarity (or distance) coefficients among the samples. The practical way to sample the vast store of information in a genotype is to sample the phenotype and accept the error introduced by the interaction of the genetic information and its milieu.

The magnitude of this error (which is implicit in virtually all systematic studies and most genetic work) cannot be estimated accurately at the present time. We need much more knowledge of phenomena of the kind that may be lumped conveniently under the heading "developmental homeostasis" [12]. Indeed, if this sampling procedure is legitimate, then patterns of (logical) relationship which are essentially congruent should be produced by working with any large sample of characters.

This hypothesis of congruence is being tested at several institutions and on diverse groups of organisms. For example, Ehrlich is now engaged in a detailed investigation of the comparative external and internal morphology of a representative series of butterflies. When his study is completed it will be possible to compute a matrix of cofficients for some 75 characters [13] from the external anatomy and another based on a roughly equivalent number of characters from the internal anatomy. To test the assumption that there is a reasonable degree of congruence in the patterns for adults and for larvae, the next step in these investigations will be to see whether the same pattern is obtained when characters of the larvae are considered. Recent work by Rohlf [14] indicates that such congruence is not complete in the patterns of relationship of mosquito larvae and adults, and other studies, by Michener and Sokal [15], of patterns for males and females and for head and body characters of bees also show incomplete congruence. Studies such as these should give information on the "reality" of currently accepted patterns of relationship and also may help shed light on basic problems of development. Present thinking leads to the assumption that systems of relationships based on adult characters will be essentially the same as those based on immature stages or alternate generations. This is an aspect of development which is poorly understood; in addition, it is not certain whether the genetic code functions cyclically or in different ways in cells at different levels of ploidy.

There seems to be no theoretical reason why there *must* be complete congruence among estimates of relationships based on characters from different developmental stages or on characters from different organ systems of the same stage. Thus, for highest information content and predictive value, specialized taxonomies designed for optimal usefulness under restricted conditions could be created. The day may be at hand when, instead of saying "mammal taxonomy" or "butterfly taxonomy," we will discuss "adult mammal taxonomy" or "pupal butterfly neurotaxonomy." In a taxonomy based on ecological requirements, whales will be more closely related to sharks than to bears. Such a relationship is no more or less "true" or "natural" than the classical one; it is merely based on different attributes. Special systems would, of course, be created on demand—not in expectation of need, as today's taxonomies are. What sort of taxonomy is desirable depends upon what one wishes to use it for. Ecologists have used special taxonomies (such as that of Raunkiaer) for many years. In dealing with a multiplicity of special taxonomies, it is obvious that the creation of structures of formal names should be avoided.

It is probable that some type of mean relationship will be utilized as a basis for a general taxonomy giving estimates of overall similarity. This presumably would provide estimates of evolutionary divergence, but the actual parameter being estimated is difficult to specify. If it were possible to compare directly the nucleotide sequences forming the entire genetic code of two organisms, would this be a "true" measure of evolutionary divergence? We think not— the code cannot be considered without its translation. Whatever kind of sampling is used as a basis for new general taxonomic systems, it appears likely that our current systems, based mainly on the external features of adult forms, will seem warped in comparison.

The Species Problem

One of the most widely accepted ideas of population biology is that higher animals tend to occur in rather well defined clusters called species. Various theoretical definitions of species have been attempted, and most of those accepted by modern evolutionists make some statement about reproductive isolation between, but not within, the clusters. In older definitions, assumptions concerning the occurrence or nonoccurrence of interbreeding are implicit. Special definitions such as those of paleontology reflect special problems. The details of such definitions doubtless are familiar. Botanists, on the other hand, have not always found such seemingly well-delimited clusters. It is commonly admitted that species in certain groups of plants simply are not as "good" as those in other groups. In some families the usual terminology may be difficult to apply at the species level [16]; in others, "species" may be well marked but higher categories may be difficult to define [17].

Contrary to widely held opinion, the situation in zoology may not be very different from that in botany. In well-investigated groups such as the nearctic butterflies, the distinctness of clusters has been vastly overrated [18]. It appears that the idea of preponderance of good species in animals is a generality without foundation—an artifact of the procedures of taxonomy. These procedures require that distinct clusters be found and assigned to some level in a hierarchy—subspecies, species, subgenus, genus, and so on. Thus, we have the fruitless arguments over whether or not a species or subspecies is "good." Interpolating additional categories (for example, superspecies) has not solved the logical problem; it has merely obscured it. The basic trouble seems to be confusion concerning the evolutionary importance of barriers to gene flow and the actual or potential utility of these barriers as a criterion in establishing a taxonomic system.

Perhaps the most unfortunate aspect of the so-called biological-species definition is the need to estimate the interbreeding potential of allopatric entities. Laboratory tests are not considered definitive. For instance, *Peromyscus leucopus* and *P. gossypianus* will hybridize in the laboratory, but where they occur together naturally in the Dismal Swamp of Virginia, they remain distinct. On the other hand, laboratory hybrids between northern and southern populations of *Rana pipiens* do not develop properly, although if intermediate populations became extinct and the terminal ones approached one another naturally, selection *might* alter them so that they would interbreed freely on meeting.

There seems to be an element of crystal-gazing in the idea of potential inter-breeding. First, the events at a hypothetical meeting must be predicted. Then, if the formation of hybrids is postulated, the fitness or viability of the hybrid population must be estimated. It need hardly be said that fitness and viability are parameters difficult to estimate in a closed laboratory population of *Drosophila,* let alone a hypothetical hybrid population. As Mayr [19] points out, unpredictability characterizes both large- and small-scale evolutionary events. These difficulties might be partially circumvented by redefining the biological species so that laboratory tests become definitive. However, the problem of cutting a continuum of different degrees of interfertility would re-main, and the amount of work required to delimit even a single species would be prohibitive. It seems clear that the biological-species definition never has been operational and never will be [20].

A serious problem facing population biologists is the necessity for developing mathematical methods of usefully describing the relationships observed. The ultimate test of a mathematical model is how well it describes a situation in nature; unfortunately, our current models are of rather uneven performance. Attempts to improve them have taken somewhat diverse paths in different fields; for instance, population ecologists have been exploring applications of information theory with rather interesting results. However, the mathematically inclined population biologists often accept badly formulated concepts of tax-onomists as facts. For example, they study "species in competition" when, at most, only individuals can compete. This unfortunate tendency of some non-taxonomists to treat species as entities reaches its naive extreme in papers on topics such as "the embryology of the monkey" or "the physiology of the frog." The partially indeterminate results of Park's sophisticated work [21] on two kinds of competing *Tribolium* beetles clearly show the dangers of treat-ing "species" as units. After a number of generations at high temperature, the surviving individuals were of one kind; at low temperatures, the survivors were of the other; at intermediate temperatures, the results varied from experiment to experiment. It is likely that, as Park suspected, the genetic variance among the beetles (all of the same kind) used to start the various experiments is one of the factors causing the indeterminacy at intermediate temperatures [22]. *Tribolium confusum* is not an entity, it is a taxonomic concept.

The term *species* should be retained only in its original, less restrictive sense of "kind." There seems to be no reason why quantitative methods should not be used to study phenetic relationships (those based on similarity rather than imagined phylogeny) at what we now loosely call the species level. These studies may reveal clusters of populations, and, where convenient for com-munication, these clusters may be given formal names. Their genetic relation-ships, when known, can be employed as characters but will not be involved in category definition. We recognize that changes which affect interbreeding are phenetic, and thus they may be used along with other features of the organism as characters in a quantitative comparison.

Recently Ehrlich [18] compared 13 male individuals of checkerspot butterflies (*Euphydryas editha* and *E. chalcedona*) on the basis of 75 characters of their external morphology, genitalia, and color pattern. Both the relationships of the individuals with each other (the Q-matrix) and of the characters (the R-matrix) were computed, with product-moment correlation coefficients as the measure of similarity. Two primary clusters were discovered in a search for structure in the Q-matrix—*E. editha* (ten specimens) and *E. chalcedona* (three specimens). *Euphydryas editha* and *E. chalcedona* occur together in many areas, but in these places intermediate individuals are unknown. Two of the individuals in the study came from a population which, on the basis of classical taxonomic procedure, could not be assigned positively to one "species" or the other.

The correlation study placed them as a distinct subgroup of the *E. editha* cluster. The remaining eight *E. editha* individuals clustered according to their overall similarities, not their populations of origin. As a test of the "reality" of the pattern of relationships observed in the original Q-matrix, additional Q-matrices were calculated on the basis of different subsets of the 75 characters. Examination of these Q-matrices based on different character combinations showed that in eight out of nine matrices the correlations among the *E. chalcedona* specimens were all higher than any *E. chalcedona-E. editha* correlation. Despite the inadequate number of characters (all but two Q-matrices were based on less than 60) and the rather crude methodology, the same gross pattern of relationships emerged repeatedly. We have here the essence of an operational definition: several operations (measurement of different sets of characters) ascribe the same value to the variable (in this case the Q-matrix). The clusters thus operationally defined could be placed at any desired level in a taxonomic hierarchy. It seems possible that studies such as this of relationships of individuals may lead eventually to the development of a genetics of populations oriented toward genotype, rather than gene, frequencies [23].

This general approach to the "species problem" would permit relaxation of the rigid hierarchic structure of taxonomic categories which requires that all entities be arbitrarily assigned to some level (deme, subspecies, species, and so on) by the complex system of guesswork outlined above. We may now modify our system to permit more accurate and thus more useful description of the intricate relationships of organisms. Just as physics has been divested of the burden of absolute time, so biologists can be freed from the necessity of imposing a platonic structure on nature. That this imposition on nature has been long recognized is shown by the following quotation from a work published in 1872 [24].

"It is of interest to note that in Aristotle the difference between plants and animals is already touched upon. . . . Regarding the nature of some marine growths one may be in doubt whether they are plants or animals. . . . Even the ascidians, says Aristotle, may properly be called plants since they give off no excrement. . . . One sees that Aristotle fell into the same error as almost all moderns. The term 'plant,' which came to us as a part of our language, was interpreted as a term that must correspond to a class of naturally occurring entities. The same thing has happened to later workers with respect to the term 'species.' Instead of investigating whether there exists in nature anything that is unchangeable and circumscribed and that corresponds to this term, and then, in the absence of such, to allow nature her liberty and only artificially to assign a meaning to it that corresponds to the current state of knowledge, one simply assumed that one was compelled to consider the word as a symbol for one of nature's secrets, a secret that one might still hope to unveil."

Mendelian Populations and Gene Flow

In contrast to the "biological species," the concept of Mendelian population (in a restricted sense) may have some merit. Studies of local populations of newts [25] and butterflies [26] have shown a remarkable lack of interchange of individuals among various parts of the colonies. Similar situations have been noted in studies of other organisms. It seems likely that we will find in these organisms that entities which may conveniently be called Mendelian populations do exist, but that they are smaller than one would have expected on the basis of casual assumptions about gene flow. The whole problem of the movement of genetic information among evolving units has been given very spotty study. Here is an area where botany and zoology differ remarkably in a number of respects, but again the difference may be more apparent than real. Botanists have for a long time accepted the fact that plant "species" and even "genera" may hybridize, and they have recognized the importance in evolution of even rare exchanges of genetic material. The concept of "introgressive hybridization" has become widely used as an explanation of taxonomic systems. It is only very recently that some zoologists have admitted that something more important than taxonomic problems is involved when individuals intermediate between accepted clusters are detected. Epling and Catlin [27], among others, have shown how our frozen concepts and terminology may have kept us from seeing important genetic relationships in natural populations. Perhaps some such neutral term as *evolutionary unit* might be used in evolutionary studies, the term *species* being reserved for pragmatic uses only, as mentioned earlier.

Community Ecology

When we turn from the level of the single evolutionary unit to associations of species in nature, we find that no field of population biology has suffered as severely from hardening-of-the-concepts as community ecology. In spite of clear and well-reasoned arguments by a number of botanists [28], one still finds discussions, obviously taken very seriously, about succession, climax, biome, flora, and so on. Even if it be granted that these terms are clearly understood by specialists in the field and that they have a certain practical value, surely they are misunderstood by workers in other areas of population biology. The literature is still permeated with terms such as *chaparral, tundra, spruce-moose biome, dominant, Madro-Tertiary flora,* and *Holarctic fauna,* which are thought to be biologically meaningful. At best they are superficial descriptions of places and situations. At worst they obscure the intricate patterning of nature and lead to a mystical approach to problems of community structure, community migration, evolution of communities, and the like. *Tundra* is perfectly acceptable as a descriptive word meaning something like "treeless northern plain"; it is not acceptable as a general biological entity (once one tries to define *tundra* as more than "the absence of large trees in certain climatic regions," one encounters great difficulties) [29].

Consider also the so-called "redwood flora," which is commonly thought to be a clearly distinct grouping of forms which can be traced well back into the Tertiary. Much effort has been spent in tracing its "migrations." Nevertheless, its floristic composition has changed drastically through time, and each entity (each interbreeding population of individuals) has had an evolutionary history dependent on, among other things, its own genetic processes. Concepts of floristic or faunistic sources or centers of origin can only obscure the genetic processes and confuse the evolutionary histories. As Mason has said: "Because of the differences in genetic constitution and in physiological capacity between the various species of the community, and because of the operation of different genetic mechanisms it is hardly to be expected that any two or more species of such a community will follow precisely the same historical pattern even for a relatively short time." That "species" occur in the same community implies to many biologists that they share the same general "adaptations" to the environment of that community. It should be obvious that the only unity such a community possesses is based upon the overlapping ranges of tolerance of the individual organisms for certain factors of the environment.

Adaptation and Population Fitness

As everyone knows, one of the less fortunate results of the publication of the *Origin of Species* was the subsequent fanatical search for "adaptations." At one time it was asserted that flamingos were pink because this gave them cryptic coloration when they flew across the sunset! Few nonevolutionists realize that the term *adaptation* is one of the least understood and most misused in population biology. The entire "adaptation" approach to evolution needs reexamination. Natural selection has become widely recognized as an a posteriori description of events (differential reproductive contributions of different genotypes greater than or less than one would expect from sampling error). A few authors persist in considering selection to be some sort of weight or burden which can be lifted from the back of a poor struggling population. This latter view is most evident in works on human evolution [30], where we find that man has finally been freed from the dire load of natural selection. On the other hand, adaptation [31], the result of natural selection, has retained rather tenaciously its status as a "thing."

It is difficult to see much merit in the term, as all known organisms are the result of more than a billion years of selection and are therefore "highly adapted." At best, "adaptation" is used in vague comparisons of the way of life of an organism with the extent of usable habitat (parasites are more "narrowly adapted" than omnivores). At worst, it is often a device for inciting wonder at the diversity of vertebrate forelimbs, bird beaks, or pollination mechanisms (one is reminded of Lincoln's remark that his legs were, miraculously, just long enough to reach the ground). In the former instance, once the relationships (perferably quantified) have been described, the comment on adaptation seems extraneous. Under present conditions elephants cannot survive in as many places as human beings; does it really help to add that "elephants are more narrowly adapted than people"? The continuing feeling that adaptation is some phlogiston-like, beneficial substance that a population may possess in varying quantities has been at least partially responsible for the difficulties (mentioned earlier) which theorists have had in coming to grips with the problems attendant on the question of population fitness.

In highly specified competition experiments, such as those with *Tribolium,* or in comparable population-cage experiments in which the standards of "success" are carefully stated [7], population fitness can be given meaning. In a provocative paper on possible game-theory approaches to evolutionary problems, Lewontin [3] suggests using the one-generation probability of survival as a measure of population fitness and briefly outlines experiments to test various strategies against this standard. At present it is difficult to visualize how such approaches can be applied to investigations of populations in the field. In most cases (if not all), expressions such as "populations with structure X are more fit than those with structure Y" or "species A is more fit than species B" are meaningless.

Evolutionary Theory

Finally, consider the third question posed earlier: "What accounts for the observed patterns in nature?" It has become fashionable to regard modern evolutionary theory as the *only* possible explanation of these patterns rather than just the best explanation that has been developed so far. It is conceivable, even likely, that what one might facetiously call a non-Euclidean theory of evolution lies over the horizon. Perpetuation of today's theory as dogma will not encourage progress toward more satisfactory explanations of observed phenomena. As Hardin puts it [9]: "There is always a considerable lag in teaching. Many years ago it was remarked that the Military Academy of St.

Cyr in France trained its students splendidly to fight the battles of the *last* war. So it is in science teaching; we too often train our students to fight battles already won, or equip them with weapons that no longer fire." We hope that population biologists will begin to break the bonds of tradition which have thus far strongly inhibited the development of a rigorous and unified approach to problems at the highest level of biological organization.

Summary

In summary, then, we would like to suggest that in broad investigations of the patterns of interaction and relationship among organisms the artificial and stultifying fragmentation of population biology into divisions such as taxonomy, population genetics, and ecology should be ignored. Care also should be taken to scrutinize current concepts such as "species," "niche," and "community." If some emergent patterns seem to correspond to a great degree with these concepts, then the concepts may be given operational definitions and the labels should be retained. If there is no such correspondence, then the concepts will have outlived their usefulness and should be discarded.

The basic units of population biology are not communities, species, or even populations, but individual organisms [32]. In populations, variation, growth, genetic equilibria, selection, behavior, and so on are not "things" but relationships. Therefore, what is of interest in population biology is the pattern in which organisms are related in space and time [33].

References and Notes

1. G. A. Radnitsky, *Behavioral Sci.* 6: 153 (1961). Until and unless the Whorfean hypothesis can be shown to be incorrect, it is very important to preserve the diversity of human languages.
2. G. E. Hutchinson and R. H. MacArthur, *Am. Naturalist* 93: 117 (1959).
3. R. C. Lewontin, *J. Theoret. Biol.* 1: 382 (1961).
4. G. E. Hutchinson, *Cold Spring Harbor Symp. Population Biol.* 22: 415 (1957).
5. H. L. Mason and J. H. Langenheim, *Ecology* 38: 325 (1957).
6. H. L. Mason, *ibid.* 42: 158 (1961).
7. J. A. Beardmore, T. Dobzhansky, O. H. Pavlovsky, *Hereditary* 14: 19 (1960).
8. K. E. Boulding, *Conflict and Defense* (Harper, New York, 1962).
9. The gaucho example is taken from Garrett Hardin, *Am. J. Psychiat.* 114: 75 (1957). Hardin is a pioneer in applying Whorf's ideas to biological problems; see, for example, is remarkable paper "Meaninglessness of the word protoplasm," *Sci. Monthly* 82: 112 (1956).
10. References to the literature of numerical taxonomy can be found in P. H. A. Sneath and R. R. Sokal, *Nature* 193: 855 (1962).
11. E. Anderson, *Introgressive Hybridization* (Wiley, New York, 1949).
12. See C. H. Waddington, *The Strategy of the Genes* (Allen and Unwin, London, 1957), and I. M. Lerner, *Genetic Homeostasis* (Wiley, New York, 1954), for discussions of this general problem.
13. The word *character* is used here in the idiom of the numerical taxonomist to mean any feature which varies in the group under study.

14. F. J. Rohlf, personal communication.

15. C. D. Michener and R. R. Sokal, personal communication.

16. W. H. Camp, *Brittonia* 7: 113 (1951).

17. R. W. Holm, *Ann. Missouri Botan. Garden* 37: 377 (1950).

18. P. R. Ehrlich, *Systematic Zool.* 10: 167 (1961).

19. E. Mayr, *Science* 134: 1501 (1961).

20. G. S. Myers, *Systematic Zool.* 9: 338 (1960).

21. T. Park, *Physiol. Zool.* 27: 177 (1954).

22. I. M. Lerner and F. K. Ho [*Am. Naturalist* 95: 329 (1961)] have shown that genotypic differences in competitive ability exist in *Tribolium confusum* and *T. castaneum*, supporting this hypothesis. Further discussion may be found in I. M. Lerner and E. L. Dempster, *Proc. Natl. Acad. Sci. U.S.* 48: 821 (1962).

23. We do not mean genotype frequencies with reference to one or two loci only. Again, the loss of detail in translation from genotype must be accepted.

24. J. V. Carus, *Geschichte der Zoologie* (Munich, 1872), p. 31. We are indebted to R. G. Schmieder for translating this passage and bringing it to our attention.

25. V. C. Twitty, *Science* 130: 1735 (1959).

26. P. R. Ehrlich, *ibid.* 134: 108 (1961).

27. C. Epling and W. Catlin, *Heredity* 4: 313 (1950).

28. H. L. Gleason, *Torrey Botan. Club Bull.* 53: 7 (1926); H. L. Mason, *Ecol. Monographs* 17: 201 (1947); R. H. Whittaker, *Botan. Rev.* 28: 1 (1962).

29. P. R. Ehrlich, *Entomol. News* 69: 19 (1958).

30. The following statement of W. La Barre [*The Human Animal* (Univ. of Chicago Press, Chicago, 1953), p. 144] is an example: "man is no longer subject as an individual to the full effects of natural selection and to the other evolutionary mechanisms which operate on wild animals." La Barre's book is, in most respects, excellent.

31. We are not considering physiological adaptation in this discussion. Adaptation clearly is a panchreston in Hardin's sense [*Sci. Monthly* 82: 112 (1956)].

32. In this article we have chosen not to discuss in detail how "individual" may be defined. Here again taxonomic concepts have biased our thinking badly. The idea of an individual connotes uniqueness. If a plant reproduces vegetatively and the various parts become separated to form a clone, are we dealing with one individual or with several? The problem as phrased is insoluble. An individual is a machine (or set of operations) programmed in advance to do a particular thing. A group of genetically identical organisms is one individual reproductively. Ecologically these organisms represent a population of individuals with different epigenetics. In an instance such as this, if historically we had begun to think about biology in ecological rather than taxonomic terms we would now deal with biological "facts" very differently.

33. We have discussed the ideas presented in this article with numerous colleagues at Stanford and elsewhere and have presented them in a series of seminars at several institutions. We have been particularly stimulated by the views of H. V. Daly and H. L. Mason (University of California, Berkeley), N. H. Russell (Arizona State University), and R. R. Sokal (University of Kansas). Daly and Sokal, C. D. Michener (University of Kansas), and W. R. Briggs and D. Kennedy (Stanford) were kind enough to read and criticize the manuscript. A long discussion with K. W. Cooper (Dartmouth Medical School) on "What is population biology?" was ur immediate incentive for writing the article.

Frank B. Livingstone

The Distributions of the Abnormal
Hemoglobin Genes and Their Significance
for Human Evolution

One of the most spectacular advances in the last 10 years in our knowledge
of human genetic diversity has been the discovery of the abnormal hemoglobin
genes. In this short space of time the distributions of these genes in the world's
populations have become one of the best known genetic systems for any animal
species. In fact, the great mass of data makes it difficult to summarize our
knowledge of these genes in a single paper, and the heterogeneity of these data
emphasizes once again the great genetic variability which exists among the
populations of the human species. Although we know more about the
hemoglobins, this is but one of the many genetic systems which the increasing
precision of biochemical techniques has brought to our attention. The hapto-
globins, transferrins, and others yet to be discovered will increase our knowledge of human genetic diversity still further.

Another significant advance in recent years, which preceded the discovery
of the hemoglobins, was the development of the modern genetic theory of
evolution. This synthesis was a theoretical advance as much as a factual one
and was developed primarily from data on animals other than man. It has been
applied to some extent to the blood group genes, but because we know so much
more about the factors of evolution as regards the abnormal hemoglobin genes,
this system is the first one for the human species for which we can discuss the
factors of evolution and their interrelationships. Since, in addition, we also
know the environmental circumstances which determine the direction of natural
selection, the principal factor of evolution, we can effectively evaluate the role
of culture as one of the environmental determinants of human evolution at
the hemoglobin locus.

While the populational aspects of the abnormal hemoglobin genes have been
of great interest to anthropologists and geneticists, biochemists have also made
significant advances in the chemical structure of hemoglobin so that hemoglobin is one of the best known complex proteins. The chemical structure of
this molecule has been directly related to gene action as no other has. We now
know that genes are composed of DNA, which, through RNA, directs the
manufacture of proteins or polypeptide chains, but for the hemoglobin mole-

Reprinted by permission of the author and publisher from *Evolution, 18:* 685–699, 1964.

cule we know the exact changes in the molecule which are associated with the gene differences. (The biochemical advances are discussed by Ingram, 1963).

As the specific changes which genes produce have been discovered, it has been realized that similar phenotypic characteristics, whether based on observation with the naked eye or biochemical tests, can result from very different genetic structures. For example, one can talk about the gene for albinism and even calculate the mutation rate to this gene, but we now realize that literally dozens of different genetic changes may result in phenotypically similar albinism. This specificity of genes also has implications for measuring gene flow between populations. Many of the characteristics which have been used to claim genetic relationships between populations may well be due to very different genes. The abnormal hemoglobins, as the first system where we know the specific chemical changes involved, have made it possible to discuss the basic concepts of mutation, gene flow, and natural selection in a much more realistic way.

In 1953 after the development of paper electrophoresis made mass surveys for the abnormal hemoglobins quite easy, an international committee was convened to establish some orderly process for the naming of the new hemoglobins which were rapidly being discovered. This committee established the letters A, F, M, and S, for normal, fetal, met-, and sickle cell hemoglobins which had been known for some time and decided that further hemoglobins would be assigned letters in order of discovery, beginning with the letter C, and working up the alphabet. At present we are up to the letter R, but further developments have rendered this system rather unworkable as originally set up. These developments were the perfection of techniques to determine the complete chemical structure of hemoglobin. They have resulted in the discovery that hemoglobins which were being called by the same letter since they had the same electrophoretic properties were actually quite different in structure. Hence, another conference has resulted in the use of subscripts to the letters to distinguish these similar hemoglobins. These subscripts designate the place of discovery so that we now have, for example, hemoglobin $G_{San Jose}$, hemoglobin $G_{Bristol}$, and hemoglobin $G_{Philadelphia}$.

With a few exceptions which are more complicated genetically, all of these newly discovered abnormal hemoglobins are due to the presence of a single gene, or in other words differ from normal hemoglobin in one part of their structure. When heterozygous, these genes are for the most part benign, while homozygosity or simultaneous heterozygosity for two of them result in conditions of variable severity ranging from lethality for the sickle cell homozygote in the absence of modern medicine to a slight anemia as in homozygosity for hemoglobin C. For many of the rare hemoglobins no homozygotes have been detected, but it would appear that these conditions may well be more like hemoglobin C in severity than the sickle cell gene.

Although the hemoglobin genes may still hold some surprises for us, the world distribution of these genes can be mapped in considerable detail. For purposes of further discussion the hemoglobin genes will be divided into three groups: (1) those which attain appreciable frequencies or more than 15% heterozygotes in some populations, (2) those found in intermediate frequencies or more than 1% but less than 15% heterozygotes, and (3) those found only occasionally or in less than 1% of the population. The letter designations of the hemoglobins will be used although it should be remembered that any one of these letters may indicate more than one specific gene. With this classification hemoglobins *S, C, E,* and thalassemia would fall into group 1; hemoglobins *D, K, N,* and *O* in group 2; and the rest in group 3. Thalassemia is a potpourri and undoubtedly contains many different "genes." This is because thalassemia is still primarily diagnosed on clinical and morphological features, and many cases which appear similar in these characteristics have been shown to have different chemical and genetic bases. Some thalassemias are chromosomal duplications due to unequal crossing over, some are probably specific structural changes in the hemoglobin molecule as are the other abnormal hemoglobins, and others may result from operator or regulator genes, whatever that means. Nevertheless, some populations have high frequencies of all thalassemias combined so that this system will be considered in the same category as hemoglobins *S, C,* and *E,* which are more specific entities.

Some 25 different rare hemoglobins have been discovered so far, although in order to discover these, extremely large samples must be collected. Many of these rare hemoglobins have been discovered in populations in the tropical and subtropical regions of the Old World which have high frequencies of abnormal hemoglobin genes, but the rare hemoglobins have also been discovered in populations outside this area. Studies from Japan indicate that these random mutants occur in about one of every 2,000 individuals examined (Shibata, 1961). We have talked about mutation as a random, recurrent process and we now have this excellent example. Furthermore, most mutations were thought to be deleterious and this appears to be true of the hemoglobins. Thus, the low frequency of abnormal hemoglobins in the Japanese, English, or Swedish populations results from a balance between mutation to these genes and selection against them. This type of selection which keeps the gene frequencies where they are has been called stabilizing selection, and the hemoglobin loci in these populations are examples of the classical theory of genetic diversity which views this diversity as a balance between mutation away from the normal genotype and natural selection weeding out these deleterious mutants. Evolution or gene frequency change has not occurred here.

The classical view of evolutionary change is usually stated as "every once in awhile a favorable mutation occurs which then replaces the older norm." For the abnormal hemoglobins this statement is wrong or at least it seems to me to be the wrong way to characterize their evolution. It is rather backward and another example of genetic determinism which is endemic in Western thought. It is important to remember that mutation is a recurrent, continuous process, and our hominid and pongid ancestors were continually mutating and producing abnormal hemoglobins. But little evolution occurred; so little, in fact, that based on peptide fingerprinting, the hemoglobin of most of mankind is more similar to that of the chimpanzee and gorilla than it is to their fellow-man, including in some cases immediate family. The cause of evolutionary change in the human hemoglobin genes is not the occurrence of favorable mutants, but changes in the amount and direction of natural selection operating on these genes, and these changes in natural selection were the result of the development of environmental circumstances in which heterozygotes for some of these abnormal hemoglobin genes possessed a selective advantage. It was only then that these genes became an important part of some human gene pools.

While all populations which have been intensively investigated have low frequencies of some abnormal hemoglobin genes, it is only populations which have been resident for a considerable length of time in the tropical and subtropical regions of the Old World which have intermediate or appreciable frequencies of abnormal hemoglobins. However, there are populations in this area, such as the Australian aborigines, some Papuans, Polynesians, and Micronesians in the Asian tropics and the Bushmen, Ethiopians, and some Nilotic peoples in the African tropics, that do not have high frequencies of any abnormal hemoglobin. With the exception of thalassemia, the hemoglobins which attain high frequencies in the tropics, hemoglobins *S, C,* and *E,* are rarely found outside their areas of high frequencies except in migrant populations. Thus, they do not seem to be frequent mutants of the hemoglobin loci, but relatively rare ones.

Although thalassemia is a genetically heterogeneous entity, hemoglobins *S, C,* and *E* are quite specific, and all differ from normal hemoglobin by only a single amino acid out of the string of about 300 amino acids which comprise the identical halves of a hemoglobin molecule. Since an abnormal hemoglobin mutation presumably could occur on most of these 300 amino acids, it is obvious that the mutation rates to the hemoglobin *S, C,* or *E* gene are much less than the mutation rate to thalassemia which includes many different changes.

Since hemoglobins *S, C,* and *E* appear to be relatively rare mutants and their distributions are contiguous and somewhat restricted, gene flow appears to have been a more important factor in determining their distributions than in the case of thalassemia which is a common mutant. Of course, to explain similar frequencies of abnormal hemoglobins in any two populations, one has to weigh the possibility of gene flow with the possibility of a separate mutation becoming established. But this is possible in the case of these three hemoglobins since all frequencies seem to be of the same specific gene mutation in each case, while for thalassemia the recognition of gene flow is difficult. It should be noted that all that sickles is not hemoglobin *S;* there are other hemoglobins which also produce the sickling phenomenon, but the distributions which will be discussed are based for the most part on electrophoresis tests and not on sickle cell tests with sodium metabisulfite.

All four of the abnormal hemoglobins which are found in high frequencies have some deleterious effects associated with homozygosity. In fact, it is rather surprising that thalassemia and hemoglobin S, the most widespread and most frequent of the four, have the most serious effects. Although some individuals who appear to be homozygous for either hemoglobin S or thalassemia have survived and reproduced, population studies indicate that in the relatively primitive medical conditions of the areas of Africa and Europe where high frequencies of these genes are found, the survival and reproduction of homozygotes for these genes is practically nil. Such selection against the sickle cell and thalassemia genes thus raises the question as to why there are high frequencies of these genes in some populations.

Neel (1951) first suggested the two possible answers, mutation or heterozygote superiority, and there were suggestions that malaria may be the factor which confers an increased fitness on the heterozygote. But Allison (1954a, 1954b, 1954c) first grasped the problem and attempted to answer it. His investigations, although providing strong evidence of an association between the sickle cell gene and malaria, were not conclusive; but since then investigations by Raper (1956), the Lambotte-Legrands (1957), Delbrouck (1958), and Firschein (1961) have demonstrated conclusively that sickle cell trait carriers have a selective advantage in an area with holocndemic malaria which is due primarily to *Plasmodium falciparum*. Although disbelief in the malaria hypothesis is still occasionally expressed, I think this work is an excellent example of progress in science. The question, why high frequencies of the sickle cell gene, is a legitimate one and must have an answer. In terms of the modern theory of population genetics there may be several answers, but I have never seen an alternative to the malaria hypothesis seriously advanced. And in terms of the total array of data we now possess on this gene, there is no other answer. Assuming that this is a balanced polymorphism, the factor which is balancing the polymorphism in many populations of Africa, Greece, and India would have to eliminate about 15% of the normal homozygotes each generation or about 11% of the total population. Malaria is the only cause of death which comes anywhere near eliminating this many zygotes. Thus, in terms of our theories, this question must have an answer and this is the only possible one.

Although the relationship between sickling and malaria has much evidence in its favor, practically no work has been done on the selective factors of the other abnormal hemoglobin genes. In Greece (Choremis, Fessas, Kattamis, Stamatoyannopoulos, Zannos-Mariolea, Karaklis, and Belios, 1963), Sardinia (Ceppellini, 1957), and New Guinea (Curtain, Kidson, Gajdusek, and Gorman, 1962) the frequency of thalassemia has been shown to be correlated with the amount of malaria, and there is some evidence from Ghana (Thompson, 1962) that hemoglobin C carriers may have some resistance to malaria infections. By analogy with hemoglobin S, it has been generally assumed that malaria is the major factor involved in the other abnormal hemoglobins, but since the differences in fitness which we are attempting to detect are so much smaller for the abnormal hemoglobins, C, E, and, in most areas, thalassemia, the task is much more difficult than for the sickle cell gene. Furthermore, malaria is rapidly being controlled as a lethal disease and even being eradicated, so that there are few places left where such a relationship could be tested. Since there are also moral problems involved, I suspect that direct proof of the factors which are balancing the hemoglobin polymorphisms will never be forthcoming, except perhaps by means of some laboratory experiments which are technically not feasible at present. But making the assumption that malaria is the selective factor balancing these polymorphisms renders the entire distributions of these genes so intelligible that I think circumstantial evidence will prevail.

In the remainder of this paper malaria will be assumed to be the major factor which is balancing these polymorphisms. However, hemoglobin S seems to be balanced by falciparum malaria while this does not seem to be the case for the other abnormal hemoglobins (Livingstone, 1961). Thalassemia, for example, seems to convey some resistance to the other widespread species of malaria, quartan and benign tertian, which are due respectively to *Plasmodium malariae* and *P. vivax*. The fourth species of malaria parasite, *P. ovale,* is so rare that it need not be considered further.

Fig. 1 shows the distribution of thalassemia in the Old World. It only shows the presence of thalassemia and not frequencies since these data are quite incomplete. Thalassemia is the most widespread of the abnormal hemoglobins and its distribution in the Old World is almost as extensive as the distribution of endemic malaria, with the very striking exception of East Africa. A very few individuals who appear to be simultaneously heterozygous for hemoglobin S

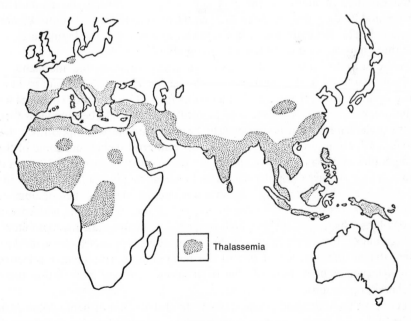

Figure 1

The distribution of thalassemia in the Old World.

and a thalassemia gene have been discovered in East Africa. Strangely enough, on the edge of East Africa among the Arab and Greek communities of Khartoum, thalassemia apparently attains its highest frequencies in the world (Vella and Hassan, 1961; Vella and Ibrahim, 1961).

Occasionally, a thalassemia gene is encountered outside this area in Swiss, German, Japanese, English, and some others. On the map I have tried to indicate the areas where there appear to be a significant number of cases or percentages of thalassemia. This association with few exceptions between endemic malaria and thalassemia, in addition to confirming the malaria hypothesis, indicates other factors in the population dynamics of the abnormal hemoglobins. Thalassemia, as a number of specific genes, has a higher mutation rate than the more specific abnormal hemoglobins; so that when malaria moves into an area, the first genes with an increased fitness which it is likely to encounter are thalassemia genes. Thus, as malaria has spread, it has brought thalassemia right behind it. For example, malaria appears to have spread rather recently through the islands of the southwest Pacific and is still spreading today through the Solomons. The Solomons and the New Hebrides are one of the few places in the tropics where there are anopheline mosquitoes and no malaria. Although malaria seems to have spread there from Southeast Asia, there has been little gene flow from the Indonesian populations to New Guinea. Hence in the New Guinea populations there are appreciable frequencies of thalassemia and another red cell gene, glucose-6-phosphate dehydrogenase deficiency, whose population genetics appears to be determined by approximately the same factors as thalassemia. In addition, there is a correlation between the amount of malaria and thalassemia in New Guinea (Curtain, Kidson, Gajdusek, and Gorman, 1962). Both are found in the lowlands but not in the highlands.

Turning now to the distribution of hemoglobin E, which is shown on Fig. 2, it can be seen to have a rather restricted distribution on the mainland of Southeast Asia and in the Indonesian archipelago. This gene appears to have spread by gene flow out through Indonesia as far as Celebes and Timor. Since the mutation rate to this very specific chemical change would be much less than that to thalassemia, gene flow seems to be a reasonable assumption for this contiguous distribution. Among the Bugis of southern Celebes and some of the other peoples in this area hemoglobin O attains frequencies of about 2% and is almost unique to these populations (Lie-Injo and Sadono, 1958). As is the case with other hemoglobins, with intermediate frequencies, hemoglobin O is found at the forefront of the wave of advance of one of the more widespread hemoglobins which are found in high frequencies, in this case hemoglobin E. Hemoglobin O, like other intermediate hemoglobins, appears to be a random mutant that in the absence of one of the hemoglobins with greater selective advantage such as hemoglobin E, has been selected for and increased in these peripheral populations.

In contrast to Africa and hemoglobin S, the distribution of hemoglobin E in Southeast Asia is more spotty and erratic. This is related to the fact that all species of human malaria are not as solidly endemic on every village and farm

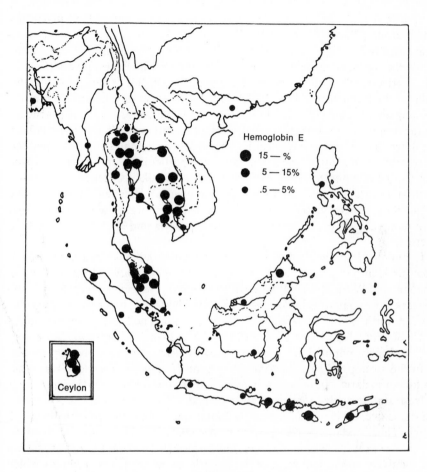

Figure 2

Percentage incidence of individuals with hemoglobin
E in the populations of Southeast Asia.[1]

in Southeast Asia. This in turn is due primarily to the vectors of malaria there. On the mainland of Southeast Asia, *Anopheles minimus* is the major vector of malaria but in Malasia it is a similar species, *A. maculatus*. These vectors breed principally in small, cool, fast-flowing, sunlit streams and hence are found in great numbers only in the hilly regions of Southeast Asia, where the

[1] The percentages computed for each population in Figs. 2, 3, 4, and 5 include both heterozygotes and homozygotes for the respective abnormal hemoglobin. Because of the problem of differentiating homozygotes from individuals simultaneously heterozygous for an abnormal hemoglobin and a thalassemia gene, estimation of the gene frequencies was not attempted. The variability in the percentages used, however, is an approximate measure of the variability in the frequency of the abnormal hemoglobin gene.

forest has been cut down. In contrast to Europe where malaria and marshes were intimately associated because of the nature of the anopheline vectors, in Southeast Asia the deltas and great river valleys are not particularly malarious. Thus, around Bangkok and in the delta of the Mekong River in South Vietnam there is little malaria and low frequencies of hemoglobin E. On the other hand, the foothills are intensely malarious and the more primitive slash-and-burn agriculturalists of these areas have high frequencies of hemoglobin E. No data on the frequency of hemoglobin E in the hunters of this area such as the Semang are available, but due to the ecology of the vectors, there is practically no malaria in the unbroken tropical forest. It is only when the forest has been cut down that A. *maculatus* becomes very frequent in Malasia and A. *minimus* elsewhere. A. *maculatus,* however, does not particularly prefer human blood and can be diverted to biting cattle if these are available. Hence, in primitive slash-and-burn agriculturalists with few cattle such as the Senoi there are high frequencies of hemoglobin E. But as more livestock are present and more human manipulation of the landscape occurs, malaria and A. *maculatus* tend to decrease.

In mainland Southeast Asia it has been recently demonstrated that A. *balabacensis* is an important vector in addition to A. *minimus* (Eyles, Wharton, Cheong, and Warren, 1964). Since this mosquito is associated with forests and appears most numerous in villages surrounded by forest, it is perhaps responsible for much of the malaria in the sparsely populated areas. In the region of Cambodia where Eyles et al. (1964) worked, the parasite rates were very high and these populations also have very high frequencies of hemoglobin E.

In the swamps of parts of Malasia and into Indonesia, there are two other vectors of malaria, *Anopheles sundaicus* and A. *umbrosus*. A. *umbrosus* breeds in fresh-water, shaded mangrove swamps and when the trees are cut down becomes scarce, while A. *sundaicus* is found only along the coast in brackish water. Thus, malaria is rather spottily distributed in Indonesia, but can become a very severe disease in places. On Borneo the efficient vectors of malaria are relatively absent and most of the malaria is due to A. *leucosphyrus* which breeds in shaded water and is associated with tropical forest. The Dyaks have less malaria and low frequencies of hemoglobin $E,$ while the Muruts of North Borneo have more malaria and a higher frequency of hemoglobin E.

To the west hemoglobin E is occasionally encountered in Nepal and in Bengal there is a frequency of about 4%, but the greater part of India is characterized by high frequencies of hemoglobin S. Some hemoglobin E has been reported in Eti-Turks and Greeks, but it may be derived from other mutations and does not represent gene flow from the east, although that possibility exists. With these exceptions there appears to be a strong border in the neighborhood of Calcutta with hemoglobin E predominating to the east and hemoglobin S to the west. This line coincides with the two general avenues of the penetration of agriculture into the South Asian tropical forest. Most of peninsular India and the Ganges River valley were populated by peoples from the west, while the Nagas and other tribes of the North East Frontier are linguistically and culturally related to peoples of Burma and southern China. However, it should be noted that few studies have been done on the Nagas or the other tribes of this area, but an assorted sample of Burmese did have a high frequency of hemoglobin E.

The only groups to the west which have high frequencies of hemoglobin E are some Vedda villages on Ceylon. An earlier report (Aksoy, Bird, Lehmann, Mourant, Thein, and Wickremaisinghe, 1955) showed a very low frequency, but recently some villages are reported to have 30% hemoglobin E carriers (Wickremaisinghe, Ikin, Mourant, and Lehmann, 1963). The investigators imply that this indicates a genetic relationship to the Senoi but there is little evidence for it. Assuming that the genes are the same, it seems to indicate gene flow from Southeast Asia. Hemoglobin E is also found occasionally in the other inhabitants of Ceylon so this seems to be quite likely. It should be noted that the Veddas are now living in settled villages, have mixed considerably with the Tamils and Sinhalese, and the villages with the high frequencies of hemoglobin E are located in the north part of Ceylon which has hyperendemic malaria. Other studies of similar villages of Tamils and Sinhalese are needed, but since they are not considered to have "ethnological" significance they have not been investigated. To postulate that the presence of this gene in the Veddas and Senoi is the result of their common ancestry which goes back to a time when hunters and gatherers were sparsely distributed throughout Southeast Asia does not accord at all with our knowledge of the operation of natural selection on this gene.

Hemoglobin E then seems to have followed the spread of malaria through Southeast Asia. On the other hand, the spread of the conditions which gave rise to holoendemic malaria in India to the west of Calcutta appear to have come from Asia Minor. This part of India has hemoglobin D and thalassemia in the north, while hemoglobin S is found over most of the Indian peninsula, as is shown on Fig. 3. Many gaps on the map are not necessarily areas where hemoglobin S is absent but just where no studies have been carried out. However, populations of the plains of Madras and Kerala have been examined and no sickling is found. And strange as it may seem, these areas also have little malaria. The populations which have very high frequencies of hemoglobin S are found in the Western and Eastern Ghats and the Bastar Hills. Here in these areas the vector of malaria, A. fluviatilis, is like those of Southeast Asia in that it breeds in the little streams in the hills. These areas are characterized by holoendemic malaria while the coastal plains have little. On the Deccan Plateau of Mysore and Hyderabad malaria tends to occur in epidemics which are dependent on the breeding of the malaria vector, A. culicifacies, which in turn is dependent on the monsoon. Although not many studies of abnormal hemoglobin have been done on the plateau, there seem to be lower frequencies.

The high frequencies of hemoglobin S in South India also are found in tribal peoples, most of whom are slash-and-burn agriculturalists but some, like the Paniyans, verge on hunting and gathering. On the other hand, the castes, with the exception of the Mahars, seem to have much lower frequencies even in the

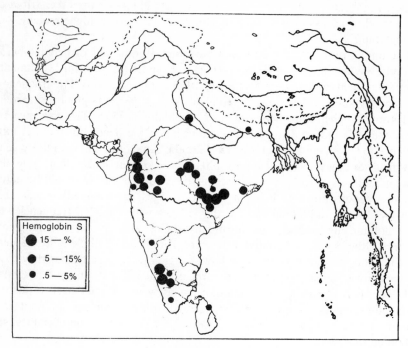

Figure 3
Percentage incidence of individuals with hemoglobin
S in the populations of India.

same general areas, than the tribal peoples. This seems reasonable since malaria is not endemic in the cities of southern India because there is no "rainbarrel" vector there.

The question as to whether the hemoglobin S genes in India are derived from the same source as those in Africa is a real problem. Assuming that these are examples of the same mutation chemically speaking, then the restricted distribution of hemoglobin S in Africa, the Middle East, and India seems to indicate that this gene is a rather rare mutant. None of the populations with high frequency are very distant from others and hence gene flow has presumably occurred.

Turning to Africa and the Middle East, Fig. 4 shows the distribution of hemoglobin C. This gene is restricted to West and North Africa and the high frequencies in West Africa are found in the more primitive tribes that speak Gur languages. The one exception is the Wakura who inhabit the northernmost mountains in the Cameroons. They appear to be long resident in the area and are surrounded by the Kanuri and Shuwa Arabs among whom there are extremely high frequencies of hemoglobin S and no hemoglobin C. One of the problems associated with hemoglobin C is whether it is replacing hemo-

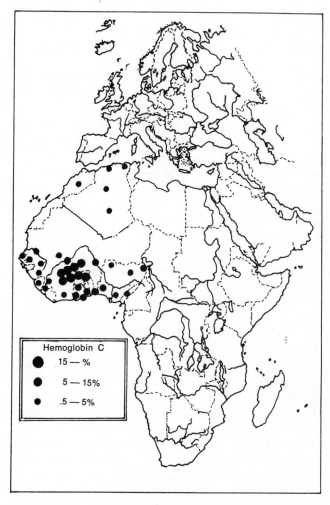

Figure 4

Percentage incidence of individuals with hemoglobin
C in the populations of North and West Africa.

globin S or vice versa, or perhaps there is an equilibrium frequency with both
present. The fitness values of the genotypes involved in this triallelic system
undoubtedly vary throughout this area, but I think a good case can be made
for the hemoglobin S gene replacing hemoglobin C. I think it can be shown
that hemoglobin S will replace almost any other abnormal hemoglobin gene or
thalassemia.

From the fact that the frequency of hemoglobin S carriers is 30 to 40% in many populations in this part of the world, one can estimate that the fitness of the AS heterozygote must be 1.2 to 1.3 times the fitness of the normal homozygote, assuming that the sickle cell homozygote has a fitness of zero. On the other hand, since thalassemia only occurs up to 25% of some populations, the fitness of the thalassemia heterozygote must be about 1.1 times that of normals. Homozygotes for hemoglobin C do not have the very serious anemia of either sickle cell or thalassemia homozygotes. If we estimate the fitness of the homozygous C genotype at from 0.6 to 0.8 that of the normal genotype, then, since a C gene frequency of 0.15 is as high as the equilibrium C gene frequency could possibly be with only C present, the maximum fitness value of the hemoglobin C heterozygote would be about 1.08 times the normal fitness, which we arbitrarily set as 1.00. Given these fitness values, we can attempt to determine which of these genes, hemoglobin C, S, or thalassemia, will replace the others or whether instead there is an equilibrium point with more than one of them present. The general conditions for the existence of an equilibrium with three genes present have been solved by Li (1955), Kimura (1956), Penrose, Smith, and Sprott (1956), and Mandel (1959), and Bodmer and Parsons (1961) have solved the conditions as to whether any one of a series of alleles will increase when introduced into a population at a low frequency. However, the differential equations involving gene frequency change at a multi-allelic locus are nonlinear and nonhomogeneous and hence a general solution is not possible by the methods of classical mathematical analysis; but one can use a computer to obtain specific solutions to these equations. I was rather amazed to find that the sickle cell gene will increase under a great variety of conditions. It will completely replace the hemoglobin C gene and will take over from the thalassemia gene although there is a stable equilibrium with about 15% sickle cell genes and 2% thalassemia. In both cases it takes about 50 generations or about 1.000 years for the sickle cell gene to replace the C or thalassemia gene. In evolutionary perspective this is a very short time span; in fact, it is about the most rapid rate at which one gene can replace another. Thus, what seem to be the most plausible estimates of the fitness values of the abnormal hemoglobin genotypes imply that the sickle cell gene is extremely predatory and will eliminate other such genes.

   This analysis has many implications for the distributions of the S and C genes. In West Africa their distributions have raised the problem as to whether there is an equilibrium with both genes present as Allison (1956) has maintained, or whether one gene is replacing the other. According to this analysis the S gene should be replacing the C gene, and this seems reasonable. Since there are populations in the western part of West Africa with low frequencies of both genes, it appears that the S gene was introduced into this area from the east and north, and historically it is known that a great deal of gene flow did occur in this direction. Since the highest frequencies of the C gene are found in the rather primitive Gur-speaking peoples who have received less such gene flow, it appears that the C gene was present here before the S gene and is now being replaced.

Fig. 5 shows how the hemoglobin S gene has spread throughout the Old World. In East Africa the S gene has replaced all the other abnormal hemoglobins, while to the north in the Mediterranean area, S is only found in high frequencies in North Africa and parts of Greece and Turkey. However, Barnicot, Allison, Blumberg, Deliyannis, Krimbas, and Ballas (1963) have shown that there is an inverse correlation between the S and thalassemia gene frequencies in the malarious areas of Greece, which indicates that they are in

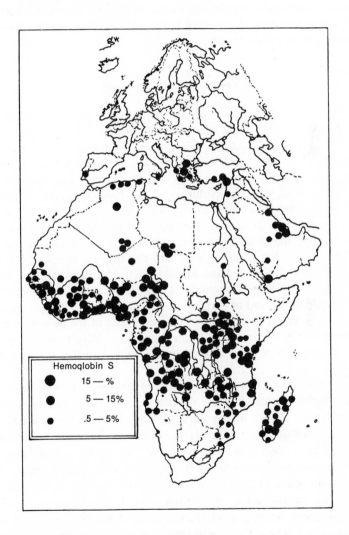

Figure 5

Percentage incidence of individuals with hemoglobin S in the populations of Africa, Europe, and Southwest Asia.

competition and that one is replacing the other. The S gene does not seem to have reached Sardinia which seems expectable since it is one of the more isolated areas of Italy with less contact with and presumable gene flow from the outside.

The fact that the S gene will increase rapidly in a malarious environment no matter what other genes are present implies that any mutant S gene would most likely increase. Thus, the fact that there are many malarious areas without high frequencies of the S gene and that the high frequencies of this gene are in rather contiguous populations indicates that the S gene is a rare mutant and that the distribution of this gene is due primarily to gene flow among the populations within which it occurs.

Conclusions and Summary

The preceding interpretation of the distributions of the abnormal hemoglobins in terms of the factors which we know control gene frequency change has several general implications. First, natural selection is the major factor determining differences in gene frequency, and for the abnormal hemoglobins this natural selection is determined by the presence of holoendemic malaria and its high cost of life. The evolution of this type of malaria is in turn dependent upon a sedentary way of life for which agriculture seems to be a necessary prerequisite in most environments. Agriculture and hence high frequencies of abnormal hemoglobins are relatively recent events in human evolution. The penetration of agriculture into the tropical regions of Asia came from two centers, China and the Middle East. The penetration from China through Southeast Asia to Indonesia is associated with the spread of hemoglobin E, while the spread of agriculture from the Middle East through peninsular India and Africa is associated with the spread of the hemoglobin S gene. Where these two movements met in the vicinity of Calcutta is also the border between the high frequencies of these genes, with S to the west and E to the east.

We have learned a great deal about the evolutionary process from the abnormal hemoglobins since they are the first genetic system in man to which we can apply genetic theory in any detailed way. They also emphasize the important relationship between man's cultural and biological evolution. The evolution of gene frequency differences has often been called "race formation." With reference to abnormal hemoglobin, such a label seems not only grossly inappropriate but false when the implications of the concept of race are taken into consideration. In addition, the distributions of the abnormal hemoglobin genes are not at all related to the traditional races of man, although one can still read that the sickle cell gene is a Negroid character. With reference to the hemoglobins, Coon (1962: 663) has recently stated, "To me, at least, it is encouraging to know that biochemistry divides us into the same subspecies that we have long recognized on the basis of other criteria," a statement which I think the detailed arguments of this paper have shown to be false with respect to the hemoglobins. If natural selection is considered to be one of the major factors contributing to the gene frequency differences which exist among the hundreds of thousands of human breeding isolates, then the gene frequencies will vary with the intensity of selection as do the abnormal hemoglobins and not with "race." If, as Mayr (1963) has recently emphasized, subspecies are artificial units of the classifier and not major units of evolution, it is time anthropologists stopped considering them as such. Between the "natural" units of species and breeding population, there is no natural unit according to the genetic theory, and to attempt to reconcile race with the genetic theory of evolution is to use old concepts to express new ideas which leads to nothing but confusion since we all learn what race basically is in childhood. In this paper I have attempted to describe and explain the distribution of one particular genetic system in man. This has been done without using the concept of race; I think the same can be done for any genetic system.

Literature Cited

Aksoy, M., G. W. G. Bird, H. Lehmann, A. E. Mourant, H. Thein, and R. L. Wickremaisinghe. 1955. Hemoglobin E in Asia. J. Physiol., 130: 56P–57P.

Allison, A. C. 1954a. Protection afforded by sickle-cell trait against subtertian malarial infection. British Med. J., 1: 290–294.

———. 1954b. The distribution of the sickle-cell trait in East Africa and elsewhere, and its apparent relationship to the incidence of subtertian malaria. Trans. Roy. Soc. Trop. Med. and Hygiene, 48: 312–318.

———. 1954c. Notes on sickle-cell polymorphism. Ann. Human Gen., 19: 39–57.

———. 1956. Population genetics of abnormal human hemoglobins. Acta Gen. et Statistica Med., 6: 430–434.

Barnicot, N. A., A. C. Allison, B. S. Blumberg, G. Deliyannis, C. Krimbas, and A. Ballas. 1963. Hemoglobin types in Greek populations. Ann. Human Gen., 26: 229–236.

Bodmer, W. F., and P. A. Parsons. 1961. The initial progress of new genes with various genetic systems. Heredity, 15: 283–299.

Ceppellini, R. 1957. I meccanismi evolutivi nelle popolazioni umane. Suppl. a La Ricerca Scientifica, 27: 3–23.

Choremis, C., P. Fessas, C. Kattamis, Stamatoyannopoulos, L. Zannos-Mariolea, A. Karaklis, and G. Belios. 1963. Three inherited red-cell abnormalities in a district of Greece, thalassemia, sickling, and glucose-6-phosphate-dehydrogenase deficiency. Lancet, 1: 907–909.

Coon, C. S. 1962. The origin of races. Knopf, New York.

Curtain, C. C., C. Kidson, D. C. Gajdusek, J. G. Gorman. 1962. Distribution pattern, population genetics and anthropological significance of thalassemia and abnormal hemoglobins in Melanesia. Amer. J. Phys. Anthrop., 20: 475–483.

Delbrouck, J. 1958. Contribution a la genetiquede la sicklemie. Ann. Soc. Belge de Med. Trop., 38: 103–133.

Eyles, D. E., R. H. Wharton, W. H. Cheong, and McW. Warren. 1964. Studies on malaria and *Anopheles balabacensis* in Cambodia. Bull. World Health Org., 30: 7–21.

Firschen, L. 1961. Population dynamics of the sickle-cell trait in the Black Caribs of British Honduras, Central America. Amer. J. Human Gen., 13: 233–254.

Ingram, V. M. 1963. The hemoglobins in genetics and evolution. Columbia University Press, New York.

Kimura, M. 1956. Rules for testing stability of a selective polymorphism. Proc. Nat. Acad. Sci., 42: 336–340.

Li, C. C. 1955. The stability of an equilibrium and the average fitness of a population. Amer. Nat., 89: 281–296.

Lambott-Legrand, J., and C. Lambotte-Legrand. 1958. Notes complementaire sur la drepanocytose. Ann. Soc. Belge de Med. Trop., 38: 45–54. I. Sicklemie et malaria.

Lie-Injo, L. E., and M. D. Sadono. 1958. Haemoglobin O (Buginese X) in Sulawesi. Brit. Med. J., 1: 1461–1463.

Livingstone, F. B. 1961. Balancing the human hemoglobin polymorphisms. Human Biol., 33: 205–219.

Mandel, S. P. H. 1959. The stability of a multiple allelic system. Heredity, 13: 289–302.

Mayr, E. 1963. Animal species and evolution. Harvard Univ. Press, Cambridge.

Neel, J. V. 1951. The population genetics of two inherited blood dyscrasiias in man. Cold Spring Harbor Symp. Quant. Biol., 15: 141–158.

Penrose, L. S., S. M. Smith, and D. A. Sprott. 1956. On the stability of allelic systems, with special reference in haemoglobins A, S, and C. Ann. Human Gen. 21: 90–93.

Raper, A. B. 1956. Sickling in relation to morbidity from malaria and other diseases. Brit. Med. J., 1: 965–966.

Shibata, S. 1961. Hemoglobinopathy, with special reference to the abnormal hemoglobins found in Japan. Bull. Yamaguchi Med. School, 8: 197–207.

Thompson, G. R. 1962. Significance of haemoglobins S and C in Ghana. British Med. Jour., 1: 682–685.

Vella, V., and M. M. Hassan. 1961. Thalassemia major in a Sudanese Arab family. J. Trop. Med. and Hygiene, 64: 199–201.

―――, and S. A. Ibrahim. 1961. The frequency of thalassemia minor in a Greek community. J. Trop. Med. and Hygiene, 64: 202–206.

Wickremaisinghe, R. L., E. W. Ikin, A. E. Mourant, and H. Lehmann. 1963. Blood groups and haemoglobins of the Veddas. J. Roy. Anthrop. Inst., 93: 117–125.

Richard Levins

The Theory of Fitness in a Heterogeneous Environment
The Adaptive Significance of Gene Flow

Gene flow has generally been regarded as detrimental to a population, its principal effect being to swamp a local population and prevent its adaptation to local conditions. The swamping effect has been considered so strong that prior isolation was thought to be a necessary first step in speciation. More recently it has been recognized that strong selection can produce divergence even in the face of a high rate of migration (Thoday and Gibson, 1962; Streams and Pimentel, 1961), while the experiments of Koopman (1950) show that sexual isolation can arise in populations in contact.

This has raised the opposite question: why do we not have local speciation on a much greater scale, why are there any widespread species at all, why is not each local ecotype a distinct species? The obvious first answer refers to population size. As the environment becomes infinitely subdivided, local population size decreases, and the probability of random extinction increases. Suppose that the average number of offspring per pair is r, and each has a probability $1/r$ of survival. Then the probability that a population of size $2n$ becomes extinct by chance is $[1 - (1/r)]^{rn}$ which approaches e^{-n} for large r. However, this probability decreases rapidly with n, and would not be an important factor for populations greater than several hundred.

A second disadvantage to small population size is the loss of genetic variance through random drift, which might be important in very small populations, but the same objection applies as in the previous argument. Drift cannot account for the paucity of abundant but local species.

It will be argued below that gene flow among populations is part of the adaptive system of a species, that there are optimal values for gene flow that depend on the statistical structure of the environment, and that natural selection can establish these optimal levels (or more precisely, that the actual levels of gene flow among populations of different species differ in the same direction as their optimal values).

The model used here is a continuation of that used in the previous papers of this series (Levins, 1962, 1963, 1964). It is assumed that corresponding to

Reprinted by permission of the author and publisher from *Evolution, 18:* 635–638, 1964.

each environment there is an optimal phenotype S, which may vary in time and space; that when the actual phenotype is the optimum, the adaptive value is maximized; and that fitness declines toward zero as the deviation of actual from optimal phenotype increases. (The phenotype is genetically determined. Any developmental or physiological modification of phenotype by the environment has the effect of reducing the environmental variance, as explained in the second paper of this series.) We further specialize the model by assuming that the fitness of each phenotype declines with the square of the deviation of that phenotype from the optimum, so that

(1) $$W_{ij}(t) = 1 - [S_i(t) - P_{ij}(t)]^2,$$

where $W_{ij}(t)$ is the fitness of phenotype j in population i at time t, $S_i(t)$ is the optimal phenotype for population i at time t, and $P_{ij}(t)$ is the jth phenotype in population i. The fitness of the whole population is found by averaging over all phenotypes to get

(2) $$W_i(t) = 1 - [S_i(t) - P_i(t)]^2 - VAPHE$$

where $P_i(t)$ is the mean phenotype in population i at time t and $VAPHE$ is the phenotypic variance within the population. Averaging over all times t we obtain the mean fitness of the population

(3) $$E(W_i) = 1 - (S - P)^2 - \text{var } (S) - \\ \text{var } (P_i) - E(VAPHE) + 2 \text{ cov } (S,P_i).$$

Thus fitness is reduced by the deviation of the mean phenotype from the mean optimum, by the variances of the environment and of the mean phenotype, and by the mean phenotypic variance, and is increased by the covariance of environment and mean phenotype.

In the previous papers it was shown that the greater the additive genetic variance, the greater also will be $VAPHE$ and the variance of the mean phenotype in a fluctuating environment. Thus, additive variance reduces fitness. However, if there is a sufficiently high autocorrelation in the environment (correlation between the environments of successive generations of the same population) then the mean phenotype can follow the environment and therefore the covariance of S and P_i can increase fitness sufficiently to compensate for the losses due to var (P) and $VAPHE$. In that case, the optimum amount of genetic variance will be greater than zero.

Migration between populations can affect each of the components of fitness. The nature of these effects can best be seen by considering three special cases. First we note that the change of mean phenotype under selection at n loci is

(4) $$\frac{dP}{dt} = \sum_i \frac{\partial P}{\partial x_i} \frac{dx_i}{dt},$$

where x_i is the frequency of the ith locus. Further, for continuous models with overlapping generations,

(5)
$$\frac{dx_i}{dt} = \frac{1}{2} x_i (1 - x_i) \frac{\partial W}{\partial x_i}.$$

In our model,

$$\frac{\partial W}{\partial x_i} = 2(S - P) \partial P / \partial x_i,$$

so that

(6)
$$\frac{dP}{dt} = (S - P) \sum_i x_i (1 - x_i) (\partial P / \partial x_i)^2.$$

The summation term is the total additive genetic variance for phenotype, so that our particular case of the fundamental theorem of natural selection becomes

(7)
$$\frac{dP}{dt} = V(S - P),$$

where V is the additive genetic variance for phenotype. For convenience we assume that V remains constant, a reasonable assumption if the fluctuations in P are not too great.

Case I: Environment constant in time, variable in space, so that the populations have permanently different environments. Then the change in mean phenotype in two populations is given by the pair of equations

(8)
$$\frac{dP_1}{dt} = V[S_1(t) - P_1] + m(P_2 - P_1),$$

and

(9)
$$\frac{dP_2}{dt} = V[S_2(t) - P_2] + m(P_1 - P_2),$$

where m is the fraction of each population exchanged with the other. Since the $S_i(t)$ are constants, an equilibrium value is reached at

(10)
$$P_1 = S_1 - m(S_1 - S_2)/(2m + V)$$

and

(11)
$$P_2 = S_2 - m(S_2 - S_1)/(2m + V).$$

Thus migration displaces the mean phenotype from its optimal value by an amount which increases with the difference between the environments and the amount of gene flow, and decreases with the additive variance. This is the familiar swamping effect. $VAPHE$ is also increased by migration since each population is a mixture of two populations with different means. Hence, gene flow between populations with different average environments reduces fitness.

Case II: Environments of both populations fluctuate independently about the same mean, and there is no autocorrelation between environments of successive generations. The pair of simultaneous differential equations (8) and (9) has the solution

(12)
$$P_1(t) = V \int_0^t e^{-V(t-\gamma)} \{ [\tfrac{1}{2} + \tfrac{1}{2}e^{-2m(t-\gamma)}] \cdot \\ S_1(\gamma) + [\tfrac{1}{2} - \tfrac{1}{2}e^{-2m(t-\gamma)}] \cdot S_2(\gamma) \} \, d\gamma,$$

where γ is a dummy variable of integration. Thus $P_1(t)$ depends on the environments of both populations, weighted in favor of recent environments. The relative weight of the environment of its own habitat is greatest for recent environments and approaches one-half for the environments of the remote past. The average P_1 is the same as P_2 and is not affected by migration. The variance of P_1 is

(13) $\text{var}(P_1) = \tfrac{1}{4}\,\text{var}(S) \cdot [1 + 1/(1 + 2m/V)].$

When m is zero, $\text{var}(P_1) = \tfrac{1}{2}\,\text{var}(S_1)$ while for m/V large $\text{var}(P_1) = \tfrac{1}{4}\,\text{var}(S_1)$. Thus migration between two populations can reduce the variance of mean phenotype by almost half (and for many populations, the effect is greater). There will be a slight increase in $VAPHE$, but the overall effect of migration is to damp the response to ephemeral fluctuations of the environment and thus to increase fitness.

Case III: Environments vary in time, but are the same for the two populations. Then

(14) $P(t) = V \int_0^t e^{-V(t-\gamma)} S(\gamma) \, d\gamma$

independently of m.

Comparing cases II and III, we see that migration damps the response of populations to local fluctuations while permitting response to widespread changes of environment. It remains to be noted that long-term or major fluctuations tend also to be widespread, while short-term oscillations of environment are more localized (see, for example, Hariharan, 1956). Since it has been shown previously that response to selection is advantageous only for environmental changes with a high autocorrelation (long-term changes), we can now assert that the adaptive significance of gene flow is that it permits the population to respond genetically to long-term, widespread environmental changes while damping the response to local, ephemeral fluctuations. Or in information terms, migration is a filter whereby spatial information is used for temporal prediction.

The above argument leads to the conclusion that the optimal amount of gene flow between populations is increased by the temporal variance of the environmental variable and decreased by the spatial gradient. From this several predictions follow:

1. In regions of temporal stability, there will be greater geographic differentiation and speciation per unit spatial heterogeneity.

2. Stable habitats (large lakes in contrast to streams, forests in contrast to open fields, subsoil as contrasted with surface) favor reduced gene flow and local differentiation.

3. Along a given transect, with a given spatial heterogeneity, herbs, weeds, and animals have a more variable lifetime environment than climax trees. Therefore, whereas the climax vegetation will be sharply zoned, the secondary species, herbs, and weeds will cross several tree zones and have more gene flow along a transect. This will be associated with simultaneous flowering along the transect for these species as contrasted with waves of flowering along the altitudinal gradient for climax trees.

4. Species may be described as having fine-grained environments if the individuals wander over many of the microclimatic patches during their lives, and coarse-grained if the individual lands at random or by habitat selection within a single patch and remains there for its whole life. The environment of a coarse-grained species without habitat selection has the greatest temporal variance from generation to generation, the fine-grained species are next, and the coarse-grained with strong habitat selection have the lowest temporal variance. Plants are in the first category with respect to soil types; most vertebrates are in the second, while the smaller invertebrates are in the last. The expected amount of gene flow decreases, and the degree of diversification increases from first to last.

The question arises, to what extent are the results dependent on the details of the model? Consider a more general case in which, instead of equation (1),

$$(15) \qquad W_{ij}(t) = W[|S_i(t) - P_{ij}|].$$

For a fixed $S_i(t)$ we can expand in Taylor's series about $S_i - P_i$:

$$(16) \quad W_{ij}(t) = W[S_i(t) - P_i(t)] + [P_i(t) - P_{ij}] \cdot$$
$$W'[S_i(t) - P_i(t)] + \frac{1}{2}[S_i(t) - P_i(t)]^2 \cdot$$
$$W''[S_i(t) - P_i(t)] + \dots$$

Now taking the expected value over all phenotypes we have

$$(17) \quad W_{ij}(t) = W[S_i(t) - P_i(t)] +$$
$$\frac{1}{2} \, VAPHE \, W''[S_i(t) - P_i(t)] + \dots$$

If the coefficient of $VAPHE$ is negative, the qualitative effects are in agreement with the previous special model. This will always be the case if P_i is not too far from S_i because $W(z)$ is a unimodal non-negative function of its argument. Only when z exceeds z_0, the point of inflection of $W(z)$, does $W'''(z)$ become positive and fitness increase with $VAPHE$. Similarly, expanding $W(S_i - P_i)$ about the mean values of S_i and P_i, we have

$$(18) \quad W(S_i - P_i) = W(\bar{S} - \bar{P}) + [(S_i - \bar{S}) - (P_i - \bar{P})] \cdot$$
$$W'(\bar{S} - \bar{P}) + \frac{1}{2}[(S_i - \bar{S}) + (\bar{P} - P_i)]^2 \cdot$$
$$W''(\bar{S} - \bar{P}) + \dots$$

which has the average value

(19) $W(S_i - P_i) = W(\bar{S} - \bar{P}) + \frac{1}{2}[\text{var }(S) +$
$$\text{var }(P) - 2 \text{ cov }(S, P)] \cdot W''(\bar{S} - \bar{P}) + \ldots$$

Once again, if the average P is not too far from the average optimum, then the coefficient of var (S) + var (P) − 2 cov (S, P) is negative and the qualitative effects are unaltered. Therefore, the conclusions of this paper hold beyond the quadratic model provided the environment is not too variable or migration too extreme.

Summary

The adaptive significance of gene flow is that it permits populations to respond under natural selection to long-term, widespread fluctuations in the environment while damping the response to local, ephemeral oscillations. The optimal level of gene flow increases with the temporal variance of the environment and decreases with the average spatial gradient.

Literature Cited

Hariharan, P.S. 1956. A study in spatial and frequency distribution of daily rainfall in relation to a network of rain recording stations. Indian J. Meteorol. Geophysics, 7 (3,3).

Koopman, K. F. 1950. Natural selection for reproductive isolation between *Drosophila pseudoobscura* and *D. persimilis*. Evolution, 4: 135–148.

Levins, R. 1962. Theory of fitness in a heterogeneous environment. I. The fitness set and adaptive function. Am. Nat., 96: 361–373.

———. 1963. II. Developmental flexibility and niche selection. Am. Nat., 97: 75–90.

———. 1964. III. The response to selection. J. Theor. Biol. (in press).

Thoday, J. M., and J. B. Gibson. 1962. Isolation by disruptive selection. Nature, 193: 201–210.

Streams, F. A., and David Pimentel. 1961. Effects of immigration on the evolution of populations. Am. Nat., 95: 201–210.

Alice M. Brues

The Cost of Evolution vs. the Cost of Not Evolving

Haldane (1957) under the title "The Cost of Natural Selection" investigated the replacement of a gene by a more favorable allele, in terms of the total number of deaths required to eliminate the less advantageous allele from the population. This he found to be relatively independent of the intensity of selection, with the number of generations required for the change varying inversely with the number of deaths per generation. He estimated the total number of deaths, where selection was moderate (not more than one-third of the adversely affected genotypes being eliminated) to be 10–20 times the number of individuals living at any one time. This figure was based on the assumption that the favored phenotype had a frequency of only 0.0001 at the beginning of the process. He pointed out that this initial frequency is the most important factor influencing the total number of deaths, since a lower frequency serves to protract the initial period during which the viability of the population is at a minimum. On the basis of the apparent burden of excess deaths involved in the process, he hypothecated a limit on the rate at which gene substitutions could take place in a natural species. Kimura (1960) referred to Haldane's work in a discussion of genetic load, which he divided into three types: (1) mutational (the type classically discussed by Muller, 1950), (2) segregational, or due to the loss of homozygotes in a balanced polymorphism (first so called by Crow, 1958), and (3) substitutional or evolutional. In reference to the latter he states "The process of substituting one allele for another through natural selection involves lowering of population fitness and thus creates a genetic load." The concept was referred to again by Mayr (1963) under the heading "The Cost of Evolution."

In order to clarify these concepts, it is necessary to review some of the conventions customarily used in setting up a mathematical model for selection. It is convenient in such problems to take the viability of the most favored known genotypes as a standard, and measure all others relative to it, so that a conspicuous parameter in the calculations is commonly one of the form $(1 - x)$ denoting the viability of a genotype that suffers a net loss of x per generation as compared with an "optimum" genotype. Another convention is to adjust

Reprinted by permission of the author and pubisher from *Evolution, 18:* 379–383, 1964.

the population size in some manner so that it appears to be constant from generation to generation. These mathematical devices, while necessary to produce a neat model of the selective process, may ignore certain realities. For instance, no account is generally taken of whether one, both, or neither of the viabilities designated by 1 and $(1 - x)$ are adequate to maintain the existence of the population at a constant level. If a population has only one genotype, that genotype will be classed as "optimum" and there can be no "inferior" genotypes. Thus the mathematical model will show no mortality at all, even though, as in the case of some egg-laying organisms, the actual average of individual survival is somewhere in the vicinity of one per million. Even worse, a one-genotype population may appear to be doing very well in the mathematical model, even though in reality it is rapidly becoming extinct because its one genotype is inadequate under current conditions. On the other hand, a population with a variety of genotypes will always show some selective losses in the model because some of its genotypes have to be rated less than 1, although it may, in fact, be increasing in numbers quite rapidly. The paradox becomes clearer if we imagine a situation in which there occurs within a population a new mutation with favorable effects on viability. In order to incorporate this into the scheme, it is necessary to *demote* the previously optimum genotype to a selection value less than 1. This creates a fictitious genetic load, since the old genotype is just as good as it ever was, and the gradual introduction of a superior one can have no effect but to continually enhance the viability of the population and presumbaly increase its numbers. This paradox has recently been alluded to by Li (1963). Now it is indeed true that limitations of habitat often tend to lop off added population if population size increases, and that if population size decreases, less vigorous individuals may be somewhat protected. One needs only to attempt to project selection effects *without* some adjustment of total population size to realize how readily species would either become extinct, or rapidly cover the globe, if this were not the case. However, it is doubtful that mortality due to overpopulation in a too vigorous species is properly classed as "load" or "cost," even if it strikes out selectively certain genes which are becoming obsolete.

Turning again to Haldane's original paper, we find that he explicitly describes the type of situation he had in mind: one in which a population, due to deteriorating circumstances, finds a previously satisfactory gene inadequate so that it comes to be replaced by a previously neutral or undesirable allele which had remained rare. It is, in fact, the resultant mortality of the old genotype, in excess of what is suffered prior to the environmental change, which is the "cost of natural selection." (There appears to be an assumption that the viability of the old genotype before the external change, and of the new one, after it, are identical.) Now it is true that under such circumstances natural selection will be costly, but we have prejudiced the case by assuming that the process begins with a serious crisis. If the terminology is subtly changed to become "the cost of evolution," as in Mayr's allusion, we now have a definite contradiction, for evolution is not natural selection, but a process which results from it. In a case such as described, the evolution, that is, the gene replacement, is a positive factor by which the population may better its condition after an environmental setback. To speak in this connection, as Kimura does, of a "substitutional load" that "involves lowering of population fitness" is to imply that the gene substitution causes the lowering of fitness when in fact it is the means of correcting it. A similar question arises in connection with the term "segregational load" (Crow, 1958). It is clear that in a case of balanced polymorphism the overall viability of the population must be *greater* than it was before the appearance of the second of the two genes involved, since prior to that time the only genotype present was one of the less viable homozygotes. Here a load is present only if we use as a standard of comparison a condition not even attainable on the population level, that of universal heterozygosity. For a further discussion of this question see Sanghvi (1963).

Perhaps we should return to examine the context in which Muller first proposed the use of the term "load" in connection with genetic lethality. He was, in the first place, deeply concerned with the possibility of a decrease in overall fitness as a result of a deterioration of the genetic material itself. Secondly, he was specifically concerned with the human species, in which humanitarian considerations make the production of a sublethal individual a source of anguish, even though the total fertility-viability of the species may, as at the present time, be a cause of serious apprehension because of the threat of overpopulation. However, it appears that the term "genetic load" is now being rather freely used in situations in which a threat to the species is initiated by environmental alterations rather than genetic ones or where there is no threat at all, but actually a newly opened possibility of "more abundant life."

Similarly, the term "cost," as applied to evolution, needs to be examined more carefully. Perhaps the concept can be put into better perspective if we compare the "cost of evolution" with the "cost of not evolving" under the same circumstances. In any selective process leading to a change in gene frequencies, the percentage of survival per generation will be a minimum at the beginning, when the population consists largely or exclusively of the less viable of the types considered. As the percentage of the more viable type increases, the survival rate increases until it finally reaches a maximum level with the fixation of the more viable types. This process will be slow at first, then accelerate, and again become slow at the end, the slowness being more apparent initially in the case of a favored recessive and terminally in the case of a favored dominant. However, the total amount of selective loss is bound to be less for the evolving population than it would have been for a population which lacked the advantageous gene altogether and therefore suffered a continual maximum mortality throughout the whole period. Thus, if a species were to be so taxed by the "cost of evolution" that it ceased to exist, nothing is more certain than that it would have become extinct with even greater promptness if it had not evolved.

In order to determine the ratio of the cost of evolution to the cost of not evolving, a number of runs were made with a simple computer program which was capable of handling differential selection, under conditions of random mating, for the three genotypes obtainable with two genes at one locus. Desired gene frequencies for an initial generation were specified; from this data genotype frequencies were calculated and multiplied by the appropriate selection factors to derive frequencies of "surviving" genotypes. From the latter figures the gene frequencies for the next generation were calculated. This process could be repeated for as many generations as desired. The usual conventions of a selection model were used in that selection factors were of the form $(1 - x)$, with the value 1, or theoretical "no deaths," being assigned to the optimum genotype. The handling of gene frequencies in per cents in effect established a constant population size. However, for each generation the amount of loss, or falling short of optimal survival, was also recorded. This latter value corresponds to the "deaths" in Haldane's calculations.

Selection both towards an initially rare dominant and towards an initially rare recessive was tested, with selection intensity varying from 50% fatality of the adversely affected genotype to only 1%. In order to truncate the time period and avoid excessive machine operation, each run was started with a 0.01 frequency of the advantageous phenotype and ended with a 0.01 residual frequency of the disadvantageous phenotype (the respective gene frequencies being 0.10 for a recessive gene and 0.005 for a dominant one). This truncation, as Haldane has predicted, resulted in considerably less total "fatalities" than if the starting point were at a lower value of the favored phenotype; in our series the total "deaths" in all generations ranged only from 4 to 11 times the number of individuals living at any one time. The "cost of evolution" was then compared with the "cost of not evolving," i.e., the number of deaths that would have occurred if the initial maximum mortality had prevailed throughout the same period of time. The resulting ratios were found to be remarkably constant in spite of the large range of selection intensities. In the case of a favored dominant, the cost of evolution ranged from 0.27 to 0.30 times the cost of not evolving, and in the case of a favored recessive, from 0.67 to 0.70. (Some portion of the small variation present may be due to cumulative errors of approximation in the method used.) The difference between dominant and recessive is due to the more rapid approach to the optimal condition where the dominant is selected for. These figures of course do not take into account the continuing disadvantage of the nonevolving group after the time at which we chose to terminate the calculations. It is clear that in any case the "cost of evolution" is the lesser of two evils by a considerable margin.

In view of the difficulties encountered in deriving a practical measure of viability by purely relative ratings of past, present, and future genotypes, it is helpful to emphasize the simple Darwinian-Malthusian equation of individual mortality with excess reproductive capacity. For practical purposes, the net viability of a species is 1 if its reproductive capacity is equal to its losses, both selective and random. Any change involving increase in this value is tolerable, a decrease is not. This will lead us to question some of Haldane's further conclusions regarding the number of loci at which gene substitutions can take place simultaneously in a population. The limitations he envisages are based on the assumption that any process of gene replacement involves a net loss to the species. It is this emphasis on the negative aspects of gene replacement which results in his calculation that a species can replace genes by selective processes at the rate of only one every 300 generations. However, it appears on closer examination that normal gene replacement due to natural selection will always represent a gain in fitness with respect to current conditions and the fact that the replacement may sometimes have been triggered by a deterioration of environment, or that ecological conditions may subsequently penalize the expanding population, is coincidental. We may then say that if at a given time the reproductive capacity of a species is adequate to compensate for its natural losses, there is no reason why there should be any limit, on the basis of the selective process alone, on the number of advantageous genes it can proceed to cultivate. The very nature of an advantageous gene is that it will salvage a certain number of individuals which would have been among the "natural" losses in former generations. More likely limiting factors on multiple gene replacement would be paucity of useful mutations, and the fact that mutations which were all individually advantageous in a particular genetic background might conflict with one another when they became common enough to interact.

In connection with the relation of viability and fecundity we might note that many of the larger mammals have attained a level of individual viability which from the point of view, for instance, of one of the egg-laying fishes, would appear to be well along the asymptotic approach to immortality. It is for this reason only that these mammals have been able to reduce reproduction to the fantastically low level of one or less offspring per year. Haldane commences the work with the comment, "It is well known that breeders find difficulty in selecting simultaneously for all the qualities desired in a stock of animals or plants. . . . In slowly breeding animals such as cattle, one cannot cull even half the females, even though only one in a hundred of them combines the various qualities desired." The situation described is one in which a species, having attained exceedingly high viability which enables it to thrive with very low fertility, is suddenly subjected to a capricious selection which involves the elimination from the breeding pool of an overwhelming number of perfectly healthy individuals whose only fault is that they lack some quality which is desired, not for the good of their own species, but for the pleasure of another one. This indeed is an externally induced catastrophe of a magnitude which would seriously threaten any species were it to arise under natural conditions. However, it is genetically determined only in the sense that the native intelligence of a cow is not adequate for her to escape from this unreasonable treatment and pursue the ultimate perfection of bovitude in her own fashion. Similarly, in the case of man, if we attempt to define a situation in which reproductive capacity would become inadequate to compensate for selection losses, we find really only three possibilities: first, a great increase of undesirable mutations—genetic load in the original Mullerian sense; second, the onset of a severe environmental stress to which present genotypes of man could not adapt in any way; or third, a drastic eugenic attempt to select for qualities other than physical vigor and fecundity, which is something quite foreign to natural selection and not pertinent to ordinary evolutionary processes.

Summary

Attention is called to certain usages of the terms "genetic load" and "cost of evolution."

The term "genetic load," first used by Muller to describe a burden on a species due to deterioration of the genetic material, has come to be applied to any situation in which one gene is replacing another due to a selection differential, even though the replacement results from the introduction of an advantageous allele, and the overall viability of the population is increasing throughout the process. This paradox is believed to arise from the mathematical convention of representing differential selection in terms of a deficiency from an "optimum" genotype, which may be a rare one which will not exist in any significant numbers until some time in the future; and from the habit of assuming for purposes of calculation that a population remains constant in size. It is also shown that a "load" due to deterioration of environment, which is later alleviated by a gene substitution, may come to be referred to as if it were genetic in its origin.

The related concept of the "cost of evolution" is examined by comparison with its alternative, the "cost of not evolving." It is shown that under the same external circumstances a species undergoing appropriate gene substitutions will always fare better in terms of total number of deaths during the period of adjustment than will a population which is unable to make such substitutions. Here, again, a mistaken concept is entertained if we compare the state of the evolving population with an idealized future, rather than with the state in which it would presently be if it were genetically static. It is also pointed out that if gene substitutions are positive in their effect, as they will normally be if they represent natural selection in the direction of greater biological fitness, there is no risk to species survival inherent in the selective process itself which will restrict the number of such substitutions which may take place in a given population during any particular period of time.

Literature Cited

Crow, J. F. 1958. Some possibilities for measuring selection intensities in man. Human Biol., 30: 1–13.

Haldane, J. B. S. 1957. The cost of natural selection. J. Genet., 55: 511–524.

Kimura, M. 1960. Optimum mutation rate and degree of dominance as determined by the principle of minimum genetic load. J. Genet., 57: 21–34.

Li, C. C. 1963. The way the load ratio works. Amer. J. Human Genet., 15: 316–321.

Mayr, Ernst. 1963. Animal species and evolution. Harvard Univ. Press.

Muller, H. J. 1950. Our load of mutations. Amer. J. Human Genet., 2: 111–176.

Sanghvi, L. D. 1963. The concept of genetic load: a critique. Amer. J. Human Genet., 15: 298–309.

3

Population Ecology

Whereas in the first section of these readings the papers reproduced were by chance from botanical authors, in the second section the subject matter was, equally fortuitously, largely of a zoological nature. In this third section, which covers the growth, regulation, and energy relations of species populations, it will be apparent that no such distinctions are or can be made. Population phenomena, and the current concepts that have developed in explanation of them, apply equally to populations of plants, animals, and microorganisms. The same worker may be investigating at one time a population from one of these kingdoms, at another time members of a different one. The range of the population ecologist has to be entirely biological. No more than the evolutionary ecologist can the population ecologist afford to specialize in one or another group of living organisms and ignore all others.

Papers reproduced in the first two sections emphasized that species populations result from processes of evolutionary ecology. The rate at which these processes develop and their direction will determine the extent of species diversity. The patterns of species diversity have received considerable attention in recent years, and one of the workers who has been especially concerned with this problem is R. H. MacArthur. Dr. MacArthur, himself a pupil of Dr. G. S. Hutchinson, has, with his group of associates, pursued the mathematical relationships of species occurrence, both in relation to new habitats (as, for example, volcanic islands) and in interspecific and intraspecific competition. In the paper reproduced here, Dr. MacArthur examines species diversity, its measurement, and its relationship with the relative abundance of species. He points out that information theory formulae can be used to measure habitat diversity and differences between communities or habitats. This permits changes in the pattern of species diversity to be compared with changes in the environment. He explains why small or remote islands have fewer species than large or complex ones. He accounts for the fact that local variations in species diversity in a restricted or a uniform habitat can usually be predicted in terms of the structure and productivity of the habitat. The theory of competition and the effects of character displacement within the habitat are also discussed in this paper. The greater species diversity of tropical areas is attributed to a finer subdivision of habitats by greater niche diversification.

The matter of species diversity has been approached from a different direction in a paper by R. T. Paine, who suggests that local animal species diversity is related to the number of predators in the system and their efficiency in preventing single-species populations from monopolizing some major and limiting resource of the habitat. Dr. Paine considers the marine rocky intertidal zone, where the limiting resource is usually space. In this situation, predators capable of preventing such monopolies are not present, and these systems are less diverse. Unlike the MacArthur correlations, Paine finds on a local scale no relationship between latitude and diversity. On a wider scale he attributes increased stability of annual production mainly to an increased capacity for the support of high-level carnivores. This he supposes is the explanation of the greater diversity of tropical ecosystems, which include disproportionately larger number of carnivores.

An examination of species abundance follows that of species diversity. The question of population numbers and their regulation in one animal species population, a vole (*Microtus agrestis*), is considered by D. Chitty, who worked for a number of years in the Bureau of Animal Population Studies founded in Oxford University by the distinguished British ecologist Charles Elton. Dr. Chitty examines the hypothesis that vole populations are a special instance of a general law that all species are capable of regulating their own population densities without destroying the renewable resources of their environment or requiring the influence of predators or environment to keep them from so doing. This hypothesis can be shown to be false or irrelevant to a given situation by proving that there are significant differences between expanding, stationary, and declining populations in the distribution of the properties of the individuals. Dr. Chitty concludes that it is improbable that the action of physical factors is independent of population density, and postulates that the effects of weather and other factors become more severe as numbers rise and quality falls.

Only recently have population processes in plants come to be investigated in the same manner as have those of animals. This new approach has been pioneered by J. L. Harper, who up to this time is the youngest man ever to be elected as President of the British Ecological Society. In a paper published jointly with some of his collaborators, Dr. Harper discussed competition between plant populations at the seedling stage. Although this may be regarded in some ways as a density-dependent relationship, it is concluded that competition between species at this stage is controlled by the nature of microsites which are available in and on the soil. Each species has particular requirements for germination and establishment, so that the numbers of seedlings that develop in each species population is related to the availability of suitable microsites.

A recent study of population growth rates by J. T. Tanner is reproduced next. The work described was carried out at Oak Ridge National Laboratory and very well illustrates the methods now being applied toward a solution of the density-independent, density-dependent argument. Dr. Tanner concludes that in most animal species populations, growth is a decreasing function of density. He points out that this explains the relative stability of animal populations, which do not appear to continue to increase at the rate their fertility would permit, and rarely decrease to extinction.

Continuing with this examination of plant populations, the sixth paper is by D. M. Gates, Director of the Missouri Botanic Garden, who at the time this was written was also a member of the Institute of Arctic and Alpine Research at the University of Colorado. Dr. Gates deals with two different but equally vital aspects of population ecology, the relationship between a species population and its environment and energy relations. He describes the environmental factors affecting the flow of energy between the plant and its environment. He considers the mechanisms of radiation and conversion that are concerned with the transfer of energy, and the ecological significance of these environmentally influenced physiological processes, in terms of productivity and competition.

These relations are also considered in the paper by L. B. Slobodkin on the energy relationships of populations. For a number of years Dr. Slobodkin has been investigating the energy relations of single-species populations in competition and in simulated food chains. His theoretical analyses and mathematical models have dealt essentially with laboratory populations, but from these he has been able to obtain data applicable to natural ecosystems that have provided information regarding energy transfer in these situations. In this major paper, Dr. Slobodkin deals with the important concepts of ecological efficiency, population efficiency, and growth efficency. He defines and illustrates these concepts and discusses their interrelationships. He then proceeds to a discussion of the development of a comprehensive, predictive, general theory of community ecology.

Robert H. MacArthur

Patterns of Species Diversity

I. Introduction

Patterns of species diversity exist. Usually there is an increasing gradient of numbers of species from the poles toward the equator. There is also a general pattern of remote or small islands having fewer species than larger islands near the source of colonization. Finally, within a fairly small region there are what might be called within- and between-habitat patterns although the distinction is vague. The within-habitat pattern is the predictable number of species which coexist in spite of regular overlap in their place of feeding, or which have made other adjustments to coexist. But the total number of species present in a geographic area usually greatly exceeds the number within a component habitat, because different species are likely to occupy different habitats; this is the between-habit pattern of diversity. If the patterns were wholly fortuitous and due to accidents of history, their explanation would be a challenge to geologists but not to ecologists. The very regularity of some of the patterns for large taxonomic groups suggests, however, that they have been laid down according to some fairly simple principles, and it is the purpose of this article to review the facts and some of the explanations which have been proposed. The reader may refer to Goodall (1962) for a very complete bibliography of the subject.

An analogy is unusually enlightening as a means of clarifying the relevant features of the problem. It we were to ask "Why does one library contain more books than another?" there would be two categories of answer. If both libraries were known to be full, the answer would have to do with the total length of the shelves and the average distance between centres of books. If, on the other hand, the libraries were not yet full, a wholly different answer would be appropriate, expressed in terms of the ages of the libraries and their rates of acquisition and elimination of books. The same categories of answer are appropriate for the species-diversity question: if the areas being compared are not saturated with species, an historical anwer involving rates of speciation and length of time available will be appropriate; if the areas are saturated with species then the answer must be expressed in terms of the size of the niche

Reprinted by permission of the author and publisher from *Biological Reviews of the Cambridge Philosophical Society*, 40: 511–533, 1965. Research supported by the National Science Foundation and the American Academy of Arts and Sciences.

space (the biological equivalent of the length of the book shelves) and the limiting similarity of coexisting species (the equivalent of the distance between books). There is of course no necessity for different aspects of the diversity to have the same type of explanation. Indeed, we shall see that there is strong evidence that species reach saturation within a habitat rather quickly even though the total number of species in all habitats combined may still be increasing. Thus it is possible that the pattern of the total number of species may be best given an historical answer, while the within-habitat patterns of diversity may have an equilibrium explanation.

II. Measures of Species Diversity

The simplest measure of species diversity is a count of the number of species. This applies to resident species and not those which are present by accident. Thus an ornithologist making a census of the breeding birds of a fifteen-acre forest will normally ignore some sea bird seen flying over once during a storm. He counts only those species which give evidence of breeding. The typical result of a breeding-bird census is a virtually accurate list of all species present with a slightly less accurate count of the number of pairs of each. In what follows we shall make considerable use of the data provided by such censuses. But the problem is much more difficult for the botanist counting tree species in the same forest, for he cannot so easily eliminate from his count an established tree which has no business there but was derived from a seed blown in many years ago from a more suitable adjacent habitat. By "no business there" we mean that the species cannot maintain itself within the forest but must rely on immigration for its continued existence. G. H. Orians (personal communication) has even suggested that only the one most shade-tolerant tree species would persist in a large forest of uniform topography and soil, and that all others are in the same sense temporary or accidental. Hence the problem may be severe. However, trees, like birds, can be counted and identified relatively easily so that many censuses are available, even if they must be interpreted with care. Both the tree and bird counts can be complete: every tree or breeding-bird species in the fifteen-acre forest will be included. Many other species counts are really samples: the soil arthropods collected in a funnel or the fish from a net do not usually include members of every species present. Some of the rare species are likely to be missing. However, after repeated sampling, a relatively complete list of species can usually be assembled, even if no accurate estimate of individuals per species is available.

Thus, species counts or fairly complete samples (with or without data on the abundances of the species) are usually available. These quite simple species counts are adequate for studying some of the patterns of species diversity.

Various authors have used refined measures of species diversity designed to overcome the two principal drawbacks of using these species counts. The potential drawbacks of species counts are that they fail to take account of species abundance and that they depend upon sample size. A census with ninety-nine individuals of one species and one of a second has the same number of species (two) as does one with fifty of one and fifty of the second. Yet most people intuitively feel that the second census should be assigned a greater species diversity. Two essentially different ways have been used to overcome this difficulty. First, it is possible to fit a variety of statistical distributions to the distribution of relative abundance of species. These may have parameters which can be used as diversity indices. Thus Fisher, Corbett and Williams (1943) guessed that a sample of species from an area should have a negative binomial distribution of abundance. They went on to approximate this by a log-series. These distributions fit the data for moth species caught in a light trap reasonably well and a parameter of the log-series is an appropriate measure of species diversity (see Williams (1964) for further results). Similarly, Preston (1948) showed that in a variety of censuses the number N of species of abundance x could be approximated by the lognormal distribution which, for convenience, Preston wrote in the form

$$y = y_0 \exp \{- aR^2\} = y_0 \exp \left\{- \frac{R^2}{2\sigma^2}\right\}, \qquad (1)$$

where R was the number of "octaves" right or left of the mode, and each "octave" is double the previous one. Thus the first octaves are 1–2 individuals, 2–4 individuals, 4–8 individuals, 8–16 individuals, etc., and the number of species, y, with abundances within these octaves are given by equation (1). Preston plots one point for each octave, giving the number of species whose abundances fall within the octave. He then fits a truncated normal distribution to the points. (Actually, since 2, 4, 8, 16, etc., are boundary substances, belonging to two octaves, the species with these abundances are half assigned to each appropriate octave.) Figure 1 shows a diatom count made by Patrick (1954) plotted by Preston's technique. (A glass slide was suspended in fresh water according to methods described by Patrick for a fixed time and then the diatoms which had settled and reproduced were identified and counted. Since freshwater diatoms are not free-living planktonic species, these slides represent very convenient communities.) On the assumption that a doubling of the sample size will approximately double the number of each species present, and add a few new species represented by one or two individuals, we see that the shape of Preston's curve is virtually (but not exactly) independent of sample size and that with a doubling of sample size it simply moves one unit to the right, unveiling its left tail by one further unit. Thus, for instance, each species which formerly had between 2 and 4 individuals now has between 4 and 8; all which formerly had 4–8 now have 8–16, and so on. The rare species will, however, only approximately double. This new curve is nearly the old one moved one unit right. Preston reasoned that an infinitely large sample would reveal all the species under the whole curve, even those parts now left of the origin and hence currently undiscovered. This number of species, N, which is $y_0\sigma\sqrt{(2\pi)}$, is a reasonable measure of species diversity. It also, as we have seen, takes species abundance into account and is nearly independent

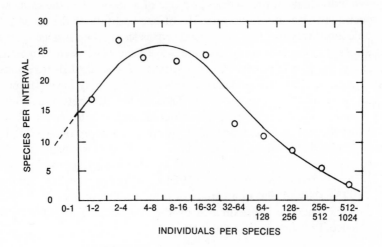

Figure 1

The abundances of diatom species on a slide are
plotted by Preston's method. The numbers of species
with abundances 1–2, 2–4, 4–8, etc., are plotted as
points and a truncated normal distribution is fitted
to the points. (From Patrick, 1954.)

of sample size. Both Preston (1960, 1962) and Patrick (1963) have made
very good use of this estimate in investigating species diversity.

A similar parameter to estimate species diversity was suggested by many
plant ecologists (see Gleason, 1922; Goodall, 1952) and independently by
Odum, Cantlon and Kornicker (1960) who kept track of the number of species
as the sample size increases. They found that if they plotted cumulative numbers of species against the logarithm of the number of individuals they got a
nearly straight line passing through the origin. The slope of this line, measuring how fast species accumulate as the number of individuals increases, has
many of the properties required of a species diversity indicator.

A second way to take account of the abundance of the species is independent
of any hypothetical distribution of relative abundance. We ask the question:
"How difficult would it be to predict correctly the species of the next individual
collected?" This is a problem which communications engineers have had to
face, because they are interested in the difficulty of predicting correctly the
name of the next letter which might appear in a message. When successive
letters are chosen independently, the formula

$$H = - \sum_{i=1}^{26} p_i \log_e p_i$$

measures the uncertainty of the next letter, where p_i is the probability of the
ith letter of the alphabet. Similarly, if successive individuals in our census are
independent of previous ones,

$$H = -\sum_{i=1}^{N} p_i \log_e p_i$$

is the appropriate measure of the uncertainty of the specific diversity of the next individual in our census. Here N is the number of species in the count and p_i is the proportion of the total number of individuals which belong to the ith species. Notice that if all N species are equally common, each is a proportion $1/N$ of the total. Thus the measure

$$-\sum_{i=1}^{N} p_i \log_e p_i \quad \text{takes on the value} \quad -N\left(\frac{1}{N}\log_e\frac{1}{N}\right).$$

This equals $\log N$, so the measure of equally common species is simply the logarithm of the number of equally common species, meaning that E equally common species would have the same diversity as the N unequally common species in our census.

Returning to the example of a census with 99 individuals of one species and 1 of a second, we calculate

$$H = -p_i \log_e p_1 - p_2 \log_e p_2 = -0.99 \log 0.99 - 0.0 \log_e 0.0 =$$
$$0.0099 + 0.0461 = 0.0560.$$

For a census of fifty individuals of each of the two species we would get

$$H = -0.5 \log_e 0.5 - 0.5 \log_e 0.5 = -\log \tfrac{1}{2} = \log_e 2 = 0.693.$$

To convert these back to "equally common species," we take $e^{0.0560} = 1.057$ for the first census and $e^{0.693} = 2.000$ for the second. These numbers, 1.057 and 2, accord much more closely with our intuition of how diverse the areas actually are, but it does not necessarily follow that E is more simple to predict from an examination of the habitat than the simple species count will be. This measure of species diversity was first used by Margalef (1957), who actually used the related measure

$$1/M \log M!/(M_1! \, M_2! \ldots M_2!)$$

in which M_1 is the actual abundance of the ith species and there are M individuals in all. By Stirling's theorem this is virtually identical to the other formula. Lloyd and Ghelardi (1964) calculated H and then gave tables relating it to what would be expected if the N species had abundances proportional to the lengths of the segments of a stick broken at $N - 1$ randomly chosen points. This measure, H, is less dependent on sample size than is the species count, for the new species added as the sample size increases will be relatively rare and will make a small contribution to H.

The main virtue of the measurement H, or E, as an index of diversity is that it can be used equally well to measure species diversity from species abundances or to measure habitat diversity from knowledge of abundances of the components of the habitat. We shall see below that this permits us to find which components of the environment control species diversity.

In what follows we shall use Preston's measure of species diversity or the information-theoretic one, H, most often, but we shall not hesitate to use counts of species where their abundances are unknown, or where the actual number of species seems most appropriate.

We can make further interesting use of the information-theory diversity formula to obtain a measure of the faunal difference between two regions. We ask "What multiple is the total fauna of the average of the simple censuses?" Suppose, for instance, each census had 8 equally common species. If they had no species in common the combined census would have 16 equally common species so $\frac{16}{8} = 2$ would be a measure of the difference—the largest this value could be. If they had no difference, but represented the same species, the total would have 8 equally common species and $\frac{8}{8} = 1$ would be the measure of difference—the minimum value the difference could take. Suppose, now, that the species in the censuses were not equally common; the information theory formula lets us convert the censuses to "equivalent number of equally common species,"

$$\exp\left\{ \sum_{i=1}^{N} p_i \log_e p_i \right\} = E = e^H.$$

We take H_1 for the first census, H_2 for the second, and H_T for the total (in which p_i is the unweighted average, $(P_i(1) + p_i(2))/2$, of the proportions in the two censuses), and we use H for the unweighted mean of H_1 and H_2 and we then use $\exp\{H_T - H\}$ as the measure of difference. This reduces to 2 and 1, respectively, for the simple cases described above, and can be applied to any censuses. It can be shown that this is approximately

$$\exp\left\{ 0.693 - 0.3(\pm 0.04) \left[\frac{O_1}{T_1} + \frac{O_2}{T_2} \right] \right\},$$

where O_1 is the number of individuals in census 1 of species also found in census 2; O_2, similarly is the number of individuals in census 2 of species also in census 1. T_1 and T_2 are the total numbers of individuals in the two censuses. This is a simpler formula and is very accurate when the censuses are rather different; for similar censuses, the correct formula must be used. For other measures of difference, see Greig Smith (1957) and Whittaker (1960).

III. The Within-Habitat Component of Species Diversity

Facts

If we examine any small, apparently homogenous, area we are likely to find that the number of species depends upon the structure of the habitat. Thus a few acres of forest support more breeding-bird species than do a few acres of field. Even if we census a field large enough to contain as many bird pairs (of all species combined), the forest has many more species. Since this aspect of species diversity is best understood for birds, we shall begin with the bird data. The experimental procedure is this: some measures of habitat complexity are guessed; to see which, if any, of these measures is responsible for the local bird species diversity it is sufficient to see, for a variety of bird censuses in a variety of different habitats, which habitat diversity measure is closely correlated with the bird species diversity. More precisely, a multiple regression of bird species diversity is calculated against all of the measures of habitat diversity which might be supposed to regulate the diversity of birds. This project has been carried out (MacArthur & MacArthur, 1961; MacArthur, 1964) and it was guessed that the species diversity of the plants and the "profile" of the foliage into horizontal layers were likely features of the habitat controlling the birds. The success of the predictions justified the guess. Plant species diversity was measured with the same formula, $- \sum_i p_i \log_e p_i$, as was bird species diversity, but for the plants p_i referred to the leaf area of the ith species of plant divided by the total leaf area of all species. The "foliage height diversity" was calculated as follows. For each height above the ground a density of foliage was estimated by optical means. A profile was constructed of height against density. By trial and error it was decided to subdivide the foliage into three layers corresponding to herbaceous ground cover (usually the part of the profile below 2 ft. in height), bushes and young trees (from 2 to 25 ft. in the profile) and canopy (usually over 25 ft. from the ground). The proportions of the total foliage area which lay in these three layers were called p_1, p_2, and p_3, and the same formula

$$- \sum_{i=1}^{3} p_i \log_e p_i$$

was used to compute the foliage height diversity. Remarkably enough, the bird species diversity was quite accurately predicted from the foliage height diversity alone (see Fig. 2) and knowledge of the plant species diversity did not enable an improved prediction to be made. The main point, however, is that there is a simple structural component to within-habitat species diversity. Furthermore, and this is more important, the prediction of Fig. 2 holds for such a wide geographic area (at least over much of the United States) that there appears to be a fairly uniform level of saturation of species. In other words, accidents of local history appear to have little or no effect on the within-habitat bird species diversity. (The between-habitat effect is another story, as we shall see later, although these facts, too, reinforce the present conclusion.)

For lizards, there are data of a similar nature, gathered by E. R. Pianka (personal communication), who found tentatively that the number of lizard species in flat, semidesert areas of western U.S.A. was proportional to various correlated structural features of the environment. For instance, the relation between the number of lizard species in nine desert areas and the average

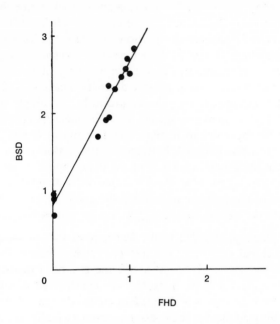

Figure 2

Bird species diversity (BSD) is plotted against foliage
height diversity (FHD) for bird censuses of a variety
of habitats, each large enough to hold twenty-five
pairs of all species combined.

volume of major shrub in cubic feet was related as in Fig. 3. Pianka's interesting study showed that most lizards, like the birds, appear to have reached
a local saturation, so that the difference between habitats is more closely
related to structure than to the time available for colonisation and rate of
speciation. (He did find two species, however, which were unable to with-
stand the colder climates of more northern deserts.) The closest parallel to
this work, for plants, is that of Whittaker (1960 and earlier) who has shown
that tree species occur, on gradients of temperature and moisture, only in
specified places. The exact prediction of species diversity is, however, much
more difficult for the trees. Whittaker recognizes the distinction between
within- and between-habitat diversities and calls them alpha and beta diversities respectively.

For most defoliating insect species, a single tree constitutes a "habitat."
Southwood (1961) showed, in apparent contradition to these results that the
numbers of species of insects inhabiting various British tree species is proportional to the cumulative abundance of the various tree species throughout
Quaternary history as measured by the total frequency of remains in the

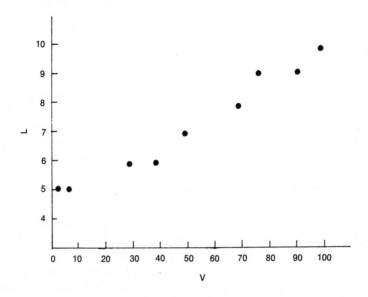

Figure 3

The number of lizard species, L, is plotted against the
average volume, V of major shrubs in cubic feet.
(From unpublished graph of E. R. Pianka.)

pollen record. These data suggest that insects inhabiting British trees have not
had sufficient time to saturate their habitats. Thus, the historical answer seems
appropriate; alternatively, we might suppose that a single tree constitutes more
than one habitat and that Southwood is not dealing with within-habitat diversity.

Another aspect of within-habitat diversity is susceptible to fairly direct observation: the limiting similarity of coexisting species. Lack (1947) and
Vaurie (1951) drew attention to the way in which the morphologies of two
species diverge in the geographic area where their ranges overlap. Brown and
Wilson (1956) reviewed many such cases, calling the phenomenon "character
displacement," and Hutchinson (1959) pointed out that there is a fairly constant relation, in the region of overlap, between the lengths of appropriate
feeding appendages of the larger and smaller of the two species. This size ratio
of larger to smaller is an indicator of how similar coexisting species can be;
Hutchinson suggested 1.3 to be a typical value of the ratio. Klopfer and
MacArthur (1961), in an attempt to show that the ratio is reduced in the
tropics, meaning that species can be more similar there, measured some birds
of species which appeared to be coexisting and found much lower values of
this ratio. As several authors have pointed out in reply, there is no reason to
think these species were character displacement pairs, so that the comparison

was not legitimate. There was nothing wrong with the idea of Klopfer and MacArthur, however, and Schoener is currently examining the whole phenomenon critically.

Theory

In Section IV it will be shown that the number of species within a habitat reaches saturation much sooner than the total number of species in a large area, since the latter continue to grow by increasing the species difference between habitats (i.e. the number of species which are found in some habitats and not others) even when each habitat is saturated. It is the purpose of this section, however, to show why there should be a limiting similarity of coexisting species, and hence a species saturation limit, and to relate this to the life-histories of the species involved.

We consider, first, the limiting similarity of resource-limited species, and defer until later those species which are limited by predators or other factors, singly or in combination. The exposition follows MacArthur and Levins (1964) and Levins and MacArthur (unpublished). A species limited by resources will normally be able to maintain its population whenever the density of the resources exceeds some threshold. Furthermore, the value of this threshold may be virtually independent of the size of the harvesting population. The rate of depletion of the resource will of course increase as the harvesters become more numerous, but at any instant of time it is the density of the resource and not of the harvesters which determines the yield to each harvesting animal. In symbols, where x is the population of a species and r_i, $(i = 1, 2, \ldots, n)$, are the densitites of the n resources,

$$\frac{dx}{dt} = \left(\sum_{i=1}^{n} a_i r_i - T \right) x,$$

where the a's are constants and the T is the threshold, so that x increases only when

$$\sum_{i=1}^{n} a_i r_i > T.$$

There are also equations for resource renewals, but they will not concern us here. For each resource, r_i, there is a value $R_i = T/a_i$ which indicates how much of resource i alone is needed to support species x. Different species, or different phenotypes within a species, will in general have different values of R_i, because they will differ in their ability to locate, capture and produce offspring from the units of resource i. In fact, the values of R_i may be expected to vary as in the left-hand graphs of Fig. 4, in which for convenience two resources are considered and the values of R_1 and R_2 are plotted against a continuum of phenotype values. There will be a phenotype, s_1, which can maintain its population at a level of resource 1 which is lower than would

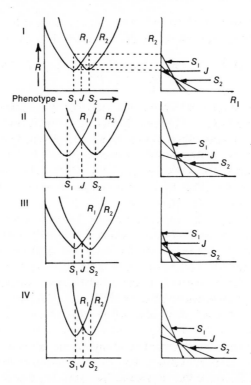

Figure 4

In the left-hand graphs the minimum quantities R_1, R_2 of two resources to support a population are plotted against the population phenotypes. These graphs are in the category of "raw data." The right-hand graphs show how the data can be analysed to predict whether the jack-of-all-trades phenotype, J, will outcompete the specialist phenotypes, S_1 and S_2, in combination. The graphs assume resource-limited populations and also that specialists tend to reduce their favoured resource, while jack-of-all-trades reduce whichever resource is commoner. For further details, see text.

be acceptable for any other phenotype. This is the specialist on resource 1. Similarly, there is a specialist, s_2, for resource 2. We can also distinguish a jack-of-all-trades, J, which is equally adept at using both resources. The curves in the figure can have a more or less arbitrary shape except that they first fall and then rise. Graph I gives a sample of two R curves such that the two specialists, in combination, are ousted by the jack-of-all-trades and kept from reinvading. This is seen from the right hand of the graphs I, which show that the curve

$$a_1(J)R_1(J) + a_2(J)R_2(J) = T(J)$$

lies inside the intersection of the two curves of the specialists. In other words, when the resources are at the level R_1, R_2, determined by the intersection of

$$a_1(s_1)R_1(s_1) + a_2(s_1)R_2(s_1) = T(s_1) \quad \text{and} \quad a_2(s_2)R_2(s_2) + a(s_2)R_2(s_2) = T(s_2),$$

which is the lowest level to which the two specialists can reduce the resources, then $a_1(J)R_1 + a_2 AJ)R_2 > T(J)$ so that the jack-of-all-trades can still increase and thereby reduce the resources to an even lower level. Furthermore, the jack-of-all-trades, if he always decreases the commoner resource, will maintain the resources about midway along the J line, so that neither specialist can enter. Thus, no more than two species can persist on two resources and, if the resources are sufficiently similar, only one can, so there is a limiting similarity to coexisting species. (MacArthur and Levins (1964) give another reason why the jack-of-all-trades can prevent the specialists from reentering.) The further biological significance of the figure comes from the comparisons of graphs II, III and IV with I. Graph II is identical to I except that the R curves are shifted farther apart (i.e. the resources are more different, requiring the specialist phenotypes to be more different). But the right-hand graph II shows that now the jack-of-all-trades line $(a_1(J)R_1(J) + a_2(J)R_2(J) = T(J)$, which is marked J in the figure) lies outside of the intersection of the specialist lines, so that the specialists in combination can oust the jack-of-all-trades and keep it from reinvading. We say the specialists are competitively superior. Graphs III show that the specialists also become competitively superior if the thresholds, $R = T/a$ are uniformly reduced, for the R curves in graph III are identical in shape and separation to those in graph I, but nearer to the phenotype axis. For birds, at least, lowering the clutch size may be expected to reduce the R curves by causing fewer mouths for the parents to feed and thus allowing the parents to bring up their brood with a lower resource density. Similarly, graphs IV show that with the same separation and threshold values as graph I, phenotypes s_1 and s_2 become competitively superior if the phenotypes become more specialized (as shown by narrower R curves). Mr. Egbert Leigh has pointed out (personal communication) that increase in specialization and lowering of the specialists' resource thresholds are likely to go hand-in-hand, combining their advantages to the specialist. Both are presumably related to climatic variability and other aspects of the physical environment, as well as to hunting strategy. In fact, an increase in productivity, by reducing the time spent searching for food, will favour an increase in specialization.

Two other cases of interest are not shown in the figure. If one of the R curves is raised higher from the phenotype axis than the other, representing unequally harvestable resources, the advantage shifts away from the jack-of-all-trades. More important, however, is the situation which arises when the resources alternate temporally, so that resource 1 is present for some time in the absence of resource 2, and then resource 2 but not 1) is present for some time. This situation clearly requires new equations and new right-hand graphs for Fig. 4, but it is clear that the advantage of the jack-of-all-trades is strengthened, since the specialists can only be as common as their respective resources will allow when these resources are minimal.

In summary, there is a limiting similarity in the species of coexisting resource-limited species and it is increased by increasing the specialization of the species, by reducing the resource thresholds (e.g. by reducing the number of young in a clutch for which the parents care), by increasing the productivity, by increasing the inequality in resource availability, and by reducing the temporal variability of the resources. Hutchinson (1965) has independently derived some of these results and applied them to the coexistence of African birds of prey.

Predator-limited species are much less simple to classify. A clever predator, such as man, can keep almost any number of prey species in a stable coexistence by maintaining each at a low population level but not so low that it becomes extinct. In fact, the most common danger is in the other direction: a species which is too common is in more danger both from diseases (a predator) and from the large ordinary predators than is a rare one (R. C. Lewontin, personal communication). Hence there is an advantage in predator-limited species being somewhat rare; yet if the individual species are rare, there can be many of them. As Lewontin has pointed out, this could conceivably be a reason why there are more tree species in a tropical habitat: each must be rare to avoid epidemics of tropical tree diseases, though why epidemics should be more prevalent in the tropics is still a problem.

If, however, the different species of prey are so similar that the predators consume them in the proportion in which they occur, then that prey species which is least tolerant of predation will be eliminated, as Leigh (1965) has pointed out to me. Hence there is also a limiting similarity to predator-limited species.

The analogy with the capacity of a library for books shows that there is another aspect of within-habitat diversity: the part analogous to the length of the shelves. Thus even though we know how similar coexisting phenotypes can be, we can only predict the within-habitat diversity if we also know what range of phenotypes are well adapted for some particular resource. Alternatively, since we know how similar the resources of coexisting species can be, we only need additional knowledge of the range of resources. It is the latter alternative which is easier to follow. The usable range of resources is not just the range of existing resources; rather it is the range of those existing resources which are maintained in sufficient quantity to support a species. Hence the more productive the habitat, the greater the fraction of existing resources which will be present in sufficient quantity. If, for instance, resources are normally distributed along an x-coordinate, with productivity determined by a constant, P, and with the actual range of resources controlled by the variance σ^2, then the usable range of resource will be the range along the x-axis, such that the distribution,

$P \exp \{-x^2/2\sigma^2\}$, exceeds some constant, c. Solving $Pe^{-x^2/2\sigma^2} > c$ we get $x < \sigma \sqrt{(2 \log_e P/c)}$ so that the usable range would be proportional to the standard deviation, σ, and proportional to the square root of the logarithm of the productivity. Of course there is no reason to think that the resources will be exactly normally distributed, so this is just an indication of how the usable range might be related to the productivity and the actual range. T. Schoener has exploited this view in an unpublished manuscript. It is dangerous, however, to assume that increases in productivity should always be accompanied by increases in diversity. In fact, where productivity is increased there is often a correlated decrease in resource variety and greater inequality of existing resources. Both of these tendencies reduce species diversity. For instance, highly productive polluted rivers show reduced species diversity (Patrick, 1954). Hence, it is only where increased productivity is unaccompanied by a reduced spectrum of resources that we have any right to expect increased diversities.

The theory of within-habitat diversity is now reasonably complete. The number of species expected is the usable range of resources divided by the limiting similarity of resources which can be used by coexisting species. Both of these are qualitatively described above, and in summary the number of species within a habitat can be expected to increase with productivity (sometimes), with the structural complexity of the habitat, the lack of seasonality in resources, the degree of specialization and with reduced family size. Of these, only the structural complexity and to some extent the productivity are likely to vary over a small geographic area; hence the local variation in within-habitat diversity is expected to be explainable in structural terms (with a smaller and somewhat ambiguous productivity term included). Actually, productivity is often correlated with structural complexity, so a structural prediction may be quite accurate. This is the theoretical justification for the facts of within-habitat diversity given in the previous section.

It is interesting that every one of the features which increases the within-habitat diversity is found to a greater degree in the tropics. Hence there is no shortage of potential causes for a tropical increase in species diversity, and there is no reason to expect this increase to be controlled by any single potential cause. Most causes should be reflected in reduced character displacement in the tropics. However, as we shall see in later sections, much of the tropical increase in species diversity is of the between-habitat rather than within-habitat type.

IV. A Theory of Within- and Between-Habitat Diversity

We begin with two premises.

Premise 1. There is a limit to the similarity of coexisting species.

Premise 2. No species voluntarily restricts its habitat, but only does so when forced to, by competition or lack of suitable conditions. (We shall say two species which are too similar to coexist belong to the same phenotype category.)

From these two premises it is simple to deduce a pattern of within- and between-habitat diversity of species. For concreteness, consider an island being colonized by an ever-increasing sample of the mainland species. The first species will, by the premises, occupy all appropriate habitats (a much wider selection of habitats than it occupied on the mainland where it was restricted by competitors). In all probability, the next species will be sufficiently different that it can coexist with the first in all suitable habitats. The third species is likely to be sufficiently different from both that it too can occupy all suitable habitats, but the probability of it being too similar to one of the previous ones to coexist is greater than it was for the second species. Eventually a species will arrive which is so similar to an existing species that both cannot coexist. Then, since both species persist on the mainland, each will be likely to find a habitat on the island in which it is superior, and the first habitat selection will have occurred. As the fauna of the island becomes quite large, it will contain a representative of each phenotype category and no further increase in the number of species per habitat will take place. Each new species will, instead, cause a further subdivision of the habitats. In summary, during the initial stages of colonization the diversity of species will be wholly within-habitat; as the fauna increases there will be more and more between-habitat diversity, and eventually all new diversity will be between-habitat. This same distinction should hold in the comparison of any rich fauna with a poor fauna occupying an environment with the same amount of structure. Before an account of the empirical evidence, an indication will be given of how this theory can be made quantitative.

Picture the possible phenotypes as a continuous space, one coordinate for each measured variable of the phenotype (say a line or a plane) and subdivide this into a mosaic of equal-sized cells corresponding to the phenotype categories. Let the incoming species fall, like raindrops, in a Poisson distribution on the phenotype plane. Then, if there are, on the average, m species per phenotype category, the expected proportion of phenotype categories with 0, 1, 2, 3, . . . species will, owing to chance, be

$$e^{-m}, \; me^{-m}, \; \frac{m^2}{2!} e^{-m}, \; \frac{m^3}{3!} e^{-m}. \ldots$$

Each habitat will be expected to contain representatives of all phenotype categories except those which have no representatives on the island. In other words, the proportion of "vacant niches" will fall according to e^{-m} and the number of species in a given habitat will grow proportionally to the formula $1 - e^{-m}$. The fraction me^{-m} of phenotype categories with a single species contains those species which have no habitat selection imposed by competition. Hence, the fraction $(me^{-m}/1 - e^{-m})$ of species within a habitat should show no competitive habitat selection and be present on other suitable parts of the island. As the species present on the island have more time together, they can make certain evolutionary adjustments, and any slight morphological change which would enable a species to move into a vacant phenotype category, or even into a less thoroughly exploited one, might be favoured. Eventually, by this process, all phenotype categories would acquire equal, or at least less unequal, numbers of species. We can use the popular term "disharmonic" to describe the initial, unadjusted, community, and can call the other community which has equally exploited phenotype categories "harmonic." Real communities presumably fall somewhere in between these extremes.

The actual data relating to this are impressive in their confirmation of the theory. Crowell (1961) confirmed the earlier impressions of Lack (1942) and others by measuring the habitats of Bermuda bird species, comparing these with mainland measurements for the same species and showing that the island birds had larger habitats than their mainland counterparts. Crowell's technique requires that the island species be also found on the mainland. Patrick (1949) has shown the same phenomenon in diatoms.

We have used a method (MacArthur and Recher, unpublished) applicable even when the island species are different from the mainland ones. Basically, the method consisted in measuring in a standard way a difference between habitats and a difference between the censuses of the birds breeding in the habitats. The difference formula of Section II was used for both the difference in bird species and the difference in profile of vegetation density between habitats. With these, one can see whether the island bird species change less with habitat changes than do mainland species. Figure 5, from the data of Recher and the author, show very clearly that the birds of Puerto Rico change much less as habitats change than do the birds of the eastern U.S.A. Similarly, Whittaker (1960) showed that a richer flora was associated with reduced habitat selection by the plant species.

V. Island Species Diversities

There are two types of possible explanation for the impoverishment of island faunas and floras compared to the adjacent mainland, and both explanations are probably appropriate for different groups of organisms. The explanation most people give is that islands are impoverished because there has not been enough time: the full quota of mainland species has never had a chance to colonize. More recently Preston (1962) and MacArthur and Wilson (1963) independently published theories accounting for an equilibrium in which the number of new immigrant species is balanced by the extinction of the rarer ones. The need for such a theory is apparent when one considers that Krakatau, which had at least all vertebrate and higher plant life destroyed by the volcanic explosion in 1883, had reconstituted a bird and insect fauna (of most orders) nearly equal to that of other islands of comparable size and remoteness within fifty years after the explosion (Dammermann, 1948). Clearly, then, birds and many kinds of insects approach equilibrium very quickly; mammals, on the other hand, are much slower and many remote islands may still be unsaturated with mammals, although the success of introductions is no proof, for the immi-

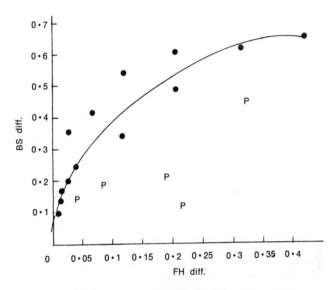

Figure 5

The difference in bird species composition (BS Diff.) between census areas differing in foliage profile is plotted against foliage profile difference (FH Diff.), showing that in Puerto Rico (*P* points) the same difference in habitat causes much less change in bird species than on the mainland of U.S.A. (• points).

gration rate is enormously higher when man introduces forms and an increase in the equilibrium fauna would be expected.

The theory of MacArthur and Wilson (1963) is summarized most conveniently in Fig. 6. It is permissible to ask what would be the rate of extinction of species and the rate of immigration of new species (not already on the island) for any number of species on the island. Thus, if the island has no species on it, all immigrants are new species and there are no species to become extinct. This is the left end of the curves in Fig. 6. As the number on the island grows, there are more species to become extinct, so this curve rises; there are also fewer new ones among the immigrants, so this curve falls, dropping to zero when the island has the full mainland fauna. Actually, the number of species will only grow until the number of new, immigrant species is balanced by the number of species becoming extinct. As Fig. 6 shows, this equilibrium number will be lower on small or uniform islands where extinction of additional species is likely (the rare ones with small niches are the likely candidates for extinction). It will also be lower on remote islands with lower rates of immigration from the sources of colonization. The multiple regression analyses of Hamilton, Barth and Rubinoff (1964) and Watson (1965) show clearly that

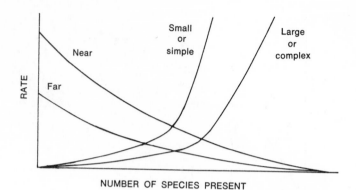

NUMBER OF SPECIES PRESENT

Figure 6

The rates of immigration (falling curves) of new species, not on the island, and of extinction (rising curves) of species on the island are plotted for all numbers of species on an island. Where they intersect, the extinction balances the immigration. This equilibrium is shown to be greater for large, complex or near islands. See text for further discussion. (From MacArthur and Wilson, 1963.)

there is a habitat diversity component to the number of species on an island. This may be reflected in the extinction curves by the rather pronounced upward bend (see Fig. 6). This takes place where the number of species on the island roughly corresponds to the capacity of the island and is assumed to be proportional to the variety of habitats; species in excess find more difficulty in surviving and thus the extinction curves become steep. When this approximate number of species has been reached, the number of species varies but little with changes in the immigration rate, and instead depends mostly upon habitat diversity. This approach to understanding island diversities has the merit of explaining qualitatively both the distance effect and the area-habitat effect (Fig. 7); statistical consequences of the theory can also be used to distinguish between saturated and unsaturated island systems (MacArthur and Wilson, 1963). The exact shape of the curves is not simply predictable, however, so quantitative *a priori* predictions of· island species diversity cannot be made. We turn to Preston's (1962) account for a better understanding of the extinction rates, and an alternate account of the whole theory in the case where the islands are of equal distance from the source of colonization.

Preston showed with considerable ingenuity how the lognormal distribution of species abundances can be used to describe species-area curves and other aspects of species diversity. (Preston's papers are too long to summarize here in their entirety.) As was shown in Section II, if a larger sample is taken from the same lognormal distribution, it essentially unveils more of the left-hand

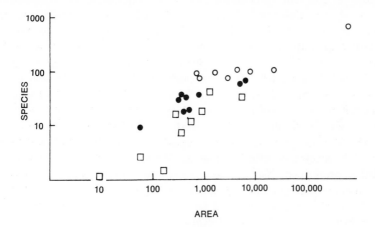

Figure 7

The number of resident bird species is plotted against the area in square miles of Pacific islands in the Moluccas, Melanesia and Oceania. Islands less than 500 miles from the presumed source of colonization (New Guinea) are represented by circles, islands farther than 2000 miles by squares. Islands of intermediate distance are represented by dots. Part, but not all, of this apparent distance effect is due to the lesser elevation of the far islands. (From MacArthur and Wilson, 1963.)

tail without altering the shape. When a biologist takes a larger sample, however, he is seldom sampling from the same distribution as in the small sample, for the large sample usually comes from a larger and hence more diverse area. Hence the unveiled curve has a slightly different shape from the original one, and we shall now show in what way it should be expected to differ. Some species will be adapted to many of the component habitats of the large area and these, the commonest, will be very abundant in the large sample—as abundant in fact as they would have been had the area sampled been uniform. Other species are adapted for only some of the component habitats, and these will not increase proportionally to the area sampled. Hence, the right-hand tail will move to the right faster than the mode, and the curve will become flatter—that is, it will be characterized by a larger value of the logarithmic standard deviation, σ. Preston obtains, by a circuitous route, an empirical relation between σ and the number of species, but it should be noted that, in his data, larger numbers of species arose from progressively larger areas sampled and not from richer faunas. In fact, as pointed out by Patrick (1963) and E. MacArthur (unpublished dissertation for Smith College, Northampton, Mass.), the value of σ decreases with the larger numbers of species in rich faunas or floras. In any case, Preston's relation between σ and the number of species reduced the number of independent constants in equation (1) to two, equivalent to the number of species, N, in the "universe" (i.e. the number of species in the whole, untruncated curve) and the number of individuals in the sample. If we were to census each area until its complete fauna were counted, Preston assumes that its distribution would reveal the complete lognormal distribution (equation (1)), including the left tail to the point at which the rarest species has m individuals. (Empirically m is not far from 1; it is because of extinction that this is the tail of the distribution, so that almost no species are as rare as this.) This gives a relation, for these complete samples, which Preston calls "isolates," between the remaining two independent constants, so that the relation between the number of species, N, in the isolate and the total number of individuals in the isolate is prescribed. Using the empirical relationships between constants, Preston obtained the equation $N = 2.07(I/m)^{0.262}$, where I is the number of individuals in the isolate. If we let p be the density of individuals and A the area of the isolate ($PA = I$), this becomes

$$N = 2.07(P/m)^{0.262}A^{0.262}, \tag{2}$$

which is the most accurate species-area curve yet devised. It shows, as Preston noted, that the number of species, N, grows, very roughly, with the fourth root of the area. This applies, of course, only to the complete samples, or isolates. Island faunas are such isolates, because extinction prevents many species from having abundance 1–2, and equation (2) describes island species diversities with considerable accuracy on the assumption that m is equal for all islands.

Both Preston's and MacArthur and Wilson's theories account for an equilibrium diversity on islands, but there is no reason to think all species on all islands have reached this equilibrium. In fact, we showed (MacArthur and Wilson, 1963) that the approach to equilibrium should be asymptotic, so virtually no island will have achieved complete equilibrium.

Dr. Ruth Patrick has carried out most interesting experiments with diatoms which duplicate the whole process of island colonization. Each empty glass microscope slide which she suspends in the water is an island to be colonized, since she has pointed out that these diatom species only reproduce while attached and the floating ones are strictly immigrants. Bearing this in mind, she suspended small and large slides in uniform currents of low and high flow rates carrying immigrant diatoms. As expected, the small slides, like small islands, ended up with fewer species. More surprising was the spectacular demonstration of competition. The small slides with low flow rates initially had colonists of many of the available species; as the colonies grew, a number of these species became extinct by being crowded off the slides. Whether there would be further reductions in diversity as time went on is not yet clear. The small slides with high flow maintained many species. In another experiment, Dr. Patrick has put slides of equal area in currents of equal flow rate and nutrient content. In one, however, the rate of immigration diatoms is reduced by a filtering of some of the water. Preliminary counts show that the slide with reduced immigration has fewer species, suggesting that immigration is balancing extinction, as in the theory of Fig. 6.

VI. Total Diversity and Tropical Diversity

In Section IV it was shown that individual habitats tend to become saturated quite soon, as a total fauna becomes richer, and that the extra species—the excess of the total diversity over the within-habitat diversity—tend to spill over into other habitats in which they are better able to compete. Thus the total diversity of a taxonomic group over a large area of several habitats and the within-habitat diversity appear to be independently controlled. Whittaker (1960) recognized the importance of total diversity and called it gamma diversity. Most of the authors who have written on species diversity have been primarily interested in discovering why there are so many species (total diversity) in the tropics; this problem has been excellently reviewed by Fischer (1960), to which paper the reader may refer for abundant documentation of the total-diversity gradient which accompanies latitude changes. Simpson (1964) and especially Terent'ev (1963) have given fairly complete descriptions of mammal and other diversities, and Patrick (1961) has discussed the similarity in species diversity in river systems, providing new examples. Here we shall review selected parts of the old data, new data and the relevant explanations which have been suggested.

Preston (1960) plotted bird species counts for temperate and tropical areas on log-log coordinates, obtaining essentially Fig. 8 of this article. If the vertical distance between these curves were uniform, it would mean that tropical counts—over no matter what magnitude of area—were a uniform multiple of temperate counts from the same size area. This would mean that within-habitat diversity was solely responsible for the extra diversity of the tropics. If, on the other hand, the tropical curve rose faster it would mean that the tropics show more between-habitat diversity. The data from Preston's graph are not adequate for discriminating between these possibilities. In fact, the data more recently collected suggest, tentatively, that for birds at least the two curves should almost meet on the left, that is, that very small tropical areas have only a few more species than temperate areas of the same size. For other organisms this is less certain. If this is confirmed, it will follow that a large part of the extra tropical diversity is "between-habitat." These considerations prompt two questions: (1) Is the tropical increase in within-habitat diversity accounted for by the factors in the theory of Section III on within-habitat diversity, or has it some other—perhaps historical—explanation? (2) Is the greater between-habitat diversity due to a greater topographic diversity, or has it an historical explanation?

For birds, question one can already be answered. The within-habitat diver-

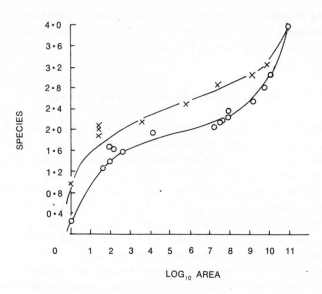

Figure 8

Species-area curves for temperate birds in the New
World (lower curve) and neotropical birds (upper
curve). N is the number of species, A is the area in
acres. (After Preston, 1960.)

sity on the relatively impoverished island of Puerto Rico is about as great as the
within-habitat diversity of the temperate habitats and is in fact nearly equal to
that of the very much richer tropical mainland. The way in which Puerto Rico
is impoverished is, as was shown in Fig. 5, that the between-habitat component
is so small. Now, all of the factors which were shown theoretically to effect
within-habitat diversity are just as tropical on Puerto Rico as on the tropical
mainland, although their histories are very different. If the island were not at
least partially saturated, the between-habitat component would not be so much
larger on the mainland.

Question two is as yet unanswered. It is perfectly plausible—perhaps even
probable—that this does have an historical answer. Perhaps more species have
evolved which are adapted to tropical conditions and, by the process described
in Section IV, the extra diversity is revealed by greater between-habitat differences. In fact, this historical explanation seems the only one that accounts for
the astonishing species diversity in ancient lakes (Brooks 1950), which at least
in some cases have no more structural diversity than the more impoverished
recent lakes. Furthermore, Richards (1952) pointed out that the richest floras
are the Mediterranean-type floras of unglaciated S.W. Australia and S. Africa,
in contrast to the Mediterranean vegetation of the north temperate zone,
which, although unglaciated, has had a more disturbed history.

There is a theoretical upper limit to total diversity set, not by limiting similarity as in within-habitat diversity, but by the abundance, or scarcity, of the species. For the total number of individuals hardly grows as the number of species increases, so the more species, the rarer each becomes. There obviously has to be at least one pair of each bisexual species, so the number of species cannot possibly rise further than half the number of individuals. In fact, of course, it cannot rise nearly that far, for the existence of many species is precarious when the abundance falls into the hundreds. More accurately, one must measure the stability, perhaps as Leigh (1965) has done but with other factors included, and compare this in temperate regions and tropics. It is conceivable that owing to fewer climatic hazards, species can be rarer in the tropics without running great danger of extinction. However, whether a limit has been reached or whether the number of species in both tropics and temperate regions is still increasing is hard to determine from present knowledge.

Various other theories of tropical total diversity have been proposed, and Connell and Orias (1964) have summarized the reasonable possibilities in one large scheme in which the roles of many mechanisms for increasing species diversity are interrelated. An increased diversity in species of lower trophic levels is certainly a potential cause of increased diversity among the species which consume them, as Hutchinson (1959) and Odum et al. (1960) have emphasized. However, this applies mostly to specialist species such as monophagous insects. It has been suggested, by analogy with human beings who have more occupations where populations are dense, that more species can persist where productivity is high. It is true that there often, but not always, seem to be more species where productivity is high. But the reason seems to be that given in Section III, where it was pointed out that only in areas of high productivity can a marginal niche support a species. Human occupations become diverse in order to exchange services effectively; such exchange of services is unknown among most organisms, so one should not be carried away by the analogy of species with human occupations.

In summary, although the total diversity—the total number of species of some phylogenetic group in a fairly wide geographic area composed of several habitats—has been the subject of a great deal of speculation and data tabulation, it is the aspect of species diversity which is least well understood.

No review of tropical species diversity could be complete without some mention of the groups which do not increase in diversity toward the tropics. Thorson (1957) pointed out that the *infauna* living in the material on the ocean bottom does not increase in diversity toward the tropics, although the *epifauna* living on the bottom does. Patrick (1964) found no increase either in the diatom diversity, the protozoan diversity or in the diversity of the freshwater insects when she sampled the upper Amazon in the same fashion in which she had sampled rivers of the eastern U.S.A. On the other hand, the fish fauna in the Amazon proper was richer. The explanation of these cases is obscure at present, but any general theory must include these exceptions.

VII. Summary

1. Species diversity is most simply measured by counting species. More complicated measures, which take into account the relative abundance of the species, have been derived from information theory or from parameters of statistical distributions fitted to the census data. The information theory formulae can also be used to measure habitat diversity and differences between communities or habitats. In this way, changes in the pattern of species diversity can be compared with changes in the environment.

2. Small or remote islands and islands with uniform topography have fewer species than large or complex islands or islands nearer the source of colonization. For birds and some orders of insects it appears that the rate of colonization of new species is virtually balanced by the rate of extinction, so that the number of species has reached equilibrium. For other organisms, such as mammals, and for all organisms on the most remote islands, this equilibrium has probably not been reached and further increases in the fauna may be expected. The comparison of impoverished island faunas with the mainland faunas whence they were derived shows the effect of relaxed competition.

3. Local variations in the species diversity of small uniform habitats can usually be predicted in terms of the structure and productivity of the habitat. Habitats of similar structure on islands and mainland often have similar species diversities; the impoverishment of the island is reflected in the fact that different habitats on the island have nearly the same species, while different habitats on the mainland have more different species. This is interpreted as evidence that uniform habitats are nearly saturated with species and that new species usually colonize by occupying different habitats from present species.

4. The theory of competition and the facts of character displacement indicate that there is a limiting similarity to species which co-exist within a habitat. Species more similar than this limiting value must occupy different habitats. According to the theory, this limiting value should be less where productivity is high, where family size is low and where the seasons are relatively uniform. It should also be less for pursuing hunters than for species which search for stationary prey.

5. Total species diversities, from areas composed of many types of habitat, are usually, but not always, much greater in the tropics than in temperate regions. This is accomplished by a finer subdivision of habitats (habitat selection) more than by a marked increase in diversity within habitats. This total diversity may still be increasing and may have not reached saturation.

I have discussed this problem profitably with biologists too numerous to name here. I am especially grateful to J. Connell, G. E. Hutchinson, P. Klopfer, E. Leigh, R. Levins, R. Lewontin, E. W. MacArthur, G. Orians, E. Orias, R. Patrick, E. Pianka, T. Schoener and G. Watson who have kindly let me see data or theories which are still unpublished. I also wish to thank M. Cody, J. MacArthur and

H. Recher who helped me to collect some of the data presented here for the first time.

References

Brooks, J. L. (1950). Speciation in ancient lakes. *Q. Rev. Biol.* 25: 30–176.

Brown, W. L. and Wilson, E. O. (1956). Character displacement. *Syst. Zool.* 5: 49–64.

Connell, J. H. and Orias, E. (1964). The ecological regulation of species diversity. *Am. Nat.* 98: 399–414.

Crowell, K. (1961). The effects of reduced competition in birds. *Proc. natn. Acad. Sci. U.S.A.* 47: 240–3.

Dammerman, K. W. (1948). The fauna of Krakatau, 1883–1933. *Verh. K. Akad. Wet (Nat.)*, 44: 1–594.

Fisher, R. A., Corbett, A. S. and Williams, C. B. (1943). The relation between the number of species and the number of individuals in a random sample of an animal population. *J. Anim. Ecol.* 12: 42–58.

Fischer, A. G. (1960). Latitudinal variations in organic diversity. *Evolution,* 14: 64–81.

Gleason, H. A. (1922). On the relation between species and area. *Ecology,* 3: 158–62.

Goodall, D. W. (1952). Quantitative aspects of plant distribution. *Biol. Rev.* 27: 194–245.

Goodall, D. W. (1962). Bibliography of statistical plant ecology. *Excerpt bot.* B, Bd 4: 253–322.

Greig-Smith, P. (1957). *Quantitative plant ecology.* London.

Hamilton, T. H., Barth, R. H. and Rubinoff, I. (1965). The environmental control of insular variation in bird species abundance. *Proc. natn. Acad. Sci. U.S.A.* 52: 132–40.

Hutchinson, G. E. (1959). Homage to Santa Rosalia, or, Why are there so many kinds of animals? *Am. Nat.* 93: 145–59.

Hutchinson, G. E. (1965). *The ecological theater and the evolutionary play.* New Haven.

Klopfer, P. H. and MacArthur, R. H. (1961). On the causes of tropical species diversity: niche overlap. *Am. Nat.* 95: 223–6.

Lack, D. (1942). Ecological features of the bird faunas of British small islands. *J. Anim. Ecol.* 11: 9–36.

Lack, D. (1947). *Darwin's finches.* Cambridge.

Leigh, E. (1965). On a relation between the productivity, biomass, stability and diversity of a community. *Proc. natn. Acad. Sci. U.S.A.*

Lloyd, M. and Ghelardi, R. J. (1964). A table for calculating the equitability component of species diversity. *J. Anim. Ecol.* 33: 217–26.

MacArthur, R. (1964). Environmental factors affecting bird species diversity. *Am. Nat.* 98: 387–97.

MacArthur, R. and Levins, R. (1964). Competition, habitat selection and character displacement in a patchy environment. *Proc. natn. Acad. Sci.,* U.S.A. 51: 1207–10.

MacArthur, R. and MacArthur, J. (1961). On bird species diversity. *Ecology,* 42: 594–8.

MacArthur, R. and Wilson, E. O. (1963). An equilibrium theory of insular zoo-geography. *Evolution*, 17: 373–87.

Margalef, R. (1957). La teoria de la inforacion enecologia. *Memorias de la real academ i de ciencias y artes (Barcelona)*, 33: 373–449.

Odum, H. T., Cantlon, J. E. and Kornicker, L. S. (1960). An organizational hier-archy postulate for the interpretation of species individual distributions, species entropy, ecosystem evolution and the meaning of a species variety index. *Ecology*, 41: 395–9.

Patrick, R. (1949). A proposed biological measure of stream conditions. *Proc. Acad. nat. Sci. Philad.* 101: 277–341.

Patrick, R. (1954). A new method for determining the pattern of the diatom flora. *Notulae Natural of the Academy of Natural Sciences of Philadelphia*, no. 259: 1–12.

Patrick, R. (1961). A study of the numbers and kinds of species found in rivers in eastern United States. *Proc. Acad. nat. Sci. Philad.* 113: 215–58.

Patrick, R. (1963). The structure of diatom communities under varying ecological conditions. *Ann. N.Y. Acad. Sci., Wash.*, 108(2): 353–8.

Patrick, R. (1964). A discussion of the results of the Catherwood Expedition to the Peruvian headwaters of the Amazon. *Verh. int. Verein. theor. angew. Limnol.* 15: 1084–90.

Preston, F. W. (1948). The commonness, and rarity, of species. *Ecology*, 29: 254–83.

Preston, F. W. (1960). Time and space and the variation of species. *Ecology*, 41: 785–90.

Preston, F. W. (1962). The canonical distribution of commonness and rarity. *Ecology*, 43: 185–215. 410–32.

Richards, P. W. (1952). *The tropical rain forest*. Cambridge.

Simpson, G. G. (1964). Species density of North American recent mammals. *Syst. Zool.* 13: 57–73.

Southwood, T. R. E. (1961). The numbers of species of insect associated with various trees. *J. Anim. Ecol.* 30: 1–8.

Terent'ev, P. V. (1963). Onit primeneneya analeza vareansi. . . . *Vest. Lenin-gradsk Univ., Ser. Biol.*, 18: 19–26.

Thorson, G. (1957). Bottom communities. In *Treatise on marine ecology and paleoecology* (ed. Ladd). *Mem. geol. Soc. Am.* 67: 461–534.

Vaurie, C. (1951). Adaptive differences between two sympatric species of nut-hatches (*Sitta*). *Proc. Xth int. Ornithol. Congr. Uppsala:* pp. 163–6.

Watson, G. (1964). Ecology and evolution of passernine birds on the islands of the Aegean Sea. Ph.D. dissertation, Yale University, New Haven.

Whittaker, R. H. (1960). Vegetation of the Siskiyou Mountains, Oregon and Cali-fornia. *Ecol. Monogr.* 30: 279–338.

Williams, C. B. (1964). *Patterns in the balance of nature*. London.

Robert T. Paine

Food Web Complexity and Species Diversity

Though longitudinal or latitudinal gradients in species diversity tend to be well described in a zoogeographic sense, they also are poorly understood phenomena of major ecological interest. Their importance lies in the derived implication that biological processes may be fundamentally different in the tropics, typically the pinnacle of most gradients, than in temperate or arctic regions. The various hypotheses attempting to explain gradients have recently been reviewed by Fischer (1960), Simpson (1964), and Connell and Orias (1964), the latter authors additionally proposing a model which can account for the production and regulation of diversity in ecological systems. Understanding of the phenomenon suffers from both a specific lack of synecological data applied to particular, local situations and from the difficulty of inferring the underlying mechanism(s) solely from descriptions and comparisons of faunas on a zoogeographic scale. The positions taken in this paper are that an ultimate understanding of the underlying causal processes can only be arrived at by study of local situations, for instance the promising approach of Mac-Arthur and MacArthur (1961), and that biological interactions such as those suggested by Hutchinson (1959) appear to constitute the most logical possibilities.

The hypothesis offered herein applies to local diversity patterns of rocky intertidal marine organisms, though it conceivably has wider applications. It may be stated as: "Local species diversity is directly related to the efficiency with which predators prevent the monopolization of the major environmental requisites by one species." The potential impact of this process is firmly based in ecological theory and practice. Gause (1934), Lack (1949), and Slobodkin (1961) among others have postulated that predation (or parasitism) is capable of preventing extinctions in competitive situations, and Slobodkin (1964) has demonstrated this experimentally. In the field, predation is known to ameliorate the intensity of competition for space by barnacles (Connell, 1961b), and, in the present study, predator removal has led to local extinctions of certain benthic invertebrates and algae. In addition, as a predictable extension of the

Reprinted by permission of the author and publisher from *The American Naturalist, 100:* 65–75, 1966. Research supported by the University of Washington (through the offices of the Organization for Tropical Studies) and by the National Science Foundation (GB–341). The author thanks Dr. Rudolf Stohler, who kindly identified the gastropod species, and A. J. Kohn, J. H. Connell, C. E. King, and E. R. Pianka, who provided invaluable criticism.

hypothesis, the proportion of predatory species is known to be relatively greater in certain diverse situations. This is true for tropical vs. temperate fish faunas (Hiatt and Strasburg, 1960; Bakus, 1964), and is seen especially clearly in the comparison of shelf water zooplankton populations (81 species, 16% of which are carnivores) with those of the presumably less productive though more stable Sargasso Sea (268 species, 39% carnivores) (Grice and Hart, 1962).

In the discussion that follows no quantitative measures of local diversity are given, though they may be approximated by the number of species represented in Figs. 1 to 3. No distinctions have been drawn between species within certain food categories. Thus I have assumed that the probability of, say, a bivalve being eaten is proportional to its abundance, and that predators exercise no preference in their choice of any "bivalve" prey. This procedure simplifies the data presentation though it dodges the problem of taxonomic complexity. Wherever possible the data are presented as both number observed being eaten and their caloric equivalent. The latter is based on prey size recorded in the field and was converted by determining the caloric content of Mukkaw Bay material of the same or equivalent species. These caloric data will be given in greater detail elsewhere. The numbers in the food webs, unfortunately, cannot be related to rates of energy flow, although when viewed as calories they undoubtedly accurately suggest which pathways are emphasized.

The Structure of Selected Food Webs

I have claimed that one of the more recognizable and workable units within the community nexus are subwebs, groups of organisms capped by a terminal carnivore and trophically interrelated in such a way that at higher levels there is little transfer of energy to co-occurring subwebs (Paine, 1963). In the marine rocky intertidal zone both the subwebs and their top carnivores appear to be particularly distinct, at least where macroscopic species are involved; and observations in the natural setting can be made on the quantity and composition of the component species' diets. Furthermore, the rocky intertidal zone is perhaps unique in that the major limiting factor of the majority of its primary consumers is living space, which can be directly observed, as the elegant studies on interspecific competition of Connell (1961a,b) have shown. The data given below were obtained by examining individual carnivores exposed by low tide, and recording prey, predator, their respective lengths, and any other relevant properties of the interaction.

A North Temperate Subweb

On rocky shores of the Pacific Coast of North America the community is dominated by a remarkably constant association of mussels, barnacles, and one starfish. Figure 1 indicates the trophic relationships of this portion of the community as observed at Mukkaw Bay, near Neah Bay, Washington (ca. 49° N latitude). The data, presented as both numbers and total calories con-

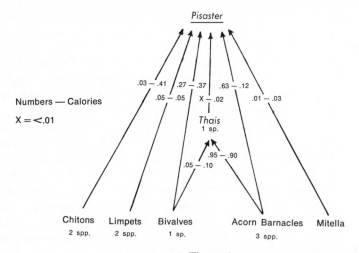

Figure 1

The feeding relationships by numbers and calories of the *Pisaster* dominated subweb at Mukkaw Bay. *Pisaster*, N = 1049; *Thais*, N = 287. N is the number of food items observed eaten by the predators. The specific composition of each predator's diet is given as a pair of fractions; numbers on the left, calories on the right.

sumed by the two carnivorous species in the subweb, *Pisaster ochraceus*, a starfish, and *Thais emarginata*, a small muricid gastropod, include the observational period November 1963, to November 1964. The composition of this subweb is limited to organisms which are normally intertidal in distribution and confined to a hard rock substrate. The diet of *Pisaster* is restricted in the sense that not all available local food types are eaten, although of six local starfish it is the most catholic in its tastes. Numerically its diet varies little from that reported by Feder (1959) for *Pisaster* observed along the central California coastline, especially since the gastropod *Tegula*, living on a softer bottom unsuitable to barnacles, has been omitted. *Thais* feeds primarily on the barnacle *Balanus glandula*, as also noted by Connell (1961b).

This food web (Fig. 1) appears to revolve on a barnacle economy with both major predators consuming them in quantity. However, note that on a nutritional (calorie) basis, barnacles are only about one-third as important to *Pisaster* as either *Mytilus californianus*, a bivalve, or the browsing chiton *Katherina tunicata*. Both these prey species dominate their respective food categories. The ratio of carnivore species to total species is 0.18. If *Tegula* and an additional bivalve are included on the basis that they are the most important sources of nourishment in adjacent areas, the ratio becomes 0.15. This number agrees closely with a ratio of 0.14 based on *Pisaster*, plus all prey species eaten more than once, in Feder's (1959) general compilation.

A Subtropical Subweb

In the northern Gulf of California (ca. 31° N.) a subweb analogous to the one just described exists. Its top carnivore is a starfish (*Heliaster kubiniji*), the next two trophic levels are dominated by carnivorous gastropods, and the main prey are herbivorous gastropods, bivalves, and barnacles. I have collected there only in March or April of 1962–1964, but on both sides of the Gulf at San Felipe, Puertecitos, and Puerta Penasco. The resultant trophic arrangements (Fig. 2), though representative of springtime conditions and indicative of a much more stratified and complex community, are basically similar to those at Mukkaw Bay. Numerically the major food item in the diets of *Heliaster* and *Muricanthus nigritus* (a muricid gastropod), the two top-ranking carnivores, is barnacles; the major portion of these predators' nutrition is derived from other members of the community, primarily herbivorous mollusks. The increased trophic complexity presents certain graphical problems. If increased trophic height is indicated by a decreasing percentage of primary consumers in a species diet, *Acanthina tuberculata* is the highest carnivore due to its specialization on *A. angelica,* although it in turn is consumed by two other species. Because of this, and ignoring the percentages, both *Heliaster* and *Muricanthus* have been placed above *A. tuberculata.* Two species, *Hexaplex* and *Muricanthus* eventually become too large to be eaten by *Heliaster,* and thus through growth join it as top predators in the system. The taxonomically difficult gastropod family Columbellidae, including both herbivorous and carnivorous species (Marcus and Marcus, 1962), have been placed in an intermediate position.

The Gulf of California situation is interesting on a number of counts. A new trophic level which has no counterpart at Mukkaw Bay is apparent, interposed between the top carnivore and the primary carnivore level. If higher level predation contributes materially to the maintenance of diversity, these species will have an effect on the community composition out of proportion to their abundance. In one of these species, *Muricanthus,* the larger members belong to a higher level than immature specimens (Paine, unpublished), a process tending to blur the food web but also potentially increasing diversity (Hutchinson, 1959). Finally, if predation operates to reduce competitive stresses, evidence for this reduction can be drawn by comparing the extent of niche diversification as a function of trophic level in a typical Eltonian pyramid. *Heliaster* consumes all other members of this subweb, and as such appears to have no major competitors of comparable status. The three large gastropods forming the subterminal level all may be distinguished by their major sources of nutrition: *Hexaplex*—bivalves (53%), *Muricanthus*—herbivorous gastropods (48%), and *A. tuberculata*—carnivorous gastropods (74%). No such obvious distinction characterizes the next level composed of three barnacle-feeding specialists which additionally share their resource with *Muricanthus* and *Heliaster.* Whether these species are more specialized (Klopfer and MacArthur, 1960)

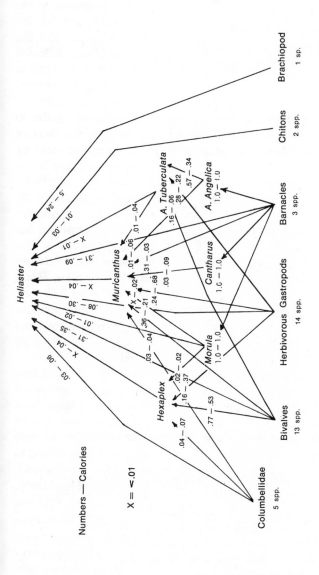

Figure 2

The feeding relatio. ' ips by numbers and calories of the *Heliaster* dominated subweb in the northern Gulf of California. *Heliaster,* N = 2245; *Muricanthus,* N = 113; *Hexaplex,* N = 62; *A. tuberculata,* N = 14; *A. angelica,* N = 432; *Morula,* N = 39; *Cantharus,* N = 8.

153

or whether they tolerate greater niche overlap (Klopfer and MacArthur, 1961) cannot be stated. The extent of niche diversification is subtle and trophic overlap is extensive.

The ratio of carnivore species to total species in Fig. 2 is 0.24 when the category Columbellidae is considered to be principally composed of one herbivorous (*Columbella*) and four carnivorous (*Pyrene, Anachis, Mitella*) species, based on the work of Marcus and Marcus (1962).

A Tropical Subweb

Results of five days of observation near Mate de Limon in the Golfo de Nocoya on the Pacific shore of Costa Rica (approx. 10° N.) are presented in Fig. 3. No secondary carnivore was present; rather the environmental re-

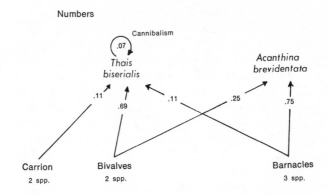

Figure 3

The feeding relationship by numbers of a comparable food web in Costa Rica. *Thais,* N = 99; *Acanthina,* N = 80.

sources were shared by two small muricid gastropods, *Acanthina brevidentata* and *Thais biserialis*. The fauna of this local area was relatively simple and completely dominated by a small mytilid and barnacles. The co-occupiers of the top level show relatively little trophic overlap despite the broad nutritional base of *Thais* which includes carrion and cannibalism. The relatively low number of feeding observations (187) precludes an accurate appraisal of the carnivore species to total web membership ratio.

Changes Resulting from the Removal of the Top Carnivore

Since June, 1963, a "typical" piece of shoreline at Mukkaw Bay about eight meters long and two meters in vertical extent has been kept free of *Pisaster*.

An adjacent control area has been allowed to pursue its natural course of events. Line transects across both areas have been taken irregularly and the number and density of resident macroinvertebrate and benthic algal species measured. The appearance of the control area has not altered. Adult *Mytilus californianus, Balanus cariosus,* and *Mitella polymerus* (a goose-necked barnacle) form a conspicuous band in the middle intertidal. The relatively stable position of the band is maintained by *Pisaster* predation (Paris, 1960; Paine, unpublished). At lower tidal levels the diversity increases abruptly and the macrofauna includes immature individuals of the above, *B. glandula* as scattered clumps, a few anemones of one species, two chiton species (browsers), two abundant limpets (browsers), four macroscopic benthic algae (*Porphyra* —an epiphyte, *Endocladia, Rhodomela,* and *Corallina*), and the sponge *Haliclona,* often browsed upon by *Anisodoris,* a nudibranch.

Following the removal of *Pisaster, B. glandula* set successfully throughout much of the area and by September had occupied from 60 to 80% of the available space. By the following June the *Balanus* themselves were being crowded out by small, rapidly growing *Mytilus* and *Mitella.* This process of successive replacement by more efficient occupiers of space is continuing, and eventually the experimental area will be dominated by *Mytilus,* its epifauna, and scattered clumps of adult *Mitella.* The benthic algae either have disappeared or are in the process of disappearing, with the exception of the epiphyte, due to lack of appropriate space; the chitons and larger limpets have also emigrated, due to the absence of space and lack of appropriate food.

Despite the likelihood that many of these organisms are extremely long-lived and that these events have not reached an equilibrium, certain statements can be made. The removal of *Pisaster* has resulted in a pronounced *decrease* in diversity, as measured simply by counting species inhabiting this area, whether consumed by *Pisaster* or not, from a 15 to an eight-species system. The standing crop has been increased by this removal, and should continue to increase until the *Mytilus* achieve their maximum size. In general the area has become trophically simpler. With *Pisaster* artificially removed, the sponge-nudibranch food chain has been displaced, and the anemone population reduced in density. Neither of these carnivores nor the sponge is eaten by *Pisaster,* indicating that the number of food chains initiated on this limited space is strongly influenced by *Pisaster,* but by an indirect process. In contrast to Margalef's (1958) generalization about the tendency, with higher successional status towards "an ecosystem of more complex structure," these removal experiments demonstrate the opposite trend: in the absence of a complicating factor (predation), there is a "winner" in the competition for space, and the local system tends toward simplicity. Predation by this interpretation interrupts the successional process and, on a local basis, tends to increase local diversity.

No data are available on the microfaunal changes accompanying the gradual alteration of the substrate from a patchy algal mat to one comprised of the byssal threads of *Mytilus.*

Interpretation

The differences in relative diversity of the subwebs diagrammed in Figs. 1–3 may be represented as Baja California (45 spp.) >> Mukkaw Bay (11 spp.) > Costa Rica (8 sp.), the number indicating the actual membership of the subwebs and not the number of local species. All three areas are characterized by systems in which one or two species are capable of monopolizing much of the space, a circumstance realized in nature only in Costa Rica. In the other two areas a top predator that derives its nourishment from other sources feeds in such a fashion that no space-consuming monopolies are formed. *Pisaster* and *Heliaster* eat masses of barnacles, and in so doing enhance the ability of other species to inhabit the area by keeping space open. When the top predator is artificially removed or naturally absent (i.e., predator removal area and Costa Rica, respectively), the systems converge toward simplicity. When space is available, other organisms settle or move in, and these, for instance chitons at Mukkaw Bay and herbivorous gastropods and pelecypods in Baja California, form the major portions of the predator's nutrition. Furthermore, *in situ* primary production is enhanced by the provision of space. This event makes the grazing moiety less dependent on the vagaries of phytoplankton production or distribution and lends stability to the association.

At the local level it appears that carnivorous gastropods which can penetrate only one barnacle at a time, although they might consume a few more per tidal interval, do not have the same effect as a starfish removing 20 to 60 barnacles simultaneously. Little compensation seems to be gained from snail density increases because snails do not clear large patches of space, and because the "husks" of barnacles remain after the animal portion has been consumed. In the predator removal area at Mukkaw Bay, the density of *Thais* increased 10- to 20-fold, with no apparent effect on diversity although the rate of *Mytilus* domination of the area was undoubtedly slowed. Clusters (density of 75–125/m²) of *Thais* and *Acanthina* characterize certain rocks in Costa Rica, and diversity is still low. And, as a generality, wherever acorn barnacles or other space-utilizing forms potentially dominate the shore, diversity is reduced unless some predator can prevent the space monopoly. This occurs in Washington State where the shoreline, in the absence of *Pisaster,* is dominated by barnacles, a few mussels, and often two species of *Thais.* The same monopolistic tendencies characterize Connell's (1961a,b) study area in Scotland, the rocky intertidal of northern Japan (Hoshiai, 1960, 1961), and shell bags suitable for sponge settlement in North Carolina (Wells, Wells, and Gray, 1964).

Local diversity on intertidal rocky bottoms, then, appears directly related to predation intensity, though other potential factors are mentioned below. If one accepts the generalizations of Hedgpeth (1957) and Hall (1964) that ambient temperature is the single most important factor influencing distribution or reproduction of marine invertebrates, then the potential role of climatic stability as measured by seasonal variations in water temperature can be examined. At Neah Bay the maximum range of annual values are 5.9 to 13.3 C (Rigg and Miller, 1949); in the northern Gulf of California, Roden and Groves (1959) recorded an annual range of 14.9 to 31.2 C; and in Costa Rica the maximum annual range is 26.1 to 31.7 C (Anon., 1952). Clearly the greatest benthic diversity, and one claimed by Parker (1963) on a regional basis to be among the most diverse known, is associated with the most variable (least stable) temperature regimen. Another influence on diversity could be exercised by environmental heterogeneity (Hutchinson, 1959). Subjectively, it appeared that both the Mukkaw Bay and Costa Rica stations were topographically more distorted than the northern Gulf localities. In any event, no topographic features were evident that could correlate with the pronounced differences in faunal diversity. Finally, Connell and Orias (1964) have developed a model for the organic enrichment of regions that depends to a great extent on the absolute amount of primary production and/or nutrient import, and hence energy flowing through the community web. Unfortunately, no productivity data are available for the two southern communities, and comparisons cannot yet be made.

Predation and Diversity Gradients

To examine predation as a diversity-causing mechanism correlated with latitude, we must know why one environment contains higher order carnivores and why these are absent from others. These negative situations can be laid to three possibilities: (1) that through historical accident no higher carnivores have evolved in the region; (2) that the sample area cannot be occupied due to a particular combination of *local* hostile physiological effects; (3) that the system cannot support carnivores because the rate of energy transfer to a higher level is insufficient to sustain that higher level. The first possibility is unapproachable, the second will not apply on a geographic scale, and thus only the last would seem to have reality. Connell and Orias (1964) have based their hypothesis of the establishment and maintenance of diversity on varying rates of energy transfer, which are determined by various limiting factors and environmental stability. Without disagreeing with their model, two aspects of primary production deserve further consideration. The animal diversity of a given system will probably be higher if the production is apportioned more uniformly throughout the year rather than occurring as a single major bloom, because tendencies towards competitive displacement can be ameliorated by specialization on varying proportions of the resources (MacArthur and Levins, 1964). Both the predictability of production on a sustained annual basis and the causation of resource heterogeneity by predation will facilitate this mechanism. Thus, per production unit, greater stability of production should be correlated with greater diversity, other things being equal.

The realization of this potential, however, depends on more than simply the annual stability of carbon fixation. Rate of production and subsequent transfer to higher levels must also be important. Thus trophic structure of a community depends in part on the physical extent of the area (Darlington, 1957), or, in computer simulation models, on the amount of protoplasm in the system (Garfinkel and Sack, 1964). On the other hand, enriched aquatic environments often are characterized by decreased diversity. Williams (1964) has found that regions of high productivity are dominated by few diatom species. Less productive areas tended to have more species of equivalent rank, and hence a greater diversity. Obviously, the gross amount of energy fixed by itself is incapable of explaining diversity; and extrinsic factors probably are involved.

Given sufficient evolutionary time for increases in faunal complexity to occur, two independent mechanisms should work in a complementary fashion. When predation is capable of preventing resource monopolies, diversity should increase by positive feedback processes until some limit is reached. The argument of Fryer (1965) that predation facilitates speciation is germane here. The upper limit to local diversity, or, in the present context, the maximum number of species in a given subweb, is probably set by the combined stability and rate of primary production, which thus influences the number and variety of non-primary consumers in the subweb. Two aspects of predation must be evaluated before a generalized hypothesis based on predation effects can contribute to an understanding of differences in diversity between *any* comparable regions or faunistic groups. We must know if resource monopolies are actually less frequent in the diverse area than in comparable systems elsewhere, and, if so, why this is so. And we must learn something about the multiplicity of energy pathways in diverse systems, since predation-induced diversity could arise either from the presence of a variety of subwebs of equivalent rank, or from domination by one major one. The predation hypothesis readily predicts the apparent absence of monopolies in tropical (diverse) areas, a situation classically represented as "many species of reduced individual abundance." It also is in accord with the disproportionate increase in the number of carnivorous species that seems to accompany regional increases in animal diversity. In the present case in the two adequately sampled, structurally analogous, subwebs, general membership increases from 13 at Mukkaw Bay to 45 in the Gulf of California, a factor of 3.5, whereas the carnivore species increased from 2 to 11, a factor of 5.5.

Summary

It is suggested that local animal species diversity is related to the number of predators in the system and their efficiency in preventing single species from monopolizing some important, limiting, requisite. In the marine rocky intertidal this requisite usually is space. Where predators capable of preventing monopolies are missing, or are experimentally removed, the systems become less diverse. On a local scale, no relationship between latitude (10° to 49° N.) and diversity was found. On a geographic scale, an increased stability of annual production may lead to an increased capacity for systems to support higher-level carnivores. Hence tropical, or other, ecosystems are more diverse, and are characterized by disproportionately more carnivores.

Literature Cited

Anon. 1952. Surface water temperatures at tide stations. Pacific coast North and South America. Spec. Pub. No. 280: p. 1–59. U. S. Coast and Geodetic Survey.

Bakus, G. J. 1964. The effects of fish-grazing on invertebrate evolution in shallow tropical waters. Allan Hancock Found. Pub. 27: 1–29.

Connell, J. H. 1961a. Effect of competition, predation by *Thais lapillus,* and other factors on natural populations of the barnacle *Balanus balanoides.* Ecol. Monogr. 31: 61–104.

———. 1961b. The influence of interspecific competition and other factors on the distribution of the barnacle *Chthamalus stellatus.* Ecology 42: 710–723.

Connell, J. H., and E. Orias. 1964. The ecological regulation of species diversity. Amer. Natur. 98: 399–414.

Darlington, P. J. 1957. Zoogeography. Wiley, New York.

Feder, H. M. 1959. The food of the starfish, *Pisaster ochraceus,* along the California coast. Ecology 40: 721–724.

Fischer, A. G. 1960. Latitudinal variations in organic diversity. Evolution 14: 64–81.

Fryer, G. 1965. Predation and its effects on migration and speciation in African fishes: a comment. Proc. Zool. Soc. London 144: 301–310.

Garfinkel, D., and R. Sack. 1964. Digital computer simulation of an ecological system, based on a modified mass action law. Ecology 45: 502–507.

Gause, G. F. 1934. The struggle for existence. Williams and Wilkins Co., Baltimore.

Grice, G. D., and A. D. Hart. 1962. The abundance, seasonal occurrence, and distribution of the epizooplankton between New York and Bermuda. Ecol. Monogr. 32: 287–309.

Hall, C. A., Jr. 1964. Shallow-water marine climates and molluscan provinces. Ecology 45: 226–234.

Hedgpeth, J. W. 1957. Marine biogeography. Geol. Soc. Amer. Mem. 67, 1: 359–382.

Hiatt, R. W., and D. W. Strasburg. 1960. Ecological relationships of the fish fauna on coral reefs of the Marshall Islands. Ecol. Monogr. 30: 65–127.

Hoshiai, T. 1960. Synecological study on intertidal communities III. An analysis of interrelation among sedentary organisms on the artificially denuded rock surface. Bull. Marine Biol. Sta. Asamushi. 10: 49–56.

———. 1961. Synecological study on intertidal communities. IV. An ecological investigation on the zonation in Matsushima Bay concerning the so-called covering phenomenon. Bull. Marine Biol. Sta. Asamushi. 10: 203–211.

Hutchinson, G. E. 1959. Homage to Santa Rosalia, or why are there so many kinds of animals? Amer. Natur. 93: 145–159.

Klopfer, P. H., and R. H. MacArthur. 1960. Niche size and faunal diversity. Amer. Natur. 94: 293–300.

――――. 1961. On the causes of tropical species diversity: niche overlap. Amer. Natur. 95: 223–226.

Lack, D. 1949. The significance of ecological isolation, p. 299–308. *In* G. L. Jepsen, G. G. Simpson, and E. Mayr [eds.], Genetics, paleontology and evolution. Princeton Univ. Press, Princeton.

MacArthur, R., and R. Levins. 1964. Competition, habitat selection, and character displacement in a patchy environment. Proc. Nat. Acad. Sci. 51: 1207–1210.

MacArthur, R. H., and J. W. MacArthur. 1961. On bird species diversity. Ecology 42: 594–598.

Marcus, E., and E. Marcus. 1962. Studies on Columbellidae. Bol. Fac. Cienc. Letr. Univ. Sao Paulo 261: 335–402.

Margalef, R. 1958. Mode of evolution of species in relation to their place in ecological succession. XVth Int. Congr. Zool. Sect. 10, paper 17.

Paine, R. T. 1963. Trophic relationships of 8 sympatric predatory gastropods. Ecology 44: 63–73.

Paris, O. H. 1960. Some quantitative aspects of predation by muricid snails on mussels in Washington Sound. Veliger 2: 41–47.

Parker, R. H. 1963. Zoogeography and ecology of some macro-invertebrates, particularly mollusca in the Gulf of California and the continental slope off Mexico. Vidensk. Medd. Dansk. Natur. Foren., Copenh. 126: 1–178.

Rigg, G. B., and R. C. Miller. 1949. Intertidal plant and animal zonation in the vicinity of Neah Bay, Washington. Proc. Calif. Acad. Sci. 26: 323–351.

Roden, G. I., and G. W. Groves. 1959. Recent oceanographic investigations in the Gulf of California. J. Marine Res. 18: 10–35.

Simpson, G. G. 1964. Species density of North American recent mammals. Syst. Zool. 13: 57–73.

Slobodkin, L. B. 1961. Growth and regulation of Animal Populations. Holt, Rinehart, and Winston, New York.

――――. 1964. Ecological populations of Hydrida. J. Anim. Ecol. 33 (Suppl.): 131–148.

Wells, H. W., M. J. Wells, and I. E. Gray. 1964. Ecology of sponge in Hatteras Harbor, North Carolina. Ecology 45: 752–767.

Williams, L. G. 1964. Possible relationships between plankton-diatom species numbers and water-quality estimates. Ecology 45: 809–823.

Dennis Chitty

Population Processes in the Vole
and Their Relevance to General Theory

Introduction

Populations of animals such as the vole (*Microtus agrestis*), which fluctuate more or less regularly in numbers, are not easy to fit into general theories about the natural regulation of animal numbers. This must mean either that these species are exceptional, and facts about them can safely be ignored, or else that the theories need to be modified, which is the alternative discussed in the present paper.

Defining the Problem

The object of many field studies is to find out (1) why population density does not go on rising indefinitely, and (2) why it varies from one type of environment to another. The first enquiry concerns a common property of all populations, the second concerns differences between them. To illustrate these definitions we may imagine two different types of environment, each starting off with the same low numbers of a certain species of animal (Fig. 1, A and B). We may also suppose that both populations expand at different rates and eventually maintain different levels of abundance. We need to explain why the populations are alike in failing to keep up their initial rates of increase, and why they differ in the levels attained.

The reason for recognizing two distinct problems is that it is not necessarily true, as is sometimes assumed, that factors associated with a difference in abundance between populations also prevent unlimited increase within them. Differences in food supply, weather, parasitism, etc. are often associated with differences in abundance, but we cannot infer that these are the factors preventing unlimited increase. Or to reverse the argument, although epidemics, or frosts, may not normally prevent unlimited increase, we cannot infer that such factors do not affect abundance. These matters must be decided empirically.

In the present paper I shall discuss only the first of the two problems

Reprinted by permission of the author and publisher from the *Canadian Journal of Zoology, 38:* 99–113, 1960.

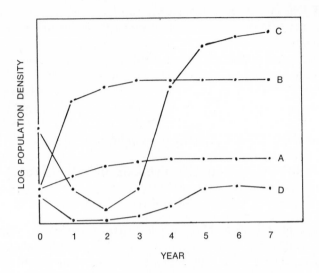

Figure 1

Curves A–D show the results of an imaginary annual
census of four populations occupying different types
of habitat. The problem is to find out if there is a
common explanation for failure of the populations
to go on increasing indefinitely. Comparisons may be
made within areas at different times (B in year 0–1
compared with year 4–5, for example) and between
areas at the same time (A and B compared with C
and D in years 0–1 or 4–5, for example). The present paper is not concerned with methods of enquiry
into the differences between good and bad habitats
(B and C compared with A and D).

mentioned above, which is seen as an attempt to discover the factors associated
with failure to go on expanding at the higher rates observed within habitats,
these rates being regarded as a control for all other rates of change. For proper
controls, however, observations must also be made on a random selection of
populations that are expanding at the same time as those that are not (Fig. 1).

Few populations are likely to conform to the simplified pattern so far
imagined; indeed the majority will have more or less severe or prolonged declines, which may or may not have to be taken into account when searching
for the factors that prevent unlimited increase. Population density may be expected to fall if the resources of the environment are reduced or the climate
deteriorates, and an instance of this sort would be a special case of the second
of the two problems; but other declines, whether they occur at regular or
irregular intervals, must be considered as possible instances, in more obvious
form, of the general phenomenon of failure to maintain a high rate of increase.
Thus the problem is here assumed to be the same whether an initial rise in

numbers is followed by a systematically recurring decline, irregular fluctuations, or a more stationary state, and the sharp distinctions drawn by some authors are not accepted.

Just as no single factor is associated with all differences in average abundance, no single factor is likely to be common to all departures from the maximum observed rates of increase. We must nevertheless avoid giving different explanations for effects that merely differ superficially, but are in fact the same. It is fortunate that in voles a specific kind of decline can be recognized, not merely by its typical periodicity, but by various other criteria, especially those based on the distribution of body weight [4, 31]. Given enough instances of a recognizable class of events it is then possible to replace unfalsifiable propositions about *some* declines by hypotheses about *all declines of a certain kind,* and hence to eliminate explanations that do not fit the facts in every case.

Throughout this paper it will be assumed that we are dealing with closed systems. As will become clear, the conclusions arrived at would not apply to populations recruited from areas in which there were fundamental differences in the conditions determining population density.

Evidence Against Proposed Hypotheses

The present section gives reasons for rejecting some of the explanations that have been advanced to explain recurrent declines in numbers in voles. The observations were made at Lake Vyrnwy in Wales, in 1936–9 [4, 5], and 1945–59 (largely unpublished).

Infectious Disease

The most reasonable hypothesis consistent with the facts available before 1938 was that overcrowded vole populations were regularly decimated by epidemics. However, the lack of any consistent association between infectious disease and population changes [14], and the discovery of vole tuberculosis [30], helped to destroy the basis for the belief that the populations were controlled by epidemic diseases. In one part of Lake Vyrnwy two-thirds of the animals were tuberculous at a time of severe mortality. This association of circumstances was similar to others described in the literature; but since several independent populations were being studied at Lake Vyrnwy it could be shown that the association was not invariant [5]. The disease was not a necessary condition for the decline of the populations, as it was almost entirely absent from other areas from which they disappeared; nor was it a sufficient condition, as some populations remained abundant in spite of being heavily infected.

Field work on tuberculosis was terminated in 1939 and no further attempt was made to study other infectious diseases, since it was realized that the original belief about the role of epidemics in the decline of animal numbers was based only on the fact that the two were sometimes associated. Although it is to be expected that diseases of various sorts are involved in most declines in numbers, there is no evidence that they are a sufficient condition for the type with which we are concerned.

Predation

If certain properties are assigned to an imaginary predator and prey, the numbers of predators and prey can be made to fluctuate in a manner superficially similar to fluctuations in nature. This superficial resemblance, however, is the same whether the predator destroys its own food supply, as in the model, or whether the prey disappears first for other reasons. In any study of predator-prey relations it is therefore essential to distinguish between these alternatives. In the case of the vole there is no reason to suppose that predation is sufficient to account for recurrent declines in numbers, since these take place whether predation is light or heavy; nor can predators be responsible for the failure of the animals to grow and sometimes to reproduce, nor for the differential survival of the sexes [6]. Similar conclusions were reached by Godfrey [17] and Lockie [23].

When predators are suddenly deprived of their normal food they may perhaps deplete some alternative. In testing this possibility care must be taken to see that any association of events is not fortuitous, especially as short-term fluctuations in the numbers of small rodents are bound to coincide with all sorts of unrelated events. An example of this occurred at Lake Vyrnwy, where foxes have always been plentiful. In 1955 large numbers of rabbits died with myxomatosis. Voles also became scarce; but this had been predicted from a knowledge of their populations in 1954. Furthermore there were other parts of Lake Vyrnwy where populations continued to build up their numbers in spite of any additional attention from the foxes. The disappearance of the rabbits thus had no detectable influence on the population trends of the voles.

Food Supply

When voles are exceptionally abundant they destroy a great deal of their food and cover; but nobody knows the proportion of occasions on which this happens, as only the abnormal instances receive attention out of several thousands of vole populations that presumably reach temporary abundance every 4 years or so. Outbreaks attended by destruction of the vegetation have thus attracted a disproportionate amount of attention, and writers who base most of their conclusions on such instances run the risks usually associated with biased sampling.

At Lake Vyrnwy it is usual to find patches of damage to vegetation at times of maximum abundance, but the subsequent scarcity of voles seems to be independent of the state of the vegetation. Thus although serious damage is sometimes associated with high numbers there are so many instances when it is not that there is no reason to suspect that malnutrition or starvation play any necessary part in the recurrent mortality. Nor are there any signs of emaciation in the animals, whose numbers may decline throughout the growing season of the vegetation, in all types of plant community, in wet and dry areas, and regardless of how few voles may be left to compete for food.

At the time of the marking-recapture study described by Leslie *et al.* [21] a botanic survey was undertaken by Mr. W. E. J. Milton of the Welsh Plant Breeding Station, and Mr. J. Lewis of the Department of Animal Health, Aberystwyth. The data from this survey have not been published but were kindly made available for use at Oxford. Damage to the vegetation was too slight to have caused any general food shortage during 1948–50, a period covering a change from great abundance to great scarcity, but the survey showed that there was an annual shortage of green material. Some areas, for example, provided only 3% green material in March 1949. It is easy to imagine that there might be competition for this seasonally reduced food supply, and that the higher the numbers of the overwintered population the higher their mortality rate from starvation; but no supporting evidence could be found. On the special study area, for example [21, Fig. 1], the verges of the road running through it provided 35–85% green material even at this time of year, and total tillers of 300 per 36 sq. in. Yet the voles living along the road did not grow or survive any better than they did anywhere else at Lake Vyrnwy.

The results of this survey thus confirmed the common-sense impression from other occasions that a general shortage of food is neither a necessary nor a sufficient condition for the recurrent type of mortality, and the findings of Summerhayes [27] that voles did not seriously reduce the total amount of vegetation, in spite of having a pronounced effect on its composition.

Weather

In order to get some idea of the influence of weather it is helpful to study populations that are fluctuating in opposite directions in neighboring habitats. Let us suppose that some populations decline in a given year, while others nearby do not (Fig. 1, year 0–1). Then, if all were similarly exposed to bad weather, we may conclude that it was not a sufficient mortality factor. This type of evidence was provided at Lake Vyrnwy, where one group of populations declined in 1938 while another group remained abundant until the following year [4], and similar evidence has been obtained since. However, although bad weather alone may not be a sufficient condition for a decline in numbers it may be sufficient in conjunction with some other condition. Random variations in weather may indeed be one of the principal factors affecting populations, and are probably a necessary part of the mechanism that tends to make them fluctuate in phase [4, 6]. Leslie [20] has constructed a numerical example to show how this effect may be produced.

Shock Disease

Determinations were made of the liver glycogen content of wild voles taken simultaneously from declining and expanding populations. The animals were killed in the field, often within an hour of capture, and their livers were put immediately into a hot solution of potassium hydroxide; other voles were kept for a few weeks in isolation before being killed. No evidence was discovered to suggest that any of them had a pathological condition that impaired their ability to store glycogen. Elsewhere [8] I have discussed the claim that a condition of this sort (shock disease) occurs among natural populations of snowshoe hares (*Lepus americanus*) and tried to show that inferences from the laboratory data are not only unjustified, but are actually contradicted by the field evidence. The conclusion of Frank [15, 16] that shock disease occurs in *Microtus arvalis* applies only to animals that had been ill-treated in captivity; the condition has not been shown to explain the natural death rate.

Adrenopituitary Exhaustion

Christian [9] wrote as follows: "Exhaustion of the adrenopituitary system resulting from increased stresses inherent in a high population, especially in winter, plus the late winter demands of the reproductive system, due to increased light or other factors, precipitates population-wide death with the symptoms of adrenal insufficiency and hypoglycemic convulsions."

This generalization is partly based on the belief, which I believe to be false [8], that shock disease occurs among snowshoe hares in nature; but the picture of adult mortality given above is not that described by Green and Evans [18], who believed that the decline in numbers could be attributed to a high juvenile death rate, probably during the summer, and continuing even at low population densities. There are no data to suggest that Christian's explanation applies to wild vole populations; nor did Clarke [12] succeed in producing a decline in numbers in his outdoor enclosures, in spite of the fact that his animals were overcrowded, and that intraspecific strife was almost certainly limiting their increase.

More recently Christian [10] has expanded his original suggestions about stress to include an effect on later generations. This he believes to come about through the impaired lactation of stressed females, which occurs fairly readily in the laboratory [6, 11]. Indeed there is no difficulty at all in interfering experimentally with reproductive processes; the difficulty comes in producing an effect which corresponds to anything going on in nature. Although Godfrey [17] found some young that were underweight at weaning during a decline, the principal problem is still to account for the disappearance of animals that seem to be perfectly normal when they first enter the active population. Their body weights do not support the idea that they are undernourished, and although there are other ways in which faulty lactation might affect them there is no evidence that it does so in nature.

Nevertheless, while I question the validity of Christian's conclusions about the mechanisms involved, his general point of view [10] has much in common with that discussed in the next section.

An Alternative Hypothesis

The present section restates an hypothesis which, though still not established, has not yet been falsified, and describes the difficulties of getting the evidence that would do so. Some of the facts that have to be taken into account [4–7, 14, 17, 21, 23, 27] are that declines in the numbers of voles can take place even though the environment seems to be favorable; that high population density is not sufficient to start an immediate decline, nor low population density to halt it; that the vast majority of animals die from unknown causes, males more rapidly than females; that the death rate can be greatly reduced by isolating the animals in captivity, and that the adult death rate, as in the snowshoe hare [8, 18], is not abnormally high during the years of maximum abundance. These facts are consistent with the proposition that susceptibility to natural hazards increases among generations descended from animals affected by adverse environmental conditions. In one form or another this idea has been put forward by writers from 1868 onwards [6], and although it cannot be accepted until a mechanism has been discovered, it fits the facts and cannot be refuted at the present time. Three components need to be considered: the original adverse changes in the environment, the resultant physiological changes, and the external factors that affect the subsequent probability of dying, or actually kill the animals.

Environmental Changes

As shown above no success was met with in the search for relevant changes in any environmental factors that included food, cover, weather, enemies, disease, etc., but excluded other animals of the same sort. For some purposes it is probably convenient to think of the environment of the population in this limited sense, but it neglects the fact that each individual is surrounded by others that differ from it, and towards which it may react differently from the way they react towards it. "Every individual in a population of animals is part of the environment of other individuals. . . . The population is then understood as a group of individuals each having an environment which resembles those of its neighbors but differs from theirs if only because the environment of an individual includes its neighbors but not itself" (Andrewartha and Birch [2, pp. 13–14]). According to this definition, even a complete knowledge of total numbers and of all factors in the "environment of the population" would give inadequate grounds for prediction, unless it could also be assumed that every individual was identical with every other alive then and at any other time. In many mathematical models this is assumed to be the case, and as a first approximation it is sometimes convenient to think of real populations in terms of total numbers or degree of crowding. The approximation, however, may be no more informative than counting a number of coins without observing their denominations or realizing that currencies may depreciate.

The inadequacy of the idea that population processes can always be related to numbers is clearly shown in experimental work. A given cage space occupied by two hostile voles is a much worse environment for both of them than the same amount of space occupied by a large family unit; and the environment of a dominant animal will be quite different from that of the animals who spend their lives being chased or keeping out of harm's way. Repeatable results cannot be expected, however carefully conditions are standardized outside the group, if interactions within it are highly variable. In the field it is even less to be expected that numbers at one time will bear any necessary relation to numbers later on, if only quantity is taken into account and quality is neglected.

Thus the change in the environment which is here postulated as a necessary antecedent to a decline in numbers of the vole is not simply an increase in numbers, but a change in the nature and frequency of the interactions, which at the present time we do not know how to observe, let alone quantify. Furthermore, if there is selection in favor of genotypes that are better able to stand these interactions [7] they will themselves produce a new kind of environment about which population density alone can tell us very little.

Physiological Changes

Although an unknown blood condition may be associated with them [13], little is known about the supposed physiological changes, and perhaps the most that can be hoped for is to get some measure of their effects. This point can be made more obviously by considering an explanation suggested by Leslie and Ranson [22]. These authors showed that a vole population with a fixed age-specific of mortality would tend to decline more rapidly than usual if it entered the non-breeding season with an unusually high proportion of the older animals. If we accept this explanation we also accept the fact of senescence in organisms without trying to explain it, and confine our attention to measuring its demographic effects. The explanation now being offered is the same in principle as that of Leslie and Ranson, the only difference being that the change in the quality of the population is no longer attributed to an increase in the proportion of older animals [4], but to an increase in the proportion of animals that are congenitally less viable. For all that is known at present these changes in constitution may also be too difficult for the ecologist to measure directly, and he may have to study them through their effects on growth rate, survival, reproduction, behavior, and reaction to standard tests of various sorts.

External Factors

In contrast to hypotheses according to which the animals die a violent death from epidemics, predators, parasites, climatic catastrophes, or shock disease, no specific causes of death are postulated. Nor for the following reasons is it thought to be profitable to try to discover them. At various times in its life an animal has a number of experiences, the last of which, naturally enough, is followed by death. If death comes through a pure accident, such as drowning, most of the animal's previous experiences will be irrelevant to its chances of survival. In other cases, however, many circumstances in its earlier life are likely to affect its probability of dying later on: quality and quantity of food, reproduction, psychological factors, chronic disease, weather, and other hazards. In order to understand a particular death rate it may be more important to examine early events of this sort than those immediately associated with death. Local forces of mortality, whatever they happen to be, will be sufficient to kill off a susceptible population, though the rate at which they do so will presumably vary.

Even when an animal dies under observation in the laboratory it is hard to determine the causes of death. It may be thought that the problem is simpler in the wild, where many deaths occur from accidents of a kind that is easier to understand than the so-called deaths from old age. This impression may be based partly on misapprehension about causes of death [24], partly on non-random sampling. Although some captive animals live long enough to become decrepit, most of them die before reaching old age, and under the harsher conditions in nature relatively more individuals may be expected to die unpredictably early deaths. Secondly the majority of corpses of animals dying in nature are never found at all, and those that are may well result from the simpler forms of accident. At present we do not know; but there is no real justification for assuming that the ecologist can expect to explain the shape of a survival curve in nature until he can do so for one in the laboratory.

This argument should not be pressed to the point where no attempt is made to find out when and how the greatest changes occur in mortality rates, for example during bad weather or at the onset of breeding. Such associations are to be anticipated, but they may contribute only part of the explanation and may not occur universally.

We may now review the course of the argument. We first considered the simplest type of explanation, that a single antecedent condition, such as an outbreak of disease, was both necessary and sufficient to bring about a decline in numbers. No such unique condition was discovered. The next most simple explanation might have been that declines occur for different reasons on different occasions, and if we knew only that animals became scarce now and then there might be some excuse for accepting almost anything as a sufficient explanation, e.g. bad weather one time, predation the next, and so on. No such solution can be regarded as satisfactory when there are enough details to show that the phenomenon is no mere reduction in numbers, but an association of fairly specific effects that are unlikely to follow except from fairly specific antecedents. We therefore had to consider a third type of explanation involving two or more factors in combination, and including at least one necessary and specific condition. This necessary condition is thought to be an interaction capable of increasing the susceptibility of certain generations to a variety of nonspecific agents, including chronic disease or parasites, further interactions with other animals, and a range of physical factors that the animals normally tolerate. According to this view both the specific and nonspecific conditions must be satisfied, a change in susceptibility being insufficient to bring about a decline in the absence of the normal mortality factors, and the latter alone being insufficient to decimate a normal population, or at least to produce the association of effects that characterize the recurrent type of decline.

It is difficult to refute this interpretation at present, since it states that an unknown kind of interaction produces an unknown change in the average properties of the individuals, whose descendants become more susceptible to unknown and principally local forms of mortality. Part of the difficulty is technical: we seldom see wild voles or find their corpses; they live too long and take up too much space when brought into the laboratory to provide data on longevity and fertility; they have too long a generation time; little is known about their genetics, and so on. Finally, we have not yet learned how to set up experimental populations to give results that are both repeatable and relevant to the problem in nature.

The latter difficulty comes from the fact that wild rodents, even when abundant, live fairly well dispersed. A population of breeding adults must be considered "crowded" at a density of 120 per acre in the best habitats at Lake Vyrnwy, or one vole to 40 sq. yd of ground covered in dense vegetation and interspersed with a network of runways in three dimensions. Elsewhere densities may be still lower [17]. Contrary, therefore, to what some authors appear to believe, useful results will not necessarily follow from keeping animals at a density several hundred times that occurring in nature, and at the same time failing to provide a substitute for their runways and cover.

Certain consequences of the hypothesis could be tested by applying experimental methods in the field, and departures from the following predictions would tend to discredit the idea in its present form. (1) If animals are prevented from interacting adversely they should go on increasing until they run out of food. (2) If large enough numbers of animals are continually removed from an expanding population, the survival rate of the remainder should continue to be high; but where an adverse physiological change has occurred no reduction in density should be sufficient to reverse a downward trend. (3) Numbers should continue to increase if animals from an increasing population are successfully transferred to an area from which a declining population has been removed; but numbers should continue to decline if animals from a declining population are transferred to a new area.

Predictions of this kind can so easily go wrong because of unforeseen practical difficulties, inadequate knowledge, and faulty logic, that the time and money required to carry them out on voles might not be well spent. Other species, however, might be easier to work with if it is reasonable to believe that the problem in the vole is merely a special case of a far more general phenomenon. We must now examine this possibility.

Relation to Other Ideas

Andrewartha and Birch [2, p. 656] summarize the principal aspect of their views in the form of three curves for each of two habitats, in one of which (area B) climatic catastrophes happen more frequently than in the other, and reduce the population to lower numbers, from which it recovers more slowly. They say "Taking all three curves into account, one can easily see that the animals would be more numerous, on the average, in area A than in area B." According to this scheme population densities are determined by the severity and frequency of bad weather, and no other factors need be postulated. We may express this point of view as implying that, in instances of this type, variations in weather are both necessary and sufficient to determine population density.

According to Nicholson [26] there is more to it than this, however. He, too, recognizes the importance of the physical factors, but argues that "they act as the tools or *instruments of destruction* used by true reactive factors." (A reactive factor is one that is influenced by changes in population density and influences it in turn.) The really essential point of his argument is that without a dependent variable the proportion of the population destroyed would be unrelated to population density, which therefore would not be "governed." However, since the death rate would be altogether different in the absence of the "instruments of destruction," much semantic difficulty can be avoided by assuming merely that both types of factor are necessary in such cases. Stripped of its surplus terminology, Nicholson's view can, I think, be reduced to the testable proposition that a set of independent variables is a necessary but not a sufficient condition determining a given population density. His other necessary condition, as already stated, is the presence of a relative factor, and it is here that the trouble arises.

In a definition of considerable importance Nicholson [25] states: *"The action of the controlling factor must be governed by the density of the population controlled."* From this it would seem important to discover factors whose *action* varies with population density; but this is not what Nicholson advises: "Instead we must find which of the factors are influenced, and how readily they are influenced, by changes in the density of the animals." A natural enemy which destroys only 1% of the population would be "wholly responsible for control," whereas climate would not, even if it destroyed 98% of the population, because "its action [is] uninfluenced by the density of the animals." A good many writers have accepted this argument uncritically apparently without recognizing the magnitude of the assumption involved or the almost complete lack of empirical evidence.

The action of a physical factor can be measured only by observing the results of a reaction on the part of the organism, and these results are predictable only if the properties of the organism can be assumed to be constant. In the case of population phenomena we can measure the action of weather only by observing its effects on death rates, birth rates, or other parameters of the population, and it seems unrealistic to assume that the characteristics of the individual animals that make up the population are constant and independent of population density. Similar considerations affect the interpretation of most mortality rates, since even the effects of biotic factors such as parasites can also be explained by changes in host resistance or in the severity of the factor.

Changes in resistance, systematically related to population density, are entirely consistent with Nicholson's main idea about the regulation of animal numbers; but not with his proposition that the action of the physical factors is independent of population density. This axiom can be abandoned, however, or restated in unambiguous terms, without affecting his main principle; and the main principle of Andrewartha and Birch may also be retained, as their idea that population density is chiefly determined by the action of the physical factors is entirely consistent with this action being governed by some population attribute. Both theories already include enough qualifications to make such a synthesis possible. The vole work suggests that population densities are indeed governed or regulated, but that this is most commonly achieved by the action of the physical factors; and since the action of any factor whatever depends upon the properties of the individuals, it seems a priori improbable that the effects of weather are independent of population density.

It is perhaps worth trying to justify the addition of fresh speculations to a subject already overburdened with them by showing their possible application to one of the many studies in which no evidence was discovered to show that numbers are regulated in the manner predicted a priori (as seems to be the case with all studies that have gone on long enough to rule out mere associations as explanations).

"It is difficult to see what factors may be responsible for regulating populations of *Glossina. Unfavourable conditions of climate are presumably independent of density and cannot regulate it* [italics mine]. Competition for blood between individual tsetse flies does not, we believe, take place. We are left to suppose that the "enemies" (using that word broadly) of the fly or the puparium must be responsible for the regulation. But it must be admitted that we have no evidence that any particular enemy becomes more numerous or effective at higher densities of the tsetse population. We have indeed very little knowledge of the causes or mechanisms which prevent an indefinite increase of these insects when external conditions are favourable, but one must certainly suppose that some such factor exists" [3].

This passage shows the remarkable persistence of the fallacy that because climatic factors are themselves unaffected by population density therefore their action is also independent of density (or other parameters). Jackson [19] also failed to realize that the effect of weather on tsetse flies can never be measured in isolation from a system involving individuals whose properties may not be constant. Although he found a long-term statistical relation between saturation deficit and birth and death rates, he could not understand why these parameters often fluctuated in opposite directions in two populations exposed to the same weather. "There is thus little doubt that the short-term fluctuations are governed by something intrinsic in the local populations, which if true is sufficient to put the detailed analysis of the effects of climate forever beyond our grasp." In contrast to this conclusion, the ideas developed in the present paper imply that results such as Jackson's are exactly what one would hope to find in order to understand the effects of climate. His results are consistent with the view that the two populations were significantly different in their properties; and such properties should be easier to investigate when simultaneous samples of animals can be examined from constrasting populations. Indeed the effects of climate are almost certain to be unpredictable until differences in the properties of the animals can be recognized.

At the present time there is an understandable reluctance to believe that the degree of crowding commonly observed in nature could possibly have profound effects on physiological condition. In the case of the tsetse fly, for example, the maximum population density may be only about 1800 ♂ ♂ per sq. mile in some places, with 2–3 times as many ♀ ♀, or about 10 flies per acre [3, 19]. Nevertheless Buxton [3] was prepared to speculate that tsetse flies might have a form of behavior that regulates their population density through dispersal; and Tinbergen [28] considers that such mechanisms may be fairly universal. As we know so little about behavior it would be wrong to assume that it has no important effects on physiology and genetics, and there is little doubt that individual properties should be taken into account more often than is customary in population studies. Perhaps the most notable exceptions are the work on locust phases [1 and earlier work], and physiological types of tent caterpillar [29].

According to the views given in this final section voles probably exemplify a general law that all species are capable of limiting their own population densities without either destroying the food resources to which they are adapted, or depending upon enemies or climatic accidents to prevent them from doing so. If this is true, self-regulatory mechanisms have presumably been evolved through natural selection, and arguments in support of this view can certainly be advanced. In the present paper, however, the only argument required is the purely methodological one that it is best to start with the fewest and simplest explanations possible, and to add to them only when it is clear that there are fundamental differences between similar phenomena in related species.

To assume that all species are capable of regulating their own numbers is entirely different from believing that all populations are in fact so regulated. In particular the assumption that a self-regulatory mechanism has been evolved by natural selection implies that it has been adapted in relation to a more or less limited range of environmental conditions. In unnatural or atypical situations, therefore, the mechanism will not necessarily prevent abnormal rates of increase or recurrent food crises.

It may be difficult to apply these views to other species until criteria have been established for recognizing instances of self-regulation and distinguishing them from instances of other phenomena. The attempt is nevertheless worth making, for birth rates and death rates are likely to be misinterpreted as long as it is assumed that the properties of the individuals are constant at all population densities.

The substance of this paper was given in some talks at the Department of Zoology, University of British Columbia, in April 1959, and I wish to thank Dr. Ian McTaggart Cowan, Dr. James F. Bendell, and other members of the department for helpful discussions. Dr. W. G. Wellington was also kind enough to read and comment on the manuscript. I am especially grateful to Dr. E. W. Fager for some very useful advice about an earlier draft of this paper, and my colleagues at the Bureau of Animal Population have, as usual, made numerous constructive suggestions that have also been incorporated in the present version.

References

1. Albrecht, F. O., Verdier, M., and Blackith, R. E. Détermination de la fertilité par l'effet de groupe chez le criquet migrateur (*Locusta migratoria migratorioides* R. et F.). Bull. biol. France, 92: 349–427 (1958). *See also* Nature, 184: 103–104 (1959).

2. Andrewartha, H. G. and Birch, L. C. The distribution and abundance of animals. The University of Chicago Press, Chicago, Ill. 1954.

3. Buxton, P. A. The natural history of tsetse flies. An account of the biology of the genus *Glossina* (Diptera). Mem. London School Hyg. Trop. Med. No. 10: 1–816 (1955).

4. Chitty, D. Mortality among voles (*Microtus agrestis*) at Lake Vyrnwy, Montgomeryshire in 1936–9. Phil. Trans. Roy. Soc. London, Ser. B, 236: 505–552 (1952).

5. Chitty, D. Tuberculosis among wild voles: with a discussion of other pathological conditions among certain mammals and birds. Ecology, 35: 227–237 (1954).

6. Chitty, D. Adverse effects of population density upon the viability of later generations. *In* the numbers of man and animals. *Edited by* J. B. Cragg and N. W. Pirie. Oliver and Boyd, Ltd., Edinburgh. 1955. pp. 57–67.

7. Chitty, D. Self-regulation of numbers through changes in viability. Cold Spring Harbour Symposia Quant. Biol. 22: 277–280 (1958).

8. Chitty, D. A note on shock disease. Ecology. In press (1959).

9. Christian, J. J. The adrenopituitary system and population cycles in mammals. J. Mammalogy, 31: 247–259 (1950).

10. Christian, J. J. A review of the endocrine responses in rats and mice to increasing population size including delayed effects on offspring. Naval Med. Research Inst. Lect. Rev. Ser. No. 57–2, 443–462 (1957).

11. Christian, J. J. and Lemunyan, C. D. Adverse effects of crowding on reproduction and lactation of mice and two generations of their progeny. Naval Med. Research Inst. Research Rept. NM 24 01 00.04.01, 15: 925–936 (1957).

12. Clarke, J. R. Influence of numbers on reproduction and survival in two experimental vole populations. Proc. Roy. Soc. B, 144: 68–85 (1955).

13. Dawson, J. Splenic hypertrophy in voles. Nature, 178: 1183–1184 (1956).

14. Elton, C. Voles, mice and lemmings: problems in population dynamics. Oxford University Press, London. 1942.

15. Frank, F. Untersuchungen über den Zusammenbruch von Feldmausplagen (*Microtus arvalis* Pallas). Zool. Jahrb. (Syst.), 82: 95–136 (1953).

16. Frank, F. The causality of microtine cycles in Germany (second preliminary research report). J. Wildlife Management, 21: 113–121 (1957).

17. Godfrey, G. K. Observations on the nature of the decline in numbers of two *Microtus* populations. J. Mammalogy, 36: 209–214 (1955).

18. Green, R. G. and Evans, C. A. Studies on a population cycle of snowshoe hares on the Lake Alexander Area. . . . J. Wildlife Management, 4: 220–238, 267–278, 347–358 (1940).

19. Jackson, C. H. N. The analysis of a tsetse-fly population. III. Ann. Eugen., Camb. 14: 91–108 (1948).

20. Leslie, P. H. The properties of a certain lag type of population growth and the influence of an external random factor on a number of such populations. Physiol. Zoöl. 32: 151–159 (1959).

21. Leslie, P. H., Chitty, D., and Chitty, H. The estimation of population parameters from data obtained by means of the capture-recapture method. III. An example of the practical applications of the method. Biometrika, 40: 137–169 (1953).

22. Leslie, P. H. and Ranson, R. M. The mortality, fertility and rate of natural increase of the vole (*Microtus agrestis*) as observed in the laboratory. J. Animal Ecol. 9: 27–52 (1940).

23. Lockie, J. D. The breeding habits and food of short-eared owls after a vole plague. Bird Study, 2: 53–69 (1955).

24. Medawar, P. B. The uniqueness of the individual. Methuen and Co. Ltd., London. 1957.

25. Nicholson, A. J. The balance of animal populations. J. Animal Ecol. 2: 132–178 (1933).

26. Nicholson, A. J. An outline of the dynamics of animal populations. Aust. J. Zool. 2: 9–65 (1954).

27. Summerhayes, V. S. The effect of voles (*Microtus agrestis*) on vegetation. J. Ecology, 29: 14–48 (1941).

28. Tinbergen, N. The functions of territory. Bird Study, 4: 14–27 (1957).

29. Wellington, W. G. Individual differences as a factor in population dynamics: the development of a problem. Can. J. Zool. 35: 293–323 (1957).

30. Wells, A. Q. The murine type of tubercle bacillus (the vole acid-fast bacillus). Special Rept. Ser. Med. Research Council, London, 259: 1–42 (1946).

31. Zimmermann, K. Körpergrösse und Bestandsdichte bei Feldmäusen (*Microtus arvalis*). Z. Säug. 20: 114–118 (1955).

J. L. Harper
J. T. Williams
G. R. Sagar

The Behavior of Seeds in Soil
The Heterogeneity of Soil Surfaces and Its Role in
Determining the Establishment of Plants from Seed

Introduction

This paper describes experiments made to determine the influence of variations in the microtopography of soil surfaces on the establishment of seedlings.
The experiments derived from the realization that at the size scale of most seeds,
the soil surface on which they are dispersed is highly heterogeneous and that
this heterogeneity of the soil is likely to provide microsites offering widely
different conditions for germination. Seeds often possess highly specific germination requirements and when seeds are dispersed onto soil surfaces, it seems
reasonable to suppose that both the numbers and proportions of species establishing may be determined by the sort of micro-environment in which each
seed lands. Unfortunately, the measurement of variations in the micro-environment at the appropriate scale is scarcely possible, and it may be for this reason
that the ecological significance of soil surface microtopography has not been
seriously considered.

Experimental

In the following experiments we have examined the influence of various artificial modifications of soil microtopography on the establishment of seedlings.
The experiments fall into two groups:
(a) A study of the effects on seedling establishment of artificial topographi-
cal modifications introduced onto a fine seed bed. For this experiment three
species of *Plantago, P. lanceolata, P. media* and *P. major,* were used.
(b) Studies of the influence of soil surface texture on seedling establishment
in which an attempt was made to express variations in surface microtopography
quantitatively. For these experiments a range of species including *Bromus* spp.,
Chenopodium album and *Brassica oleracea acephala* "green marrow stemmed
kale" were used.

Reprinted by permission of the authors and publisher from the *Journal of Ecology, 51:*
273–286, 1965.

The Influence of Small Modifications of Soil Microtopography on the Germination of Seeds of *Plantago* spp.

A series of attempts to establish populations of *P. lanceolata, P. major* and *P. media* in open plots under field conditions showed that establishment frequently bore very little relationship to the germination capacity of the seed samples as shown by laboratory tests. Moreover, germination was very erratic from place to place within plots. On one occasion the experimental plots were trodden by pigs and there was rapidly produced a stand of *Plantago* seedlings wherever hoof marks had been made. This suggested that disturbance of the soil surface had created special conditions suitable for seedling establishment. An experiment was designed to test the influence of various kinds of soil disturbance on the ability of *Plantago* seeds to germinate in the soil. An artifical seed bed was constructed, 150 cm square and 30 cm deep, overlying a free draining gravel soil surface. The seed bed was prepared from John Innes Compost No. 2, finely sifted, with coarse particles at the bottom of the seed bed and with a fine crumb soil to a depth of 2 in. at the surface. The seed bed was watered frequently after preparation.

Each plot was sown evenly with 500 seeds of each of the three species, *P. lanceolata, P. media* and *P. major*. The seed used had been collected from the Ridgeway on the Berkshire Downs in 1958, and stored in the laboratory throughout the winter of 1958–59. The area was divided into four blocks, each of nine plots, which were treated as follows:

(1) A hole 12.5 cm square and 1.25 cm deep was made by pressing a square of glass to the required depth and then removing it.

(2) A hole 12.5 cm square and 2.5 cm deep was prepared as in (1).

(3) A sheet of plate glass 12.5 cm square and 0.6 cm thick was placed horizontally on the soil surface.

(4a) A sheet of plate glass 12.5 cm long and 3.75 cm high was inserted vertically into the soil to a depth of 1.25 cm, thus leaving 2.5 cm standing vertically above the soil surface. The glass was aligned from north to south.

(4b) As (4a) but with the glass aligned east to west.

(5) A thin walled wooden box 12.5 cm × 12.5 cm without top or bottom and with sides 3.75 cm high was pressed 1.25 cm into the soil, leaving 2.5 cm projecting above the soil surface.

(6) A similar wooden box with sides 2.5 cm high was pressed 1.25 cm into the soil, leaving 1.25 cm projecting above the soil surface.

(7) A similar box with sides 1.25 cm high was pressed 1.25 cm into the soil leaving the top of the box flush with the soil surface.

(8) A control plot received no special treatment.

The layout of this experiment is shown in Fig. 1 (a) and Phot. 1. The seed was sown and treatments applied on 14 April 1959, and the experiment received only natural rainfall from that time. Seedlings started to emerge on 1 May

Table 1

The Emergence of Seedlings of Plantago *Species in Relation to the Distribution of Various Modifications in the Soil Surface**

Treatment	Percentage of Total Emergence for Each Species		
	P. lanceolata	P. media	P. major
1. Hole 1.25 cm deep	7.3	4.8	8.0
2. Hole 2.5 cm deep	23.5	11.4	18.5
3. Glass sheet flat on surface	9.6	46.7	11.6
4a. Glass sheet vertical N–S	2.3	2.9	3.3
4b. Glass sheet vertical E–W	3.8	1.9	2.2
5. Box 2.5 cm above surface	10.6	3.8	4.7
6. Box 1.25 cm above surface	11.0	4.8	8.7
7. Box 0 cm above surface	23.2	13.3	12.0
8. Control—no treatment	0.4	0.0	3.3
9. Seedlings not associated with treatments 1–8 (43.5% of total sown area)	8.3	10.5	27.9
Total number of seedlings emerged	689	105	276

* All seedlings found within the treated area (12.5 × 12.5 cm) and including a 2.5 cm broad surrounding border were regarded as associated with a treatment. Figures are means of four replicates accumulated over two sampling dates, 1 May and 11 June 1959.

1959, and 9 days later the position of all emerged seedlings was recorded and the seedlings were removed. A second flush of seedlings was mapped and removed on 11 June 1959. Maps of the distribution of seedlings from these two harvesting dates are presented together in Fig. 1(b, c and d). It is apparent that the seedlings were not evenly distributed throughout the sown area, but arose in close relation to the objects placed on the surface. Apart from the pattern of seedling distribution associated with applied treatments, two worm casts were formed on the soil surface during the course of the experiment and a mass of seedlings of both *P. lanceolata* and *P. major* appeared in association with these. Table 1 summarizes the establishment of seedlings of the three species under the various treatments.

A first and obvious conclusion is that *c*. 90% of the seedlings of *P. lanceolata* and *P. media* developed close to the objects or depressions on the surface. In contrast, the distribution of *P. major* was largely independent of the distribution of objects. The emergence of all species was increased by compressing the soil, but the most striking increase was of *P. lanceolata* and *P. major*. In contrast, seedling emergence of *P. media* was greatly favored under a glass sheet lying flat on the soil surface, but this had relatively little effect on *P. lanceolata* and *P. major*. The establishment of *P. lanceolata* and *P. media* was increased by the presence of boxes placed on the soil surface and the effect was greatest when the boxes scarcely projected above the soil. It was least with the most projecting boxes. This difference is interesting as all boxes were pressed to an equal depth in the soil—the extent of projection above the soil was the only variable. The effect of glass sheets placed on edge was much the same as one side of a box with no difference between N–S and E–W orientation.

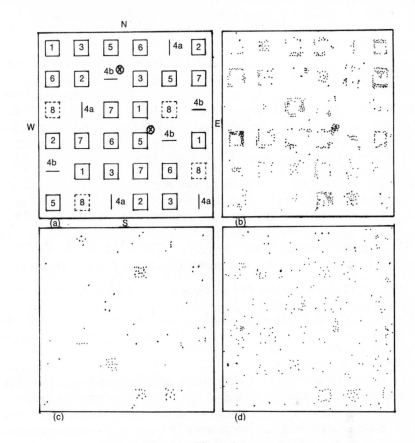

Figure 1

(a) Plan showing the distribution of various types of
objects placed on a soil surface sown with seeds of
Plantago species (see text and Phot. 1). ⊗ = worm
casts. (b) The distribution of seedlings of *P. lanceolata* in relation to objects and depressions on the soil
surface. Combined records of 1 May and 11 June
1959; all seedlings were counted and removed on each
date. (c) As (b) for seedlings of *P. media*. (d) As
(b) for seedlings of *P. major*.

A Study of the Establishment of a Variety of Species on Artificially Prepared Soil Surfaces of Varied Texture

The topography of soil surfaces varies not only with the frequency of ob-
structions, but also with the condition of the soil itself. In nature, variations in
the wetting and drying cycles to which the soil has been exposed result in varied

degrees of cracking. The activities of the soil fauna result in variations in the tilth of the soil surface, the presence and decay of leaf litter provides a changing soil surface and the activities of man may provide a variety of tilths as a result of cultivation.

An attempt was made to provide a graded series of soil surfaces. It was considered important to avoid sifting the soil as this results in a seperation of fractions which differ not only in structure but also in nutrient content (Hammerton, 1961). Large clumps of soil were therefore taken and broken by hand into fragments of the required size and these were used to form seed beds on which seeds of various species were sown. Seeds were dropped on to the soil surface from 30 cm height to simulate natural dispersal.

The Establishment of Species of *Bromus* **on Yolo Silty Loam** Plant pots 20 cm diameter were filled to within 10 cm of the rim with a 3 to 1 mixture of fine sand and Yolo silty loam. Yolo silty loam was available in a dry caked condition, having been stored wet and allowed to dry. From this a series of soil surfaces of graded structure was prepared. The large clods of soil, many of which were originally >30 cm in diameter, were broken by hand to give four grades:

(A) A large grade in which the unit clods were *c*. 5 cm diameter.

(B) A slightly smaller grade 3–5 cm diameter.

(C) A grade of soil clods 2–2.5 cm diameter.

(D) In which the large lumps were broken into fragments 1.25 cm diameter or less.

Sufficient large clods of grade A were placed on top of the soil-sand mixture to bring the average level of the soil to the top of the plant pot. The same weight of soil of the remaining grades was added to other pots. Eight pots were prepared from each soil grade except grade D from which sixteen pots were prepared. Eight pots of grade D were watered heavily and then allowed to dry for 3 weeks to give a fifth type of surface, E, hard capped with deep cracks (Phot. 2).

The soil surfaces prepared for the experiments were superficially similar to many of the soil surfaces observed on the coastal ranges of central California. Frequently soil disturbance results in clod sizes comparable with grades A, B and C. Grade E corresponded to soil surfaces which had been rained on and then cracked during drying. Simple equipment was designed to permit measurement of the roughness of the soil surface. This consisted of a frame holding a line of ten pins arranged so that they were free to move vertically. The tops of the pins were fitted with pointers which rested against a graph paper scale (Fig. 2). The frame was lowered horizontally onto the soil surface until the points of all the pins rested on the soil. Readings were then taken of the heights of the pointers. Three such sets of ten readings were taken from each pot of soil. The absolute values obtained from such readings have no very useful meaning but the variance of the values gives a measure of the soil microtopography. This parameter may be called "soil microtopographical

Phot. 1

The arrangement of objects on a soil surface sown with seeds of *Plantago* species (compare with Fig. 1a).

Phot. 2

Various soil surfaces, prepared from Yolo silty loam, on which seeds of *Bromus* species have been dropped. The long awns of *B. rigidus* are conspicuous on the surface.

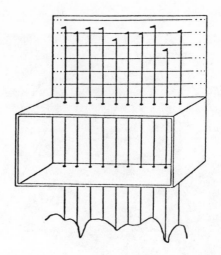

Figure 2

Ten-pin frame used for the measurement of soil
roughness.

variance" (S.M.-T.V.). The values for S.M.-T.V. represent the error variance
in an analysis of variance of pointer readings, after partitioning and removing
the variance due to differences between replicate pots and due to differences
between the three positions of the aligned pins in each pot. Determination of
the S.M.-T.V. in this way makes it irrelevant whether or not the apparatus is
held at the same height for every set of ten readings, and makes this measurement possible as a field operation. It is of course essential that the frame is
horizontal when readings are taken.

There was a high degree of constancy in the variance obtained from eight
pots of similar soil grade. The S.M.-T.V. of the five grades was as follows: (A)
189.48 mm^2, (B) 166.49 mm^2, (C) 60.59 mm^2, (D) 6.43 mm^2, (E) 2.78
mm^2.

Seeds of *B. rigidus* and *B. madritensis* were sown on the varied soil surfaces.
Both species are annuals. They differ in vigour of growth, *B. rigidus* being the
more vigorous (see Harper, Clatworthy, McNaughton and Sagar, 1961), and
they differ in shape and size of the dispersal unit. The grains are dispersed together with enclosing lemma and palea and the lemma of *B. rigidus* bears a
straight awn. The grain of *B. madritensis* is smaller and lighter and the awn is
slightly curved. It was obvious on scattering the grains on the soil that those of
B. rigidus often fell like darts, entering the cracks and crevices between soil
clods and leaving only the awn showing. In contrast, grains of *B. madritensis*
fell more slowly and the slight winging of the grains seemed to cause them to
land horizontally more often than vertically on the surface of the soil. Sowings
were made at four densities of 10, 30, 60 and 100 seeds per pot and each

density was obtained from a mixture of seeds of the two species in equal proportions by number.

The design of the experiment was therefore as follows: Five soil grades; four sowing densities; the whole being replicated twice. The soil was watered from above by simulant rainfall from a fine hose; 1.25 cm of rain was given immediately on sowing. Seven days later the soil had dried and no germination was observed. The equivalent of 2.5 cm of rainfall was then applied and followed by a further 2.5 cm a week later.

Rapid germination of both species was observed and when no further emergence occurred and the established seedlings had wilted, all seedlings were removed and counted. The results of this experiment are shown in Fig. 3, and the changes in relative proportion of the two species with soil microtopography are shown in Fig. 4. The effects of soil surface were significant at $P<0.001$, and there were significant interactions between soil surface and species ($P<0.05$), and between soil surface and sowing density ($P<0.01$).

On the three soil surfaces with high values of S.M.-T.V. there was a linear relationship between the number of seeds sown and the number of seedlings

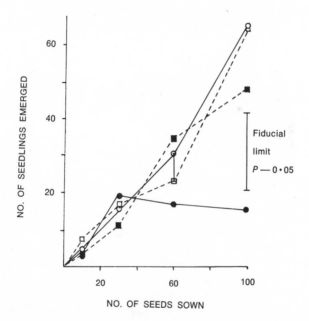

Figure 3

The relationship between the numbers of seed of *Bromus* species sown and the numbers of seedlings establishing on soils of varied microtopography. A (□) Soil microtopographical variance = 189.5 mm²; B (o) = 166.5 mm²; C (■) = 60.6 mm²; E (•) = 2.8 mm².

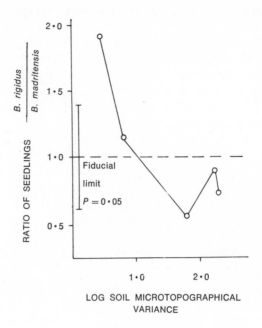

Figure 4

The ratio of numbers of seedlings of *Bromus rigidus* and *B. madritensis* establishing from an equiproportioned mixture sown on soils of varied microtopography.

established. On the soil which had been watered and allowed to crack, a very different relationship developed. Here the population of seedlings was not increased by a further increase in sowing density from 30 to 100 seeds per pot, and it is concluded that on this soil surface there was a very limited number of sites suitable for establishment under the conditions of this experiment, and that the sites were quickly saturated by increasing the density of seeds sown. The model soils provided in this experiment illustrate two contrasting conditions which may be expected to occur in the field: one in which population sizes are not limited by the availability of suitable microsites within the range of densities examined and one in which a relatively low population size is maintained despite wide variations of sowing density.

Although seeds of the two species used in this experiment were sown in equal proportions at every density and on every soil surface, there were striking differences in the proportions of the two species in the seedling populations. There was a significantly higher proportion of *B. rigidus* on the soils of low S.M.-T.V. and a higher proportion of *B. madritensis* on the rougher soils. This may perhaps be explained in terms of the different types of contact made by the grains with the soil surface. On the very rough soils the curved awn of *B.*

madritensis ensures that the grain often comes to lie curved around a soil clod making good and close contact with the water supplying soil surface. Such contact is minimized on a flat surface. In contrast, *B. rigidus* lies flat and was apparently more efficient at making contact with a flat soil surface (or entering a very narrow crack or crevice).

The Establishment of Chenopodium album and Kale on Heavy Clay Soil A heavy clay soil was obtained from Griffith's Crossing workings at Port Dinorwic, Caernarvonshire. Pots of 23 cm diameter were filled two thirds full with a 50/50 mixture of the clay with John Innes'Compost No. 2. Further samples of the clay were dried and broken by hand to give a range of clod sizes as in the previous experiment. Subsequent preparation and arrangement of the clods followed the procedure described for *Bromus* experiments. The range of surface roughness obtained in this experiment was (S.M.-T.V. values) A, 214.47 mm^2, B, 74.39 mm^2, C, 29.31 mm^2, D, 7.20 mm^2 and E (dried and cracked from D as previously) 9.98 mm^2. One hundred seeds of kale and 100 seeds of *Chenopodium album* were broadcast onto each soil surface. The experiment was replicated five times and arranged as a randomized block within a cool glasshouse. The seeds were sown broadcast onto the soil surface and it was immediately obvious that the two species took up different positions of rest in the soil. The heavier kale seeds tended to roll down between the clods, although a few lodged on the sides of the larger clods. Seeds of *C. album* usually remained where they first landed and most became lodged on the rough sides of clods. Seed sown on the caked cracked soil E rolled into the cracks. Every 4 days 2.5 cm of water was applied. At weekly intervals counts were made of the number of seedlings emerged, discarding a border 1.5 cm wide around the side of each pot. The experiments were continued for 6 weeks until no further seedling emergence occurred in the experiments. The number of seedlings present at each count and the ratio between the two species is shown in Fig. 5. Seedlings of kale emerged more quickly than those of *C. album*. The most successful emergence of both the species was from the soil surface of variance 29.31 mm^2 and the worst emergence of kale was from the smoothest soil and of *C. album* from the roughest. Kale was much more sensitive to soil roughness than *C. album*. Because the species differed in the speed with which they germinated, the ratio of the number of seedlings of kale to *C. album* started high and then fell rapidly. More seedlings established on the soil which had dried and then cracked than on the fine soil surface from which it had been prepared, because the seeds falling into cracks tended to germinate quickly and regularly.

Modification of Soil Microtopography by Compaction or Enclosure Subsequent to Seed Dispersal

Seed boxes, 100 × 62 × 37 cm deep, were prepared with three soil microtopographies corresponding approximately to A, C, and D in the previous experiments (S.M.-T.V. = 258.50, 55.75 and 9.90 mm^2). A mixture of 200

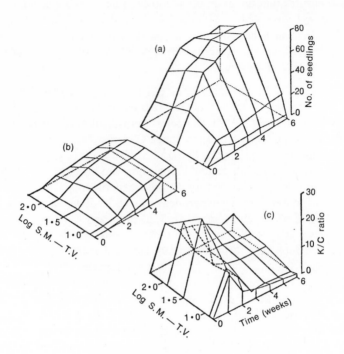

Figure 5

The establishment of seedlings of kale and *Cheno-podium album* on soils of varied microtopography.
(a) Kale; (b) *C. album;*

$$(c) \text{ the ratio } \frac{\text{Number of seedlings of kale}}{\text{Number of seedlings of } C. \text{ album}}.$$

seeds of *C. album* and 200 seeds of kale were broadcast on each soil surface. After sowing the seed, the soil in one half of the boxes was compacted by rolling with a linoleum roller. The boxes were laid out as a randomized block with five replicates each of six treatments. The boxes were placed in the open and received natural rainfall. There was a period of dry weather immediately after sowing and additional water was given at this time. The number of seedlings present at each count and the ratio between kale and *Chenopodium* is shown in Fig. 6. The establishment of *C. album* was greatly reduced by compaction but kale was much less affected, particularly on the rougher soils. Clearly the influence of soil roughness on seedling emergence can be modified by compaction. Not only were the number of potential germination sites altered by compaction, but the treatment affected the establishment of the species differentially.

One of the most obvious ways in which soil microtopography might be expected to influence seedling establishment is by determining the extent to which seeds are exposed to the atmosphere. If this is the case, then the effects

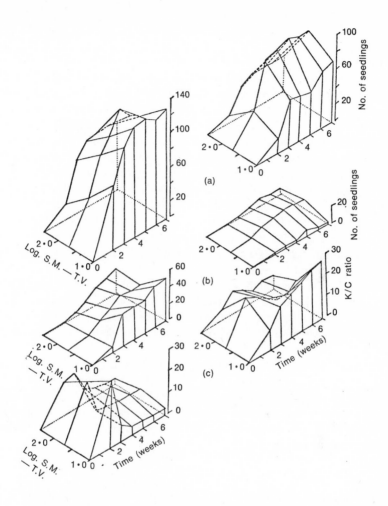

Figure 6

The influence of surface compaction on the establishment of seedlings of kale and *Chenopodium album* on soils of varied microtopography. Left-hand side—no compaction; right-hand side—with compaction. (a) Kale; (b) *C. album;*

(c) the ratio $\dfrac{\text{Number of seedlings of kale}}{\text{Number of seedlings of } C.\ album}$

of varied topographies might be reduced if the soil surface were protected by restricting evaporation from the surface. Three series of soil surfaces were prepared, S.M.-T.V. 212.62, 56.23 and 6.08 mm². A mixture of 100 seeds of *C. album* and 100 seeds of kale was broadcast on each plot. Half of the pots were covered with clear polythene held tightly across the rim by rubber bands. The pots were laid out as a randomized block with five replicates of each of the six treatments. The pots were kept in a cool glasshouse and were buried to their rims in soil to avoid excessive drying of the side of the pots. Every 4 days 2.5 cm of water was applied to the soil surface from a fine spray. A high relative humidity was maintained under the polythene covers, which carried a continuous film of water droplets. The covers were removed after 2 weeks. During bright sunlight the temperature of the soil at 5 cm depth under polythene covers was raised by between 2 and 3.1° C above that of uncovered soil. The mean number of seedlings present at each count is shown in Fig. 7.

The effect of the polythene covers was particularly marked on the emergence of kale, causing a much more rapid flush of germination and largely eliminating variations due to soil microtopography. The experiment was complicated, however, by much damping-off of seedlings which had emerged under polythene. The damping-off occurred 4 weeks after emergence even though the polythene had been removed after 2 weeks. The seedlings which had developed under polythene tended to be straggly and slightly etiolated. After 6 weeks the populations on the rough soils were smaller under polythene than without, but the populations on smooth soils were larger under polythene. The greater liability to damping-off on the rough soils may well be explained by the humid environment maintained around the hypocotyls as they elongated between the large soil clods (see Hammerton, 1961). The seeds usually fell deep in such surfaces in contrast to their behavior on fine soils where the hypocotyls were quickly free from the soil micro-environment.

The establishment of C. album was less influenced than kale by the presence of polythene covers, but in general, the effect of covering the pots with polythene was to reduce the differences due to soil microtopography. It is suggested that variations in soil microtopography affect the establishment of these species by determining the frequency on the soil surface of microsites sufficiently humid for germination.

Water Uptake by Seeds and Germination on Four Graded Soil Surfaces

An experiment was designed to examine the rates of water uptake by seeds sown on soils of varied microtopography with the aim of determining whether this was correlated with seedling establishment on such soils. Four soil surfaces were prepared (S.M.-T.V. = 332.27, 128.69, 63.94 and 8.40 mm^2) and twenty seeds of kale and twenty seeds of C. album were broadcast on to each surface. The treatments were replicated four times and the pots arranged in a randomized block design. The pots were sunk to the rim in damp soil in a cool glasshouse and after sowing the seed the pots were given 2.5 cm of water from a fine spray. The seeds had been desiccated for 2 days over calcium chloride before sowing and they were recovered after 24 h in the soil, weighed and the percentage increase in weight was calculated. Immediately after recovering the seeds, a mixture of 100 seeds of kale and 100 seeds of C. album was sown on each of the soil surfaces to obtain a measure of ssedling emergence from the same soils. Seedling emergence was recorded. The change in weight of the first batch of seeds sown in the soil and the ultimate emergence of seedlings from

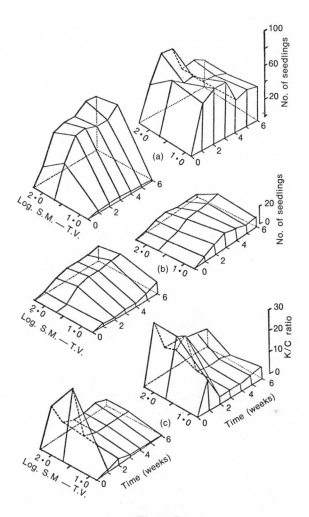

Figure 7

The influence of surface protection on the establishment of seedlings of kale and *Chenopodium album* on soils of varied microtopography. Left-hand side—no polythene; right-hand side—with polythene. (a) Kale; (b) *C. album*;

(c) the ratio $\dfrac{\text{Number of seedlings of kale}}{\text{Number of seedlings of } C.\ album}$.

the second batch of seeds sown in the same soil are shown in Fig. 8. The soil roughness which was optimal for seedling establishment was different for the two species and the optima coincided with the optima for water absorption. The results of this experiment support the hypothesis that an important role of vary-

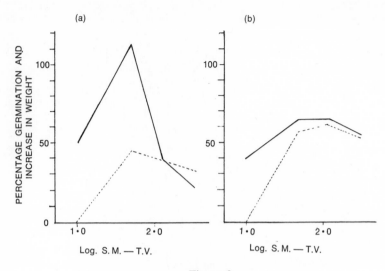

Figure 8

Percentage increase in weight over 24 h (———) of
seeds of (a) *Chenopodium album* and (b) kale sown
on soils of varied microtopography. Plotted on the
same graphs are percentage germination of these
species sown on the same soils (- - -).

ing soil microtopography in seedling establishment is to determine the ease
with which water is taken up by the seeds which fall in different positions and
make different contacts in the various soil surfaces.

Discussion

The experiments described in this paper are all concerned with the behavior
of seeds falling on a soil surface—imitating natural seed fall or the agricultural
practice of "broadcasting" seed. All the experimental results emphasize that
the heterogeneities of a soil surface may determine the chance of a seed finding a suitable crevice for germination. It is obvious that in these experimental
systems the density of the plant population is a function of the soil surface
and the population may be said to be regulated by the frequency of "safe sites"
(Harper *et al.,* 1961).

In all the experiments two or more species were sown on each type of soil
surface, and the relative proportion of the species were changed with varying
surface roughness. This suggests that there is considerable subtlety in the requirements of different species for "safe sites." The densities of species in a
mixture may be independently determined for each species because of specialized requirements for germination which are satisfied at different places on a
rough soil surface. This is particularly strongly suggested by the experiments
with *Plantago* spp. in which the density of seedlings of each species was largely

a function of the frequency of the different types of disturbance made on the soil surface.

A part of the effect of soil microtopography would seem to be due to the degree of protection of seeds against water loss—for protection of the soil surface with polythene removed much of the difference in seedling establishment on different soil surfaces. This could, however, have been due, in part, to the raised soil temperature under polythene. The observation that the different optimal topographies for establishment of *Chenopodium album* and kale corresponded with the different optimal topographies for water uptake by the seeds, supports the view that microtopography exerts its effects through modifying seed-water relationships.

It seems likely that subtle differences in seed shape and surface interacting with subtle variations in the structure of the soil surface may influence both the abundance of particular species and the balance between species. Unfortunately techniques are not available for the direct measurement of the physical properties of the minutely varying soil environment. The subsequent paper in this series analyses the behaviour of seeds in laboratory models on which the soil micro-environment of seeds may be rigidly controlled.

One feature of special interest concerns the manner in which plant population may be regulated. It is commonly argued that the regulation of densities of organisms must be by density-dependent processes (see for example, discussion by Haldane, 1963), in which increasing density is responsible for reducing the chance of individual survival. In many of the model populations examined in this paper, the number of individuals becoming established is a direct function of the number of suitable or "safe" microsites provided on the soil surface and a maximum population size is therefore determined directly by the physical environment. When the number of "safe sites" is limited, the chance of a seed producing a plant will be reduced as the density of sowing is increased—giving the spurious impression that density is causal in controlling establishment. A suitable analogy is found in the sampling of an egg cup full of beans from a sack of beans—the sample is independent of the number of beans in the sack above a critical value (only the leftovers are density-dependent).

A further point of significance in these experimental results lies in the differential response of species to the configuration of microsites. Apparently the numbers of two species establishing from seed on a soil surface may be independently determined, because of different requirements of the seeds for suitable micro-environments for germination. Such factors may need to be taken into account in analysing fluctuations in natural populations and in accounting for the ability of several species to cohabit successfully within the same area.

Summary

Seeds of different species differ in their requirements for conditions suitable for germination. The varied micro-environments provided on a soil surface act selectively on mixed seed populations and determine the numbers of "safe" germination sites. Experiments involved placing various objects, or making depressions, on soil surfaces on which seed had been sown, and of creating artificial soil surfaces of varied microtopography.

Species used in the experiments were *Plantago lanceolata, P. major, P. media, Bromus rigidus, B. madritensis, Chenopodium album* and *Brassica oleracea acephala.*

A ten-point frame was used to obtain a measure of soil microtopography. It is argued that the availability of suitable microsites on a soil surface may offer a means by which the numbers of plants establishing from seed is regulated and the relative abundance of different species is determined.

References

Haldane, J. B. S. (1953). Animal populations and their regulation. *New Biol.* 15: 9–24.

Hammerton, J. L. (1961). Studies of the effects of soil aggregate size on the emergence and growth of beet. *J. agric. Sci., Camb.* 56: 213–28.

Harper, J. L., Clatworthy, J. N., McNaughton, I. H. and Sagar, G. R. (1961). The evolution and ecology of closely related species living in the same area. *Evolution, Lancaster, Pa.* 15: 209–27.

James T. Tanner

Effects of Population Density on Growth Rates of Animal Populations

Introduction

Changes in size of animal populations usually follow seasonal and other variations in the environment. An important question is: Are these changes determined solely by the environment, or does the density of the population itself affect these changes? This study aimed at determining the relation between the rate at which a population grows or declines and the population density. Two approaches were used: 1) an examination of mathematical models of populations and 2) an analysis of the records of many different animal populations. In the second approach, data were obtained from the literature and statistically analyzed to test whether the growth rate of each population was or was not a function of population density.

The change in numbers of a population with respect to time, dN/dt, equals rn, where N is the number in the population and r is the rate of change per unit of population; $r = dN/Ndt$. For conciseness r will hereafter be called a population's "growth rate," even though it can measure a decrease as well as an increase in population size. The growth rate equals the conventional birth rate (number born per unit population per time) minus the death rate (number died per unit population per time), and the growth rate will be positive, negative, or zero depending on the relative values of its two components.

If r is a positive constant, the population will grow exponentially; if it is a negative constant, the population will decline exponentially; and if it is zero, the size will not change. Since populations never do any of these for an indefinitely long period, the value of r must vary from time to time. If its value is determined solely by the environment, r is independent of the population density. Otherwise r is some function of the population density. If r is a decreasing function of density, declining as the density increases as in Fig. 1A, and if the environment is relatively stable for a sufficiently long time, the popu-

Reprinted by permission of the author and publisher from *Ecology, 47:* 733–745, 1966. This research was completed while the author was working in the Radiation Ecology Section, Health Physics Division, Oak Ridge National Laboratory, and he thanks members of this section who helped clarify many of the ideas expressed in this paper. Most of the statistical calculations were performed by the Mathematics Panel at Oak Ridge.

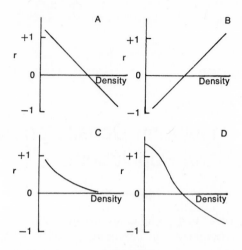

Figure 1

Graphs of r, population growth rate (r = dN/Ndt) as a function of population density. A. r is a decreasing linear function of density; B. r is an increasing linear function of density; C. r is a decreasing nonlinear function of density, found in growing Daphnia populations (Smith 1963b); D. r is a decreasing nonlinear function of density, from the reproduction curves of Ricker (1954).

lation will stabilize at the density where r is zero (or if there is a time lag, that is if r is determined by the density at some previous time, the population will oscillate about the central density). If r is an increasing function of density, as in Fig. 1B, the populations will increase to infinity or decline to extinction, again assuming that r is not changed by environmental changes.

Rates in Mathematical Models

Mathematical models for animal populations present the population size, N, as a function of time, or the derivative of this with respect to time, dN/dt. The growth rate of the population, r, equals this derivative divided by N. The relation between r and N in these equations can be determined by differentiating r with respect to N. If the resulting derivative is negative, r is a decreasing function of N (Fig. 1A); if it is positive, r is an increasing function (Fig. 1B); if it is zero, r is independent of N. The only models examined here are those which have been found to describe the changes in actual populations.

The logistic equation, widely used in population studies, is discussed by Allee, Emerson, Park, Park and Schmidt (1949, Ch. 21), who give numerous examples of this equation fitted to the growth of actual populations. The derivative, dr/dN, of the logistic equation is negative, showing that the growth rate decreases with increasing N, as in Fig. 1A. Several persons (Gause and Witt, 1935; Smith, 1963b) have modified the logistic for one reason or another, but in these modified forms r remains a decreasing function of N.

Neyman, Park, and Scott (1958) constructed mathematical models for *Tribolium* populations based on extensive experiments in rearing these beetles; one model is for the numbers of a species living alone and another consists of two equations for two species of *Tribolium* living together. Nicholson and Bailey (1935) developed equations for the numbers of a host and its parasite; the first part of the oscillating curve predicted by these equations was followed by seven generations of a host-parasite population (DeBach and Smith, 1941). In all of these equations the derivative of the growth rate with respect to numbers is negative. Utida (1957b) presented different equations which predicted the course of his oscillating host-parasite populations. The derivative for the parasite population is negative; that for the host population is positive or negative depending upon conditions other than the density of the host.

In summary, in mathematical models which have been shown to parallel the changes of actual populations, the derivative of r with respect to N is usually negative, i.e., the growth rate is a decreasing function of the density.

Rates in Animal Populations

Objective of Analysis

Few persons have appraised the direct effect of population density on population growth rates. Errington (1945, 1954) plotted per cent gain in Bobwhite and muskrat (scientific names are listed in Appendix B) populations as a function of density and obtained curves showing smaller rates of increase with higher densities. Smith (1961, 1963a) found that in populations of thrips the growth rate over a month was negatively correlated with the population density at the start of the month. He also (1963a) showed that cultured *Daphnia* populations possessed growth rates that were nonlinear decreasing functions of density.

For this part of the study, I obtained from the literature the records of many different animal populations, calculated the growth rates from the recorded numbers, and tested the hypothesis that these rates were independent of the population densities.

Methods of Analysis

A population record consists of a series of numbers, N_0, N_1, ... N_t, ... At time t the population size is N_t and its growth rate is r_t, which may be positive, negative, or zero. Expressing this rate in terms of the observed change in number, ΔN, over the period between successive numbers Δt,

$$r_t = \frac{1}{N_t} \cdot \frac{\Delta N}{\Delta t} . \tag{1}$$

Let $\Delta t = 1$, which can be done if the population was censused at regular intervals, then

$$r_t = \frac{N_{t+1} - N_t}{N_t} = \frac{N_{t+1}}{N_t} - 1. \tag{2}$$

Therefore r_t is determined by the relation between N_t and N_{t+1}. This relation needs to be examined to evaluate the effects of random variations in the data on the estimation of r_t.

N_{t+1} must be some function of N_t and the environmental conditions, which will vary with time. The nature of the function relating N_{t+1} to N_t and E_t, the environmental conditions affecting population growth at time t, is unknown, but to fit some biological facts the function has the following constraints: 1) if $N_t = O$, $N_{t+1} = O$; 2) an increase in N_{t+1} over N_t must have an upper limit which is a function of N_t, because the capacity for increase is limited; 3) a decrease cannot exceed N_t in absolute value, because a population cannot go below zero.

A function of the following form meets the above conditions:

$$N_{t+1} = bN_t \, [f(N_t, E_t)]; \, b > O,$$
$$O \leqq f(N_t, E_t) \leqq 1. \tag{3}$$

The function in brackets, $f(N_t \, E_t)$, denotes the interaction of numbers and environment. Because of random variation in the environment, variation independent of N_t, the successive values of this function will have some random variation. In the extreme case this entire function may vary independently of N_t; i.e., the coefficient of N_t in $f(N_t, E_t)$ may be zero. Then for a given value of N_t, $f(O, E_t)$ will have an expected value denoted by $E(f)$ which is estimated by the mean value of $f(O, E_t)$. Under these conditions the expected value of N_{t+1},

$$E(N_{t+1}) = bN_t \, [E(f)] = bN_t \, \overline{[f(O, E_t]}. \tag{4}$$

Substitution of equation (3) in equation (2) shows that the relation between r_t and population density is determined by $f(N_t \, E_t)$, the interaction of numbers and environment. Substitution of equation (4) in equation (2) shows that, when there is no interaction between numbers and environment, r_t will vary about its expected or mean value independent of population density.

Finally, it is possible for the successive values of N to be like a series of random numbers, with no correlation between N_t and N_{t+1}. This may occur because of large and random errors in estimating population size or because the intervals between counts were so long that numerous intervening events destroyed any correlation between successive counts. If the successive values of N are like a series of random numbers, r_t as determined by equation (2) will be a decreasing function of N_t. The proof of this is presented by Watt (1964). Therefore, to avoid obtaining fallacious results from a random series, it is necessary to check each population record to insure that the successive values are correlated and therefore that N_{t+1} is some function of N_t. Each series of population counts examined in this study was tested for nonrandomness by the method of runs. Those in which the probability of randomness was not less than 5% were eliminated.

The preceding arguments lead to the conclusion that a record of a population, N_0, N_1, ... N_t, ..., can be used to calculate the population's rate of growth for each interval, by equation (2), and that the relation between growth rate and population density may be determined statistically if the following three conditions are met: 1) N_t and N_{t+1} are correlated; 2) the population was censused at constant intervals so Δt can have the value 1; and 3) the counts, censuses, or estimates reflect the actual density of the population.

From the population record will be obtained a series of r_t and N_t, of growth rates for each interval and of numbers or density at the beginning of that interval. It would be logical to consider r_t as a function of N_t and to use regression methods to test the nature of this function. Regression methods, however, assume that the independent variable (N_t in this case) is known or measured without error, and this certainly is not true for many population records. By contrast, calculation of a correlation coefficient does not require that one variable be free of error, and therefore correlation is preferable to regression in this analysis.

The correlation coefficient is applicable only when the two variables are linearly related or approximately so. Smith (1963b) found that in Daphnia populations r is the nonlinear function of density shown in Figure 1C. Ricker (1954) postulated a series of reproduction curves for different animals; from the curves which he considered to best fit the data from actual populations can be constructed the relation between r and density shown in Fig. 1D. Both of these curves can be satisfactorily approximated by straight lines. After the computations had been completed, I read the paper by Morris (1963) in which he stated that, at least for the insect populations he studied, log N_{t+1} is a linear function of log N_t. If this is so, then log $(r_t + 1)$ is a linear function of log N_t and a correlation coefficient of these logarithms would be larger than one using actual values. To test this, seven population records, whose correlation coefficients based on actual values were not quite large enough to be significantly different from zero, were analyzed using logarithms. The resulting correlation coefficients were larger by an average of 13%, but in only one case, that of the Fulmar, was the improvement great enough to produce a coefficient significantly different from zero. The correlation coefficients reported in Table 1 for these seven populations were calculated using logarithms; they are identified by the symbol "a." The above considerations justify the use of the correlation coefficient for testing the relation between growth rate and population density.

If two or more population records of the same species are available, the best estimate of the correlation can be obtained by calculating a joint correlation coefficient, as follows. First, since the growth rate is expected to be related to the density of each population, each N_t was divided by the average size of

Table 1

Populations Subjected to Correlation Analysis, the Correlation Coefficient (Between r_t and Population Density), and Results of Tests of Significance on the Correlation Coefficient

Columns A: Nature of population and source of data. See Appendix B for scientific names; B: Number of populations combined; C: Average size of population(s); D: Interval between counts or measurements; E: Number of intervals (avarage number if two or more populations have been combined); F: Correlation coefficient; *, calculated from logarithms; see text for discussion. G: Level of significance; the probability is less than this figure that the null hypothesis (correlation coefficient equals zero) is true; [b], see also further analysis in text and Table 2.

A	B	C	D	E	F	G
Herbivore mite in culture (Huffaker 1958)	4	2,586	5 day	30	-.5030	0.001
Predatory mite in culture (Huffaker 1958)	1	17	5 day	30	-.4350	0.02
Daphnia magna in cultures (Pratt 1943)	1	41	4 day	53	-.3252	0.02
Daphnia obtusa in cultures (Slobodkin 1954)	2	284	10 day	29	-.5553	0.001
Thrips in roses in garden (Davidson and Andrewartha 1948)	1	352	1 month	80	-.1489	0.20[b]
Florida wax scale on citrus leaves (Bodenheimer 1958)	1	322	1 month	95	-.0635	0.50[b]
Chaff scale on citrus leaves (Bodenheimer 1958)	1	282	1 month	87	-.4246	0.001
Bordered white moth pupae hibernating in forest floor (Varley 1949)	1	1,214	1 yr	59	-.1564	0.30[b]
Pine spinner moth larvae hibernating in forest floor (Varley 1949)	1	672	1 yr	59	-.0848	0.50[b]
Pine hawk moth pupae hibernating in forest floor (Varley 1949)	1	38	1 yr	49	-.1451	0.40[b]
Pine beauty moth larvae hibernating in forest floor (Varley 1949)	1	43	1 yr	59	-.1379	0.30[b]
Rice weevil in culture (Birch 1953)	2	533	4 week	23	-.7221	0.001
Bean weevil in culture (Utida 1957a)	1	382	1 generation	111	-.4260	0.001
Red flour beetle in culture (Park and Frank 1950)	1	157	30 day	68	-.3686	0.01
Confused flour beetle in culture (Park et al. 1941; Park and Frank 1950)	2	1,361	30 day	43	-.3796	0.001
Parasitic wasp in culture (Utida 1957a)	1	358	1 generation	111	-.4282	0.001
Sheep blowfly in culture (Nicholson 1954)	1	2,544	2 day	132	-.1705[a]	0.10
Housefly in culture (Pimentel et al. 1963)	1	4	7 day	82	-.1746	0.20
Sewage fly in sewage beds (Lloyd 1943)	1	1,703	1 month	79	-.3139	0.01
Atlantic salmon weight of catch (Allee et al. 1949)	1	(56,300 pounds)	1 yr	63	-.3520	0.01
Lake trout abundance index based on fisheries catch (Eschmeyer 1957)	1	(2,218,000 pounds)	1 yr	25	+.4385	0.10
Goldeye abundance index based on fisheries catch (Smith & Krefting 1954)	1	(66,659 pounds)	1 yr	23	-.2371	0.30
Northern pike abundance index based on fisheries catch (Smith & Krefting 1954)	1	(39,100 pounds)	1 yr	23	-.4313	0.05
Yellow perch abundance index based on fisheries catch (Smith & Krefting 1954)	1	(212,365 pounds)	1 yr	23	-.4553	0.05
Walleye abundance index based on fisheries catch (Pycha 1961)	1	(258,034 pounds)	1 yr	28	-.5044	0.01
Freshwater drum abundance index based on fisheries catch (Smith & Krefting 1954)	1	(17,108 pounds)	1 yr	23	-.2538	0.30
Fulmar breeding birds in Britain (Fisher 1952)	1	23,000	5 yr	14	-.5622[a]	0.05
Gannet estimated world population (Fisher and Vevers 1944)	1	102,600	5 yr	24	-.3060[a]	0.20

Census (source)						
Heron nesting birds (Lack 1953)	3	423	1 yr	19	−.3743	0.01
Stork nesting birds (Lack 1954)	1	342	1 yr	24	−.0572	0.80
Ruffed Grouse census in habitat (Hickey 1955; 1944)	2	278	1 yr	30	−.2579	0.05
Red Grouse game bag records (Mackenzie 1952; Middleton 1934)	6	1,387	1 yr	66	−.3624	0.001
Sharp-tailed Grouse census in habitat (Hickey 1955)	1	28	1 yr	34	−.3800	0.05
Prairie Chicken counts of displaying males (Shelford and Yeatter 1955)	1	66	1 yr	17	−.4569[a]	0.10
Partridge game bag records; breeding birds (Middleton 1934; Severtzoff 1934)	4	1,010	1 yr	86	−.3315	0.001
Pheasant introduced population (Lack 1954)	1	405	1 yr	5	−.8411	0.10
Pied Flycatcher breeding population (Lack 1954)	1	66	1 yr	9	−.7407	0.05
Coal Tit breeding population (Kluyver 1951)	1	20	1 yr	31	−.4608	0.01
Blue Tit breeding population (Kluyver 1951)	1	27	1 yr	31	−.5805	0.001
Crested Tit breeding population (Kluyver 1951)	1	10	1 yr	31	−.4560	0.02
House Wren breeding bird census (Kendeigh 1944; Kendeigh et al. 1948–63)	2	41	1 yr	24	−.5448	0.001
Wood Thrush breeding bird census (Williams 1947–50)	1	29	1 yr	18	−.4581	0.10
Starling breeding bird census (Kendeigh 1944; Kendeigh et al. 1948–63)	1	51	1 yr	23	−.2419	0.30[b]
Red-eyed Vireo breeding bird census (Kendeigh 1944; Kendeigh et al. 1948–63; Williams 1947–50)	2	38	1 yr	20	−.3542	0.05
Indigo Bunting breeding bird census (Kendeigh 1944; Kendeigh et al. 1948–63)	2	44	1 yr	23	−.4991	0.02
Wolverine fur yields (Buckley 1954)	1	311	1 yr	41	−.2915[a]	0.10
Fisher fur yields (Keith 1962)	2	860	1 yr	38	−.5402	0.001
Mink fur yields (Keith 1962)	1	10,570	1 yr	43	−.0773	0.70
Weasel game bag returns (Middleton 1934)	2	198	1 yr	49	−.4596	0.001
Arctic fox fur yields (Buckley 1954)	1	4,772	1 yr	41	−.4266	0.01
Coyote fur yields (Keith 1962)	2	18,600	1 yr	34	−.4106	0.001
Wolf fur yields (Buckley 1954)	1	325	1 yr	41	−.3209	0.05
Gray fox bounty records (Richmond 1952)	1	8,724	1 yr	34	−.2511[a]	0.20
Colored fox fur yields (Keith 1962)	1	7,927	1 yr	36	−.2884[a]	0.20
Lynx fur yields (Buckley 1954; Elton and Nicholson 1942b; Keith 1962)	1	1,932	1 yr	55	−.2149	0.001
Fur seal census on breeding grounds (Scheffer 1955)	5	547,300	1 yr	19	−.6040	0.01
Levant vole census in habitat (Bodenheimer 1958)	1	8	1 month	82	−.1227	0.30
Muskrat census in habitat, fur yields (Buckley 1954; Elton and Nicholson 1942a; Errington 1954, 1957; Keith 1962)	1	207,379	1 yr	48	−.1983	0.001
Snowshoe hare fur yields (Lack 1954; MacLulich 1957)	6	112,682	1 yr	37	−.2504	0.05
European hare game bag records (Middleton 1934)	2	209	1 yr	80	−.4602	0.001
European rabbit game bag records (Middleton 1934)	2	5,071	1 yr	66	−.3224	0.001
Reindeer introduced population (Scheffer 1951)	2	302	1 yr	30	−.3578	0.01
Pronghorn census in habitats (Shelford 1954)	2	545	1 yr	18	−.5606	0.02
Human population of the world (various sources)	1	844 × 10⁹	50 yr	6	+.8815	0.05

Note: The following censuses were eliminated from the analysis because the series of counts were not significantly different from a series of random numbers: Clams in ocean beach (Coe 1957). Broad-horned flour beetle in culture (Park et al. 1941). Granary beetle in culture (Park et al. 1941). Lake trout fisheries catch (Fry 1949). Walleye fisheries catch (Smith and Krefting 1954). Bobwhite Quail census in habitat (Errington 1957). Ruffed Grouse census in New Jersey habitat (Hickey 1955). Great Tit breeding population (Kluyver 1951). Ovenbird breeding bird census (Williams 1947–50). Hooded Warbler breeding bird census (Williams 1947–50). Arctic fox fur yields (Elton 1942). Mink fur yields (Buckley 1934).

population; dividing by the area inhabited would have been better but this was usually unknown, and the area inhabited should be directly proportional to the average population size. Second, the sums of cross-products and of squares used in calculating the joint correlation coefficient involved the deviations from the separate means of each population.

In this study, a correlation coefficient was calculated for the paired variables, r_t and N_t, of each population record (or a joint correlation coefficient for two or more records of the same species). The null hypothesis that the correlation coefficient is zero was tested. If the null hypothesis was accepted, r_t was considered to be independent of N_t. If the null hypothesis was rejected, r_t was identified as a decreasing function of N_t if the correlation coefficient was negative, or an increasing function if the coefficient was positive.

Sources of Data

The data were obtained from censuses of animal populations that met the following requirements: 1) actual counts of a population inhabiting a definite space so that density was directly proportional to the number, or a reliable index of the density of the population; 2) counts or estimates made periodically so that the growth rates were based on constant intervals (Δt); 3) a sufficiently long series of such counts to enable a meaningful test despite random variations.

About half of the populations reported in Table 1 were censused. For the remainder an index of density was available. This index for the fish populations was calculated from the annual commercial catch corrected for variations in fishing intensity. Fur returns were used as indexes of density for some northern mammals; Keith (1962) gave reasons for believing that these were valid indexes of density when the returns came from constant geographic areas where fur prices had not failed. Hunting kill statistics were not considered to be a reliable index of density because of variations in hunting pressure with periods of war, changing economic conditions, and changing recreational habits. Exceptions to this were some bag records made on British game preserves which had been managed intensively for decades; Keith (1962) believed that these were reliable indexes of density. Fur returns from the Hudson Bay Company and game bag records for some British preserves supplied the longest series of records for this study.

I found records of 111 populations, representing 71 species, that met the requirements of this study.

Results and Discussion of Results

The results of the correlation analyses are presented in Table 1. For each species the table contains information on the populations, on the censuses or other measurements, and on the correlation coefficient. The probability of the results under the null hypothesis (the correlation coefficient equalling zero) is in the last column. The populations eliminated because their records were not significantly different from a series of random numbers are listed at the end of the table.

The results in Table 1 were obtained by using each entire population record without regard to changes in the environment. If different periods of a population's existence possessed distinctly different environmental conditions known to affect reproduction and survival, a better estimate of the correlation between growth rate and density can be made by a joint correlation coefficient, in which the deviations are measured from the means for the different conditions. This was done for two species, thrips and Starling. The number of thrips (Davidson and Andrewartha, 1948) increased each year to a high level during the Australian spring and then dropped to a low level during approximately 10 months of drouth and low temperatures. The Starling population inhabited an area where the death of many trees beginning about the 16th year of the series (Kendeigh, 1956) produced many more nesting sites and a period of relative abundance of these birds. The joint correlation coefficients for these two species and their significance are shown in Table 2; they are very significantly different

Table 2

Species Analyzed During Their Periods of Abundance and Scarcity, or During Periods of Scarcity Only

See Table 1 for more information. Columns A: Species; B: Number of intervals; C: Correlation coefficient; D: Level of significance

A	B	C	D
Joint correlation coefficient calculated from periods of abundance and of scarcity:			
Thrips	67	−.4277	0.001
Starling	22	−.7609	0.001
Correlation coefficient calculated only from periods of scarcity:			
Florida wax scale	60	−.2841	0.05
Bordered white moth	27	−.5202	0.01
Pine spinner moth	42	−.2726	0.01
Pine hawk moth	26	−.2968	0.20
Pine beauty moth	30	−.5580	0.01

from zero although the correlation coefficients (in Table 1) calculated without regard to periods of abundance and scarcity are not so. This procedure can be justified only when there is direct evidence of environmental changes.

Another situation requiring separate analysis is that of the five species of insects listed in the lower part of Table 2. Populations of these five species are similar in that they occasionally erupt, becoming very abundant for short periods after which the numbers fall to low levels for comparatively longer periods. The calculations made for Table 1, using the entire population record irrespective of population level, indicate a growth rate independent of density. The results are different, however, when the population record of each of these species was divided into periods of scarcity and abundance, and the correlation analysis was conducted only on the data from the long periods of scarcity. The results are shown in Table 2; four of the five correlation coefficients from periods of scarcity are negative and significantly different from zero.

The results of Tables 1 and 2 are summarized in Table 3. Of the 64 species

Table 3

Summary of Results in Tables 1 and 2

Columns A: Total number of species; B: Number of species eliminated because the population record was not significantly different from a random series; C: Correlation coefficient not significantly different from zero, probability of the null hypothesis exceeding 0.05; D: Coefficient positive and significantly different from zero; E: Coefficient negative and significantly different from zero

Category	A	B	C	D	E
Invertebrates other than insects	5	1	—	—	4
Insects	17	2	3	—	12
Fish	7	—	3	—	4
Birds	23	4	5	—	14
Mammals	19	—	5	1ᵃ	13
Totals	71	7	16	1	47

ᵃ The human population of the world.

remaining after 7 were eliminated because their population records were not different from a random series, 47 species had coefficients that were significantly different from zero and were negative. Only one, the human population of the world, which has been increasing at a greater rate with the increase in population density, has a coefficient that is significantly positive. Furthermore, of the 16 species for which the correlation coefficient did not differ significantly from zero, only one did not have a negative estimated value (see Table 1). Population rates of change are usually, therefore, a decreasing function of population density; as can be seen from Table 3, this conclusion applies to animals which are taxonomically very different.

Changes Between Spring and Fall

Spring and fall censuses over a number of years were made for the four species listed in Table 4, enabling a test of whether or not the population rate of change is a function of density during a period of increase, from spring to fall, and during a decrease, from fall to spring. The procedure is the same as that described for equation (2) except that, when considering spring to fall changes, N_t becomes the number in spring and N_{t+1} the number the following fall; there is a parallel procedure in studying fall to spring changes.

The results of the correlation analyses are shown in Table 4. For the muskrat, the coefficient was negative and significantly different from zero for both seasons. For the three bird species, the coefficients were significantly negative for the spring to fall changes, but for the fall to spring changes the coefficients are not significantly different from zero. Possible explanations for these differences are discussed in the following section.

Table 4

Results Based on Spring and Fall Censuses of Wild Populations

Columns A: Species and source of data; B: Number of populations combined; C: Average size of spring population(s); D: Number of intervals (average number for the six muskrat populations); E: Correlation coefficient; F: Level of significance; the probability is less than this figure that the null hypothesis (correlation coefficient equals zero) is true

			Spring to Fall			Fall to Spring		
A	B	C	D	E	F	D	E	F
Bobwhite Quail (Errington, 1957)	1	145	17	−.7842	0.001	18	−.0241	0.40
Ring-necked Pheasant (Lack, 1954)	1	405	6	−.8433	0.05	5	+.5666	0.40
Ruffed Grouse (Bump et al., 1947)	1	117	13	−.5781	0.05	12	−.4521	0.20
Muskrat (Errington, 1954, 1957)	6	283	16	−.2717	0.02	15	−.3821	0.001

Causes of Population Changes

The analyses just described have shown that in most of the species tested the population growth rate is a decreasing function of density. Different ways of saying the same are 1) that as a population increases, its growth rate decreases, or if it is declining the negative rate increases toward zero, so that a curve depicting its rise or fall will flatten as it approaches a certain level; or 2) that as a population becomes more dense the probability of a further increase becomes less and that of a decrease becomes greater, and vice versa. The net result is that population numbers tend to remain stable, rarely increasing to excessive numbers and rarely decreasing to extinction. It is true that many animal populations in constant environments do fluctuate in size, but fluctuation within limits is a degree of stabilization. Many fluctuations or oscillations of animal populations result from a delay or time lag in the response of growth rate to density (Frank, 1960; Wangersky and Cunningham, 1957).

My purpose now is to discuss the causes of population change, or the processes that affect the size of a population, to determine which are responsible for the growth rate being a decreasing function of density.

I am avoiding the use of the term "density-dependent factor" which has been used frequently in connection with this subject but with different meanings by different ecologists; see Macfadyen (1963, p. 152 to 157) for a review of the literature concerning this term. The phrase "increasing (or decreasing) function of density" is explicit and is used here for any change whose rate increases (or decreases) with increasing population density, and for the processes causing such a change. The term "density-independent" is used in the absence of any relation between rate and density.

The growth rate equals the birth rate minus the death rate. If the growth rate is a decreasing function of density and only the birth rate varies, the birth rate must also be a decreasing function of density. Ecologists often assume that each species has a potential reproductive rate determined by its physiology and life history, and that environmental factors reduce the actual rate to something below the potential. These factors reducing the birth rate at higher densities must then be operating as increasing functions of density. If, on the other hand, only variations in the death rate are producing the changes in the growth rate, death rates are increasing with greater population density and so must the effectiveness of the processes producing the mortality. In summary, the growth rate is usually a decreasing function of density, but the causes of population change operate as increasing functions of density.

The statistical analyses of population changes do not give any clue as to which processes are producing the changes, except that in three bird species (Table 4) changes that were functions of density occurred only between spring and fall and therefore the processes must be confined to that season. The most frequently suggested processes that may operate as increasing functions of density are competition, predation, and disease.

Competition results when the supply of some resource is inadequate for the population, or if interference or struggle for a common resource results in harm to individuals. Competition is obviously an increasing function of density. Examples of scarcity of a resource, usually food, limiting a population, lowering fertility, or increasing mortality are many (Andrewartha and Birch, 1954, p. 368 to 376; Andrewartha and Browning, 1961; Armstrong, 1964; Gibb, 1960; Klomp, 1964; Lack, 1954, Ch. 7 and 11; Slobodkin, 1954). Among vertebrates, competition for food frequently results in higher mortality of juvenile individuals rather than of adults; examples of this are known for fish (Beverton, 1962; Ivlev, 1961), for owls (Southern, 1959), for voles (Hoffmann, 1958), and for deer (Leopold, Sowls, and Spencer, 1947).

Individuals of some species defend a territory against encroachment by other individuals, and in these territorial species the amount of suitable habitat may be a limiting resource. Examples of vertebrates where the size of the breeding population appears limited by the number of suitable territories are Golden Eagles (Brown and Watson, 1964), Red Grouse (Jenkins, 1963), Titmice (Kluyver and Tinbergen, 1953), Chaffinches (Glas, 1960), Song Sparrows (Tompa, 1962), several bird species nesting in the spruce-fir forest (Hensley and Cope, 1951; Stewart and Aldrich, 1951), and muskrats (Errington, 1946). Dragonflies (Odonata) offer one example of this phenomenon in insects (Moore, 1964).

The amount of suitable habitat for a territorial species may limit the population in another way. Errington (1946, 1956) has shown that in muskrats mortality from predation is much higher among individuals that fail to establish themselves in a suitable territory than among territory holders. Mortality is also higher in Red Grouse that do not obtain territories in suitable habitats (Jenkins, 1963; Jenkins, Watson, and Miller, 1963).

The information included in Table 4 is consistent with the hypothesis that the populations of these four species are regulated by competition, either by territoriality determining the size of the breeding population or by competition for food and perhaps other resources determining the survival of the juveniles. The growth rate for the three bird species was a decreasing function of density only during the period from spring to fall; it was density-independent for the rest of the year when no reproduction was occurring and when these birds do not hold territories. Muskrats hold territories the year around; Errington (1946) stated that mortality is heaviest in juveniles that are unable to establish territories because suitable habitats are preempted by older animals.

Interference between individuals affects population growth, as is illustrated by the following examples. Allee et al. (1949, p. 349 to 352) summarize the detrimental effects of interference on the reproductive rates of a few species of insects. The food intake of individual fishes in a crowded situation decreased because of interference from others, fright, or actual fighting (Ivlev, 1961, Ch. 5). Titmice fought over food most often in midwinter when they spent the greatest proportion of their time searching for food (Gibb, 1954). As a result of stress from increased social contacts with increasing population density, the birth rate of rodents and hares decreased, the mortality of infant rodents increased because of failure of lactation, and sexual maturity was delayed (Christian, 1963; Christian and Davis, 1964).

Predation is a cause of mortality that may be an increasing function of density under some conditions and density-independent or even a decreasing function under others. Holling (1961), in a review of the effects of predation on insect numbers, concluded that the number of prey killed per predator generally increases with prey density, until prey density becomes so great that either the predators are satiated or the prey obtains protection from the large group; predation may therefore be an increasing function of density at low prey densities and a decreasing function at high densities. Holling's conclusions are supported by studies of predation on insects by birds made by Buckner and Turnock (1965), Gibb (1962), Tinbergen (1960), and Tinbergen and Klomp (1960).

The role of predation among vertebrates appears to be more complex. Errington (1946, 1956) was convinced that in territorial species those individuals that failed to establish good territories were removed by predation, which therefore removed only the surplus, but in nonterritorial species whose behavior allows crowding, predation may determine the size of the population. Deer are nonterritorial species and deer populations were at least originally controlled by predators, as all overpopulations of deer in the United States followed, and none preceded, the disappearance of large predators or the initiation of predator control (Leopold, Sowls, and Spencer, 1947).

The effects of predation on populations of small mammals were studied by Craighead and Craighead (1956) on an area in Michigan for two fall and winter seasons. Their published results do not contain an estimate of the mortality rate due to predation, but from some of their data I have estimated this rate for four species of small mammals preyed upon by nine species of hawks and owls; mammalian predators appeared to be insignificant. Appendix A describes the method of estimating the rate. Table 5 summarizes the results.

Table 5
Rates of Mortality Due to Predation by Nine Species of Hawks and Owls During Fall and Winter

| | Prey Species | | | |
Period and Statistic	Meadow vole	White-footed mouse	Cotton-tail rabbit	Fox squirrel
1941–42				
Population	303,000	33,000	300	300
Lost by predation	55,600	8,066	162	10
Predation rate	0.184	0.244	0.540	0.033
1947–48				
Population	75,000	27,000	1,200	1,000
Lost by predation	13,500	6,200	234	11
Predation rate	0.180	0.230	0.195	0.011

Estimated from the data of Craighead and Craighead (1956).

Large mouse populations were present in the 1941–42 fall and winter, smaller numbers in the 1947–48 season. The rate of mortality due to predation on the two species of mice was about the same for each year, or density-independent. The rabbit and fox squirrel populations were, on the other hand, lowest in 1941–42 but suffered the higher mortality rate from predation this year; for these two species predation was a decreasing function of density. The obvious reason for this is that the large numbers of mice present in 1941–42 attracted to the area many more hawks and owls than normal, and this increased the probability of an attack upon an individual rabbit or squirrel.

The results presented in Table 4 show that for the three bird species the rates of population decline from fall to spring were independent of population density. Since predation probably was responsible for most of this decline, it apparently operated as a density-independent cause of mortality.

Young or juvenile individuals are more likely to be killed by predators than are adults. Beverton (1962) concluded that populations of plaice are regulated by varying mortality from starvation and predation of the larval fish. Murie (1944) reported that predation on caribou and Dall sheep was concentrated on young animals.

Cannibalism is a special case of predation, resembling competition in that the process is intraspecific. It appears to be an increasing function of density in flour beetles, *Tribolium* (Allee et al., 1949, p. 370 to 371; Neyman, Park, and Scott, 1958), and it is at least an important cause of mortality in planarian worms (Armstrong, 1964). Ricker (1954) discusses the hypothetical effects of cannibalism on population size.

Mortality due to parasites or disease is an increasing function of density for insects and does regulate population size according to ⁼Macfadyen (1963, p. 263). Neilson and Morris (1964) report evidence for parasites and disease being primarily responsible for the regulation of an insect population. For birds and mammals, however, Lack (1954) believes that disease is with few exceptions not a cause of mortality increasing with density. The evidence for both of these conclusions was obtained from a few cases, and the conclusions may not have general validity. Disease often follows starvation, and then starvation should be considered the primary cause of mortality.

There are two other possible mechanisms for regulating population size, although few observations and measurements pertain to either. The secretion of substances into the environment which inhibit the activities of other organisms would have results similar to those of competition; this subject is briefly reviewed by Rose (1960). Wynne-Edwards (1962) describes a number of behavior patterns which he suggests can reduce reproductive rates in dense populations.

Some tentative conclusions can now be made. The statistical analyses have shown that usually a population's growth rate is a decreasing function of population density, and that this will result in regulation of its numbers. The mechanisms of this process are clear for some kinds of animals: herbivorous insects and some vertebrates.

Herbivorous insects are normally regulated by disease, parasites, and predators. When favorable conditions for reproduction and survival exist, the numbers of insects may increase so rapidly as to "escape" their predators and parasites and an outbreak occurs. The peak population is subdued by the favorable period ending or by parasites and disease overtaking the dense population. This hypothesis is supported by the results presented in Table 2, showing that only the low or "normal" levels of these herbivorous insects had population growth rates which were decreasing functions of density.

In vertebrates, the processes controlling population size are different between nonterritorial and territorial species. Nonterritorial species like fish and deer are normally regulated by predation on juvenile individuals. When this fails, as when predators of deer are removed by man, competition for food becomes important, and in deer and probably in fish, this results in starvation of younger individuals. In small rodents and possibly in hares, population regulation results from lowered reproductive rates produced by endocrine disturbances stimulated by overcrowding. The numbers of territorial species are determined by competition for suitable territories. Those that fail to obtain territories, usually immature individuals, are not able to reproduce and are the first to be eliminated by predation or starvation. It is significant that the processes known to regulate vertebrate populations affect either reproduction or the survival of juveniles; adults are relatively exempt from these processes, but the production of young adults is regulated.

Hairston, Smith, and Slobodkin (1960) inferred from some obvious facts that populations of herbivores are generally controlled by predators and those of predators by competition. This generalization is supported only in part by my conclusions presented above. Although herbivorous insects and some herbivorous mammals are normally controlled by predators or parasites, competition is important for territorial herbivores like muskrat and Red Grouse and also in some rodents whose reproductive rate falls with increased crowding.

Competition through the mechanism of territoriality does seem the regulating mechanism in predaceous birds and mammals, which compose by far the majority of species known to be territorial.

APPENDIX A. Calculation of Predation Rate

Data published in the book by Craighead and Craighead (1956) were used to calculate the mortality rates due to avian predators shown in Table 5. Because this calculation involved drawing data from scattered parts of the book, and because the conclusion drawn from Table 5 does not agree with their conclusion (p. 309) that the predation observed tended to regulate the prey populations, the procedure I used is here outlined. Table and page numbers cited below refer to Craighead and Craighead (1956).
Let:

W_r, grams of food consumed by each species of raptor during fall and winter (from Table 90).

w_s, average individual weight for each prey species (from Table 100).

n_{sr}, number of individuals of each prey species (s) consumed during fall and winter by each species of raptor (r).

N_r, total number of all prey individuals consumed by each species of raptor, $= \sum_s n_{sr}$.

f_{sr}, frequency of each prey species in food of each species of raptor, $= n_{sr}/N_r$ (estimated in samples reported in Tables 25 to 28).

$$W_r = \sum_s n_{sr}w_s = \sum_s N_r f_{sr}w_s = N_r \sum_s f_{sr}w_s$$

N_r can then be calculated since the other factors have been estimated.
Total number of each prey species consumed $= \sum_r N_r f_{sr}$.

The rate of mortality due to predation is this number divided by the size of the prey population (p. 356 to 357).

APPENDIX B. Scientific Names of Species

PELECYPODA. Clam *Tivela stultorum*.

ARACHNIDA. Herbivorous mite *Eotetranychus sexmaculatus*. Predatory mite *Typhlodromus occidentalis*.

CRUSTACEA. Daphnia *Daphnia magna* (unless otherwise stated).

INSECTA. Thrips *Thrips imaginis*. Florida wax scale *Ceroplastes floridensis*. Chaff scale *Parlatoria pergandei*. Bordered white moth *Bupalus piniarius*. Pine spinner moth *Dendrolimus pini*. Pine hawk moth *Hyloicus pinastri*. Pine beauty moth *Panolis griseovariegata*. Rice weevil *Calandra oryzae*. Bean weevil *Callosobruchus chinensis*. Broad-horned flour beetle *Gnathocerus cornutus*. Red flour beetle *Tribolium castaneum*. Confused flour beetle *Tribolium confusum*. Granary beetle *Trogoderma versicolor*. Parasitic wasp *Heterospilus prosopidus*. Sheep blowfly *Lucilia cuprina*. Housefly *Musca domestica*. Sewage fly *Spaniotoma minima*.

OSTEICHTHYES. Atlantic salmon *Salmo salar*. Lake trout *Salvelinus namaycush*. Goldeye *Hiodon alosoides*. Northern pike *Esox lucius*. Yellow perch *Perca flavescens*. Walleye *Stizostedion vitreum*. Freshwater drum *Aplodinotus grunniens*. Plaice *Pleuronectes platessa*.

AVES. Fulmar *Fulmarus glacialis.* Gannet *Morus bassanus.* Heron *Ardea cinerea.* Stork *Ciconia ciconia.* Golden Eagle *Aquila chrysaetos.* Ruffed Grouse *Bonasa umbellus.* Red Grouse *Lagopus scoticus.* Sharp-tailed Grouse *Pedioecetes phasianellus.* Prairie Chicken *Tympanuchus cupido.* Bobwhite Quail *Colinus virginianus.* Partridge *Perdix perdix.* Ring-necked Pheasant *Phasianus colchicus.* Pied Flycatcher *Muscicapa hypoleuca.* Coal Tit *Parus ater.* Blue Tit *Parus caeruleus.* Crested Tit *Parus cristatus.* Great Tit *Parus major.* House Wren *Troglodytes aedon.* Wood Thrush *Hylocichla mustelina.* Starling *Sturnus vulgaris.* Red-eyed Vireo *Vireo olivaceus.* Ovenbird *Seiurus aurocapillus.* Hooded Warbler *Wilsonia citrina.* Chaffinch *Fringilla coelebs.* Song Sparrow *Melospiza melodia.* Indigo Bunting *Passerina cyanea.*

MAMMALIA. Wolverine *Gulo luscus.* Fisher *Martes pennanti.* Mink *Mustela vison.* Weasel *Mustela vulgaris.* Arctic fox *Alopex lagopus.* Coyote *Canis latrans.* Wolf *Canis lupus.* Gray fox *Urocyon cinereoargenteus.* Colored fox *Vulpes fulva.* Lynx *Lynx canadensis.* Fur seal *Callorhinus ursinus.* Fox squirrel *Sciurus niger.* Levant vole *Microtus guentheri.* Meadow vole *Microtus pennsylvanicus.* Muskrat *Ondatra zibethicus.* White-footed mouse *Peromyscus leucopus.* Snowshoe hare *Lepus americanus.* European hare *Lepus europaeus.* European rabbit *Oryctolagus cuniculus.* Cottontail rabbit *Sylvilagus floridanus.* Caribou *Rangifer arcticus.* Reindeer *Rangifer tarandus.* Pronghorn *Antilocapra americana.* Dall sheep *Ovis dalli.*

Literature Cited

Allee, W. C., A. E. Emerson, O. Park, T. Park, and K. P. Schmidt. 1949. Principles of animal ecology. Saunders, Philadelphia. 837 pp.

Andrewartha, H. G., and L. C. Birch. 1954. Distribution and abundance of animals. Univ. Chicago Press, Chicago. 782 pp.

————, and T. O. Browning. 1961. An analysis of the idea of "resources" in animal ecology. J. Theoret. Biol. 1: 83–97.

Armstrong, J. T. 1964. The population dynamics of the planarian, *Dugesia tigrina.* Ecology 45: 361–365.

Beverton, R. J. H. 1962. Long-term dynamics of certain North Sea fish populations, pp. 242–259. *In* E. D. LeCren and M. W. Holdgate [ed.] The exploitation of natural animal populations. Wiley, New York.

Birch, L. C. 1953. Experimental background to the study of the distribution and abundance of insects. II. The relation between innate capacity for increase in numbers and the abundance of three grain beetles in experimental populations. Ecology 34: 712–726.

Bodenheimer, F. S. 1958. Animal ecology today. W. Junk, The Hague. 276 pp.

Brown, L. H., and A. Watson. 1964. The Golden Eagle in relation to its food supply. Ibis 106: 78–100.

Buckley, J. L. 1954. Animal population fluctuations in Alaska—a history. Trans. 19th N. Amer. Wildl. Conf. pp. 338–357.

Buckner, C. H., and W. J. Turnock. 1965. Avian predation on the larch sawfly, *Pristophora erichsonii* (Htg.). Ecology 46: 223–236.

Bump, G., R. W. Darrow, F. C. Edminster, and W. F. Crissey. 1947. The Ruffed Grouse. Life history, propagation, management. New York State Cons. Dept., Albany. 915 pp.

Christian, J. J. 1963. Endocrine adaptive mechanisms and the physiologic regulation of population growth, pp. 189–353. *In* W. V. Mayer and R. G. VanGelder [ed.] Physiological mammalogy. Vol. 1.

Christian, J. J., and D. E. Davis. 1964. Endocrines, behavior, and population. Science 146: 1550–1560.

Coe, W. R. 1957. Fluctuations in littoral populations, pp. 935–940. *In* J. W. Hedgpeth [ed.] Treatise on marine ecology and paleoecology. Geol. Soc. Amer. Mem. 67, Vol. 1.

Craighead, J. J., and F. C. Craighead, Jr. 1956. Hawks, owls and wildlife. Wildl. Mgmt. Inst., Washington. 443 pp.

Davidson, J., and H. G. Andrewartha. 1948. Annual trends in a natural population of *Thrips imaginis* (Thysanoptera). J. Animal Ecol. 17: 193–199.

DeBach, P., and H. S. Smith. 1941. Are population oscillations inherent in the host parasite relation? Ecology 22: 363–369.

Elton, C. S. 1942. Voles, mice and lemmings. Clarendon Press, Oxford. 496 pp.

———, and M. Nicholson. 1942a. Fluctuation in numbers of muskrat (*Ondatra zibethicus*) in Canada. J. Animal Ecol. 11: 96–126.

———, and ———. 1942b. The ten-year cycle in numbers of the lynx in Canada. J. Animal Ecol. 11: 215–244.

Errington, P. L. 1945. Some contributions of a fifteen-year local study of the Northern Bobwhite to a knowledge of population phenomena. Ecol. Monogr. 15: 1–34.

———. 1946. Predation and vertebrate populations. Quart. Rev. Biol. 21: 144–177, 221–245.

———. 1954. On the hazards of overemphasizing numerical fluctuations in studies of "cyclic" phenomena in muskrat populations. J. Wildl. Mgmt. 18: 66–90.

———. 1956. Factors limiting higher vertebrate populations. Science 124: 304–307.

———. 1957. Of population cycles and unknowns. Cold Spring Harbor Symposia Quantitative Biol. 22: 287–300.

Eschmeyer, P. H. 1957. The near extinction of lake trout in Lake Michigan. Trans. Amer. Fisheries Soc. 85: 102–119.

Fisher, J. 1952. A history of the Fulmar *Fulmarus* and its population problems. Ibis 94: 334–354.

———, and H. G. Vevers. 1944. The breeding distributions, history and population of the North Atlantic Gannet (*Sula bassana*). Part 2. The changes in the world numbers of the gannet in a century. J. Animal Ecol. 13: 49–62.

Frank, P. W. 1960. Prediction of population growth form in *Daphnia pulex* cultures. Amer. Naturalist 94: 357–372.

Fry, F. E. J. 1949. Statistics of a lake trout fishery. Biometrics 5: 27–67.

Gause, G. F., and A. A. Witt. 1935. Behavior of mixed populations and the problem of natural selection. Amer. Naturalist 69: 596–609.

Gibb, J. A. 1954. Feeding ecology of tits, with notes on treecreeper and goldcrest. Ibis 96: 513–543.

———. 1960. Populations of tits and goldcrests and their food supply in pine plantations. Ibis 102: 163–208.

———. 1962. L. Tinbergen's hypothesis of the role of specific search images. Ibis 104: 106–111.

Glas, P. 1960. Factors governing density in the Chaffinch (*Fringilla coelebs*) in different types of wood. Arch. Neerland. Zool. 13: 466–472.

Hairston, N. G., F. E. Smith, and L. Slobodkin. 1960. Community structure, population control, and competition. Amer. Naturalist 94: 421–425.

Hensley, M. M., and J. B. Cope. 1951. Further data on removal and repopulation of the breeding birds in aspruce-fir forest community. Auk 68: 483–493.

Hickey, J. J. 1955. Some population research on gallinaceous birds, pp. 326–396. *In* A. Wolfson [ed.] Recent advances in avian biology. Univ. Illinois Press, Urbana.

Hoffmann, R. S. 1958. The role of reproduction and mortality in population fluctuations of voles (*Microtus*). Ecol. Monogr. 28: 79–109.

Holling, C. S. 1961. Principles of insect predation. Ann. Rev. Rev. Entomol. 6: 163–182.

Huffaker, C. B. 1958. Experimental studies on predation: dispersion factors and predator-prey oscillations. Hilgardia 27: 343–383.

Ivlev, V. S. 1961. Experimental ecology of the feeding of fishes. Translated by Douglas Scott. Yale Univ. Press, New Haven. 302 pp.

Jenkins, D. 1963. Population control in Red Grouse (*Lagopus lagopus scoticus*). Proc. XIII Intern. Ornithol. Congr.: 690–700.

———, A. Watson, and G. R. Miller. 1963. Population studies on Red Grouse, *Lagopus lagopus scoticus* (Lath.) in north-east Scotland. J. Animal Ecol. 32: 317–376.

Keith, L. B. 1962. Wildlife's ten-year cycle. Univ. Wisconsin Press, Madison. 201 pp.

Kendeigh, S. C. 1944. Measurement of bird populations. Ecol. Monogr. 14: 67–106.

———. 1948. Census 10. Audubon Field Notes 2.

———. 1949. Census 13. Audubon Field Notes 3.

———. 1950. Census 10. Audubon Field Notes 4.

———. 1951. Census 21. Audubon Field Notes 5.

———. 1952. Census 15. Audubon Field Notes 6.

———. 1953. Census 21. Audubon Field Notes 7.

———. 1954. Census 14. Audubon Field Notes 8.

———. 1955. Census 38. Audubon Field Notes 9.

———. 1956. Census 36. Audubon Field Notes 10.

———. 1957. Census 26. Audubon Field Notes 11.

———. 1958. Census 24. Audubon Field Notes 12.

———. 1959. Census 27. Audubon Field Notes 13.

———. 1960. Census 29. Audubon Field Notes 14.

———. 1961. Census 36. Audubon Field Notes 15.

———. 1962. Census 37. Audubon Field Notes 16.

———. 1963. Census 36. Audubon Field Notes 17.

Klomp, H. 1964. Intraspecific competition and the regulation of insect numbers. Ann. Rev. Entomol. 9: 17–40.

Kluyver, H. N. 1951. The population ecology of the Great Tit, *Parus major* (L.). Ardea 39: 1–135.

———, and L. Tinbergen. 1953. Territory and the regulation of density in titmice. Arch. Neerland. Zool. 10: 265–289.

Lack, D. 1953. The stability of the Heron population. British Birds 47: 111–121.

———. 1954. The natural regulation of animal numbers. Oxford Univ. Press, London. 343 pp.

Leopold, A., L. K. Sowls, and D. L. Spencer. 1947. A survey of overpopulated deer ranges in the United States. J. Wildl. Mgmt. 11: 162–177.

Lloyd, L. 1943. Materials for a study in animal competition. II. The fauna of the sewage beds. Ann. Appl. Biol. 30: 47–60.

Macfadyen, A. 1963. Animal ecology, aims and methods. 2nd ed. Pitman & Sons, London. 344 pp.

Mackenzie, J. M. D. 1952. Fluctuations in the numbers of British tetraonids. J. Animal Ecol. 21: 128–153.

MacLulich, D. A., 1957. The place of chance in population processes. J. Wildl. Mgmt. 21: 293–299.

Marshall, W. H. 1954. Ruffed Grouse and snowshoe hare populations on the Cloquet Experimental Forest, Minnesota. J. Wildl. Mgmt. 18: 109–112.

Middleton, A. D. 1934. Periodic fluctuations in British game populations. J. Animal Ecol. 3: 231–249.

Moore, H. W. 1964. Intra- and interspecific competition among dragonflies (Odonata). J. Animal Ecol. 33: 49–71.

Morris, R. F. 1963. Predictive population equations based on key factors. Mem. Entomol. Soc. Canada 32: 16–21.

Murie, A. 1944. The wolves of Mount McKinley. U. S. Nat. Park Service, Faunal Series No.' 5. 238 pp.

Neilson, M. M., and R. F. Morris. 1964. The regulation of European sawfly numbers in the Maritime Provinces of Canada from 1937 to 1963. Can. Entomol. 96: 773–784.

Neyman, J., T. Park, and E. L. Scott. 1958. Struggle for existence; the Tribolium model: biological and statistical aspects. Gen. Systems 3: 152–179.

Nicholson, A. J. 1954. An outline of the dynamics of animal populations. Australian. J. Zool. 2: 9–65.

————, and V. A. Bailey. 1935. The balance of animal populations. Part I. Proc. Zool. Soc. London, 1935: 551–598.

Park, T., and M. B. Frank. 1950. The population history of Tribolium free of sporozoan infection. J. Animal Ecol. 19: 95–105.

————, E. V. Gregg, and C. Z. Lutherman. 1941. Studies in population physiology. X. Interspecific competition in populations of granary beetles. Physiol. Zool. 14: 395–430.

Pimentel, D., W. P. Nagel, and J. L. Madden. 1963. Space-time structure of the environment and the survival of parasite-host systems. Amer. Naturalist 97: 141–167.

Pratt, D. M. 1943. Analysis of population development in Daphnia at different temperatures. Biol. Bull. 85: 116–140.

Pycha, R. L. 1961. Recent changes in the walleye fishery of northern Green Bay and history of the 1943 year class. Trans. Amer. Fisheries Soc. 90: 475–488.

Richmond, N. D. 1952. Fluctuations in gray fox population in Pennsylvania and their relationship to precipitation. J. Wildl. Mgmt. 16: 198–206.

Ricker, W. E. 1954. Stock and recruitment. J. Fish. Res. Bd. Canada, 11: 559–623.

Rose, S. M. 1960. Feedback mechanism of growth control in tadpoles. Ecology 41: 188–199.

Scheffer, V. B. 1951. The rise and fall of a reindeer herd. Sci. Monthly 73: 356–362.

————. 1955. Body size with relation to population density in mammals. J. Mammal. 36: 493–515.

Severtzoff, S. A. 1934. On the dynamics of populations of vertebrates. Quart. Rev. Biol. 9: 409–437.

Shelford, V. E. 1954. The antelope population and solar radiation. J. Mammal. 35: 533–538.

————, and R. E. Yeatter. 1955. Some suggested relations of Prairie Chicken abundance to physical factors, especially rainfall and solar radiation. J. Wildl. Mgmt. 19: 233–242.

Slobodkin, L. B. 1954. Population dynamics in *Daphnia obtusa* Kurz. Ecol. Monogr. 24: 69–88.

Smith, F. E. 1961. Density dependence in the Australian thrips. Ecology 42: 403–407.

————. 1963*a*. Density dependence. Ecology 44: 220.

————. 1963*b*. Population dynamics in Daphnia magna and a new model for population growth. Ecology 44: 651–663.

Smith, L. L., Jr., and L. W. Krefting. 1954. Fluctuations in production and abundance of commercial species in the Red Lakes, Minnesota, with special references to changes in the walleye population. Trans. Amer. Fisheries Soc. 83: 131–160.

Southern, H. N. 1959. Mortality and population control. Ibis 101: 429–436.

Stewart, R. E., and J. W. Aldrich. 1951. Removal and repopulation of breeding birds in a spruce-fir forest community. Auk 68: 471–482.

Tinbergen, L. 1960. The natural control of insects in pine woods. I. Factors influencing the intensity of predation by song birds. Arch. Neerland. Zool. 13: 265–343.

————, and H. Klomp. 1960. The natural control of insects in pine woods. II. Conditions for damping of Nicholson oscillations in parasite-host systems. Arch. Neerland Zool. 13: 343–379.

Tompa, F. S. 1962. Territorial behavior: the main controlling factor of a local song sparrow population. Auk 79: 687–697.

Utida, S. 1957a. Cyclic fluctuations of population density intrinsic to the host-parasite system. Ecology 38: 442–449.

————. 1957b. Population fluctuation, an experimental and theoretical approach. Cold Spring Harbor Symposia Quantitative Biol. 22: 139–151.

Varley, G. C. 1949. Population changes in German forest pests. J. Animal Ecol. 18: 117–122.

Wangersky, P. J., and W. J. Cunningham. 1957. Time lag in prey-predator population models. Ecology 38: 136–139.

Watt, K. E. F. 1964. Density dependence in population fluctuations. Can. Entomol. 96: 1147–1148.

Williams, A. B. 1947. Climax beech-maple forest with some hemlock (15 year summary). Audubon Field Notes 1: 205–210.

————. 1948. Census 8. Audubon Field Notes 2: 231.

————. 1949. Census 14. Audubon Field Notes 3: 262–263.

————. 1950. Census 7. Audubon Field Notes 4: 297–298.

Wynne-Edwards, V. C. 1962. Animal dispersion in relation to social behavior. Oliver & Boyd, Edinburg. 653 pp.

David M. Gates

Energy, Plants, and Ecology

Introduction

A living plant is affected by the flow of energy, water vapor, carbon dioxide, oxygen, and ions between the plant and the environment. Energy will flow to or from the plant by radiative transfer. Energy also will flow to or from a plant by conduction along a temperature gradient or by mass flow by convection. Water vapor and carbon dioxide will flow to or from a plant along a concentration gradient of these gases. Those environmental properties which are important for energy transfer are sunlight, thermal radiation from ground and atmosphere, air temperature, wind, water vapor concentration of the air, and soil characteristics including moisture content and temperature.

The degree to which the energy content of a plant is affected by the incident radiation is determined by the absorptance to radiation of the plant surface and by the plant shape and orientation. If the plant has a high absorptance, its temperature and energy content is strongly affected by the incident radiation. If the plant has a low absorptance, its temperature is weakly affected by the incident radiation. For example, the energy content, and hence temperature, of a black object is strongly affected by incident radiation. On the other hand, the energy content of a perfect reflector would not be influenced at all by the incident radiation. The energy content of plants is moderately coupled to the incident sunlight, but strongly coupled to the infrared thermal radiation from the surrounding surfaces.

The flow of air across the surface of a plant transfers energy to or from the plant by convection. Natural convection occurs in still air and forced convection in wind. The size, shape, and orientation of the plant surfaces determine, in part, the efficiency with which energy is transferred by convection. The energy content, and temperature, of a plant with small, finely divided parts, e.g. pine needles, will be strongly affected by the air temperature. The energy content, and temperature, of a plant with broad dimensions and extensive surface, e.g., a banana leaf, will be lightly affected by the air temperature.

A plant in full sunlight, which receives more radiation than it emits and which is affected weakly by the air temperature, will have its temperature above air temperature by many degrees. On the other hand, a plant which is affected

Reprinted by permission of the author and publisher from *Ecology, 46:* 1–13, 1965.

strongly by the air temperature will have its temperature near to air temperature for normal amounts of incoming radiation. If a plant loses a strong net flux of radiation, its temperature will be substantially below air temperature if it is of broad structure and only slightly affected by the air temperature.

The temperature of a plant is also affected by the transpiration since energy is consumed with the evaporation of water. The resistance of the pathway through which the water vapor will flow from within the leaf to the free air beyond the leaf will determine the flow rate. A high resistance will result in a low rate of flow and a low resistance in a high rate for a given concentration gradient.

Hence, a plant is affected by certain environmental factors through transfer mechanisms which influence the energy content and temperature of the plant. The amount of influence is determined by the absorptance and emittance to radiation, the resistance to transpiration, and the conductance or convection coefficient to convection. The coefficients of absorptance, emittance, conductance, and resistance are characteristic of a particular plant.

The rate of energy transfer between the plant and the environment will determine the temperature of the plant. Each part of the plant, e.g. the root, stem, leaf, flower, etc., may be at a different temperature because of the rate of energy transfer between that part of the plant and its environment. The temperature of each part of the plant is important with regard to the physiological processes of the plant. Cell enlargement, photosynthesis, respiration, and other processes within the plant are temperature dependent. Certain processes, such as photosynthesis, are light dependent as well as temperature dependent.

Some of the environmental factors which determine the flow of energy between a plant and the environment affect the plant temperature or energy content to the same extent, and hence are interchangeable. A warm wind transferring energy to a plant may result in the same plant temperature as would a definite flux of incident radiation.

The intent of this paper is to describe the plant environment characteristics which affect the energy content of a plant; to describe the transfer mechanisms and the plant properties which limit the rate of energy transfer; and to discuss the physiological consequences of energy transfer and the ecological implications.

Environmental Factors

Those environmental factors which are most relevant to the energy transfer process of the aerial parts of a plant are: sunlight; skylight; thermal radiation from ground, atmosphere, and nearby objects; air temperature; wind; and water vapor concentration in the air. The only environmental factors requiring detailed discussion here are sunlight, skylight and thermal radiation. The other factors are more generally understood whereas some ambiguity exists with respect to radiation.

Radiation coming directly to the plant from the sun will be referred to as sunlight, S. Solar radiation which is scattered by air molecules and dust of the atmosphere will be referred to as skylight, s. Skylight originates over much of the upward hemisphere, as seen from the plant, while sunlight originates with nearly a point source. Sunlight and skylight vary enormously in intensity and spectral quality with location, time of day, time of year, and atmospheric conditions. The properties of sunlight and skylight and the measurement thereof have been discussed by Gates (1962, 1963b). In Fig. 1 is shown the

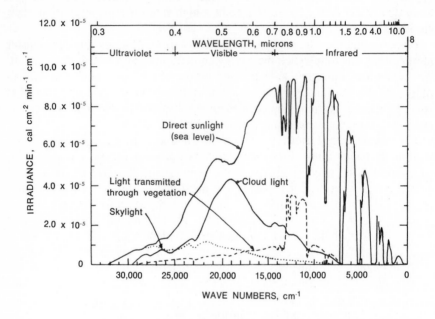

Figure 1

Spectral distribution of direct sunlight, skylight, cloudlight, and light transmitted through vegetation as a function of the frequency of radiation in wavenumbers. Wavelengths in microns is given at the top.

spectral distribution of sunlight, skylight, cloudlight, and light transmitted by vegetation. By plotting the monochromatic intensity as a function of the wavenumber the full spectrum of sunlight is shown in the figure, whereas on a wavelength plot this is not the case. A more detailed explanation of this is given by Gates (1963b). A wavenumber is the reciprocal of the wavelength and is proportional to the frequency of the radiation. For reference purposes, the equivalent wavelength scale is shown across the top of Fig. 1. The vastly different spectral distributions of sunlight, skylight, and cloudlight, and light transmitted by vegetation should be noted. Approximately 50% of sunlight is of frequencies beyond the visible in the infrared portion of the spectrum, while only a very small fraction of cloudlight occurs at infrared frequencies. Cloudlight is defined as the solar radiation reaching the ground which has been diffusely scattered by a complete overcast. It has a similar geometrical distribution to skylight in that it comes from most of the upward hemisphere, as seen from the plant. Skylight is relatively more intense in ultraviolet and blue frequencies than it is in red. At high mountain elevations the skylight is particularly rich in ultraviolet frequencies. The spectral distribution of radiation reaching plants is highly variable with time of day, altitude, latitude, and atmospheric conditions. Very few observations of the spectral quality of the radiation at the earth's surface, for conditions other than clear sky, have been made.

Radiation emitted from various surfaces or gases, which are at a low ambient temperature, will be referred to as thermal radiation. Although, strictly speaking, solar radiation also originates thermally, it is treated separately because of its unique character. An object at a temperature above absolute zero radiates energy proportional to the fourth power of its absolute temperature. The law describing this, known as the Stefan-Boltzmann Law, is written as follows:

$$\text{Radiation} = \epsilon \sigma T^4 \tag{1}$$

where ϵ is the surface emittance, σ is the Stefan-Boltzmann constant (8.12×10^{-11} cal cm^{-2} °K^{-4} min^{-1}), and T is the surface temperature in °K. For objects whose surface temperature is in the vicinity of 300° K (23° C) the emitted energy occurs as a continuum of wavelengths from 4 to 50 μ with a broad peak at about 10 μ. Hence, all surfaces at the ambient temperature of the ground or atmosphere emit infrared radiation.

A plant extending above the ground receives thermal radiation, R_g, from the ground surface, and thermal radiation, R_a, from the atmosphere. The ground radiates very much as a blackbody at the ground surface temperature. Because atmospheric water vapor, carbon dioxide, and ozone absorb effectively at infrared frequencies they also radiate efficiently at these frequencies. Gates (1962) has discussed in detail the properties of atmospheric thermal radiation.

In Fig. 2 are illustrated some environmental factors characteristic of a warm, clear, relatively dry, summer day. The values given here are not observed directly but are realistic values based on numerous measurements during warm, clear days. The numerical values of sunlight plus skylight ($S + s$) should be noted in comparison with the thermal radiation from the ground, R_g, and the atmosphere, R_a. The thermal radiation represents the total radial on environment at night and represents an amount during the daytime which is nearly equal to the sunlight and skylight contribution. The curve in Fig. 2 marked H_{av} represents the average total incident radiation per unit area of leaf surface as follows:

$$H_{av} = \frac{(1 + r)\ (S + s) + R_g + R_a}{2} \tag{2}$$

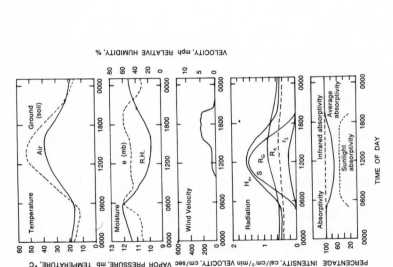

Figure 2

Environmental factors for the diurnal cycle of a clear summer day, the coefficients which couple the plant to the environment, such as absorptivity, convection coefficient, the radiation absorbed, the resulting leaf temperature, and the subsequent predicted leaf activity.

The air temperature throughout a warm, clear summer day varies from a low of 16° C to a high of 38° C with the maximum temperature occurring during midafternoon. The evening hours are distinctly warmer than the early morning hours. The relative humidity may vary enormously, but the vapor pressure of the air relatively little. The afternoon period may be more windy and turbulent than the night or morning.

Transfer Mechanisms

A plant may receive energy by radiation, by convection if the plant is cooler than the air, and by condensation if the plant temperature is lower than the dew point. A plant loses energy by radiation, by convection if the plant is warmer than the air, and by transpiration. A small amount of energy is consumed by photosynthesis or is generated by respiration. If the small amounts are neglected, the energy budget for a plant may be written as follows:

$$a_s \frac{(1 + r)\,(S + s)}{2} + a_t \frac{(R_g + R_a)}{2} - \epsilon_t \sigma T_l^4 \pm C \pm LE = 0 \qquad (3)$$

where a_s = mean total absorptance of a plant to sunlight and skylight, r = reflectance of the underlying ground or plant surface to sunlight and skylight, a_t = absorptance of plant to thermal radiation, ϵ_t = emittance of plant to thermal radiation, T_l = leaf temperature in ° K, C = energy gained or lost by convection in cal cm^{-2} min^{-1}, L = latent heat of evaporation in cal gm^{-1} of water at the leaf temperature, and E = transpiration rate of the leaf in gm cm^{-2} min^{-1}. The radiation terms, S, s, R_g and R_a, have been previously defined and are measured in cal cm^{-2} min^{-1}. The sum of the first three terms in equation (3) represents the net radiation available to the plant as energy.

A plant absorbs a fraction of the incident radiation of all wavelengths. The spectral or monochromatic absorptance of a leaf surface is the fraction of incident monochromatic radiation absorbed by the surface. The spectral absorptance of a leaf is strictly a characteristic property of the leaf. The mean absorptance of a leaf surface is the fraction of total incident radiation absorbed by the surface; it is a function of the spectral quality of the incident radiation, and not solely a characteristic of the leaf. If only the total intensity of radiation incident on the leaf is known, and not the spectral distribution of the radiation, then the mean absorptance of the leaf to this radiation must be known in order to determine the energy absorbed.

Recently Gates et al. (1959) have reported on the spectral absorptance of many species of plants. The spectral absorptance curve for *Populus deltoides* is shown in Fig. 3. The spectral absorptance of other plants is similar. A plant typically has a high absorptance to ultraviolet and visible radiation. Hence, the energy content or temperature of a plant is strongly influenced by radiation of these wavelengths. At approximately 0.7 μ or 14, 300 cm^{-1} the reflectance and transmittance of a plant surface increase considerably and the absorptance

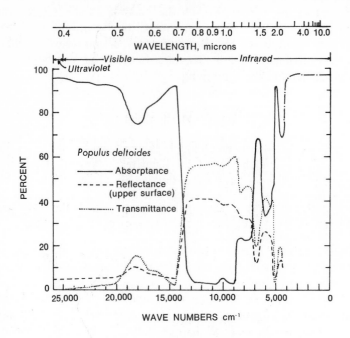

Figure 3

Spectral absorptance, reflectance, and transmittançe of *Populus deltoides* leaf as a function of the frequency of the incident radiation in wavenumbers. The measurements are for nearly normal incidence including the specular and diffuse components.

becomes very low from 0.7μ, to about 1.1 μ. The plant temperature is only slightly influenced by incident radiation of these wavelengths. The reason for this low absorptance has been discussed by Gates et al. (1965). A substantial fraction of the total incident sunlight is contained between 0.7 μ and 1.1 μ. If a plant absorbed most of the incident radiation between 0.7 and 1.1 μ it would become substantially warmer than it does without absorbing it and the plant proteins probably would be destroyed. At wavelengths greater than 1.1 μ the incident radiation becomes increasingly absorbed until beyond 2.5 μ a plant is nearly black with an absorptance of about 0.97. This high absorptance to infrared radiation of wavelength greater than 2.5 μ means that the emittance of a plant is also 0.97 at these wavelengths. Gates and Tantraporn (1952) reported the infrared spectral absorptance of many plants.

The mean absorptance of most deciduous plant leaves to incident sunlight and skylight is between 0.45 and 0.60 (Birkebak, private communication). Gates et al. (1965), from detailed spectral absorptance observations, computed the mean absorptance to a representative amount of incident sunlight and skylight. They found mean absorptance values from 0.50 to 0.60 for some deciduous leaves, from 0.60 to 0.80 for desert succulents, and 0.88 for *Thuja occidentalis* and *Pinus resinosa*. The mean absorptance to cloudlight with a complete overcast condition gave values from 0.60 to 0.70 for the broad deciduous leaves, 0.66 to 0.76 for desert succulents, and 0.88 for *Thuja* and *Pinus*. The mean absorptance of a leaf will be strikingly different for sunlight, cloudlight, incandescent light, fluorescent light, or any other source.

More precisely, the radiant energy absorbed by a leaf depends on the geometry of the leaf and its orientation relative to the source of radiation. A cylindrical needle would absorb less energy from a point source, such as the sun, than would a broad leaf normally exposed to the sun's rays, if each had the same absorptance. In order to properly evaluate the geometrical effect, however, one must take into consideration the orientation of a collection of leaves or needles on a branch. The effective area of a spruce branch and of a fir branch have been evaluated by Tibbals et al. (1964). Much work remains to be done concerning the geometrical relationships of leaves on a branch to the absorption of radiation from the sun.

An example of the influence of environmental factors on the energy content and temperature of a leaf will be given using the data presented in Fig. 2. Throughout the major portion of the day the mean absorptance to sunlight and skylight is assumed to be 0.50. Towards dawn and dusk the mean absorptance to sunlight is diminished, since at either end of the day sunlight becomes relatively richer in red and near infrared frequencies which are absorbed less than frequencies throughout the visible. During the night the absorptance is entirely to far infrared radiation and is assumed to be 0.97. The absorptance to thermal radiation during the day is also 0.97. The mean absorptance to the total incident radiation on a plant at any given time is determined by the proportion of sunlight and skylight to thermal radiation. The mean absorptance, $\bar{a}$, was computed as follows:

$$\bar{a} = \frac{a_s(1 + r) (S + s) + a_t (R_a + R_g)}{(1 + r) (S + s) + R_a + R_g}$$

$$= \frac{0.5 (1 + r) (S + s) + 0.97 (R_a + R_g)}{(1 + r) (S + s) + R_a + R_g} \tag{4}$$

The mean absorptance is given as a function of the time of day in Fig. 2. The total amount of radiation absorbed by the leaf as a function of the time of day is also shown in Fig. 2.

Air temperature influences the energy content or temperature of a plant by the convection of energy to or from the plant. A detailed discussion of this influence is given by Gates (1962) and by Gates and Benedict (1963). The temperature of a plant is nearly always different than the air surrounding the plant. This difference in temperature or temperature gradient results in energy being transferred to or from the plant. If energy is transferred from warmer air to a cooler plant, the air will cool in the process, and the cool air will descend towards the ground. If energy is transferred from a warmer plant to cooler air, the air will warm in the process, and the warm air will ascend from near the plant. Hence, even in the absence of wind the air is nearly always in motion around a plant. This movement of air, and the transfer of energy, is termed free convection. The transfer of energy by free convection may be expressed in the following manner:

$$C = h_c \Delta T = 6.0 \times 10^{-3} \left(\frac{\Delta T}{L} \right)^{1/4} \Delta T \tag{5}$$

where C is the energy transferred in cal cm^{-2} min^{-1}, ΔT is the temperature difference between plant and air in °C, h_c is the convection coefficient in cal cm^{-2} min^{-1} °C^{-1}, and L is the mean width of the leaf or the diameter of a needle in centimeters.

The transfer of energy from a plant in the presence of wind is known as forced convection. The complicated process of forced convection is described by Tibbals et al. (1964). As an example, the transfer of energy by the laminar or streamline flow of air across the surface of a flat leaf is as follows:

$$C = h_c \Delta T = 5.7 \times 10^{-3} \left(\frac{V}{L} \right)^{1/2} \Delta T \tag{6}$$

where V is the wind speed in cm sec^{-1}. In the case of a cylinder, which is a reasonable approximation for needles, the energy transferred by forced convection takes the form:

$$C = h_c \Delta T = 6.2 \times 10^{-3} \frac{V^{1/3}}{D^{2/3}} \tag{7}$$

The complications which arise with regard to heat transfer by wind involve turbulence and the intricate behavior of a complex of leaves forming a branch. As moving air passes through a canopy of vegetation it becomes very turbulent. In addition, one leaf may be in the lee of another so that the rate of energy transfer from the air to the leaves is very different than for a single isolated leaf in wind. Some of these details have been treated by Gates et al. (1965).

The example illustrated in Fig. 2 is one in which there is no wind during the night time and early morning hours. The late morning and afternoon is windy. The convection coefficient, h_c, shown in Fig. 2 is for the case of no wind all day and some wind during the midday and afternoon as illustrated elsewhere in Fig. 2. The convection coefficient was calculated for free convection using equation (5) and for forced convection using equation (6). A leaf dimension $L = 1$ cm was used. The convection coefficient determines the influence of the air temperature on the energy content or temperature of the leaf. It is readily seen from equations (5), (6), and (7) that a small leaf or a needle of small diameter has a large convection coefficient and hence the leaf temperature is strongly affected by the air temperature. On the other hand a broad leaf, such as a banana or tobacco leaf, has a small convection coefficient and the leaf temperature is only slightly affected by the air temperature.

The energy content and temperature of a plant is influenced by the transpiration rate. Transpiration of water vapor from a plant leaf is a diffusion phenomenon. The water vapor diffuses from the mesophyll cell walls lining the substomatal cavity to the free air beyond the boundary layer next to the leaf surface. It is assumed that the air next to the mesophyll cell walls is saturated with moisture at the temperature of the leaf, T_l. The saturation water vapor density is $_s\rho_l (T_l)$. The water vapor density of the free air, at a temperature, T_a, is $\rho_a (T_a)$, which is equal to the product of the relative humidity, $r.h.$, and the saturation water vapor density of the free air, $_s\rho_a (T_a)$. The flow of moisture, E, in gm cm^{-2} min^{-1}, from the substomatal cavity through the stomatal channel, through the boundary layer of air adhering to the leaf surface, to the free air beyond the leaf may be written:

$$E = \frac{_s\rho_l(T_l) - \rho_a(T_a)}{R} = \frac{_s\rho_l(T_l) - r.h. \, _s\rho_a(T_a)}{R} \tag{8}$$

where R is the total resistance of the diffusion pathway expressed in min cm^{-1}. Characteristic values of R are from 0.1 to 0.2 min cm^{-1}. Higher values may also exist. Lee and Gates (1964) have recently discussed the problem of computing transpiration resistance based on leaf anatomy. By measuring the leaf and air temperatures and the relative humidity the transpiration rate can be computed for a given plant resistance.

Wind influences the transpiration rate by reducing the boundary layer next to the leaf surface and thereby reducing the diffusion resistance. The reduced resistance increases the transpiration rate which in turn produces greater cooling of the leaf. It may be that stomatal opening is affected by leaf temperature for a given light intensity, but information concerning the temperature behavior is nearly nonexistent.

In Fig. 2 is shown an estimated transpiration rate for our model leaf for still air conditions and for windy air conditions. The transpiration rate shown is a reasonable one and corresponds to a diffusion resistance of 0.2 min cm^{-1}. The diffusion resistance increases with diminished light intensity towards dawn and dusk when the stomates close and the transpiration rate decreases accordingly.

Plant Response to the Environment

The environmental factors affecting plant temperature and energy content have been described. The transfer mechanisms responsible for the flow of energy between a plant and its environment have been discussed. The rate of flow of energy between the environment and the plant is governed by certain coefficients which are characteristic of the plant. The coefficients of interest are the mean absorptance, the thermal emittance, the convection coefficient, and the transpiration resistance. Energy will flow to and from the plant and the plant temperature will adjust for energy equilibrium. For the example illustrated in Fig. 2, if the plant absorbs the amount of radiation shown, and if convection and transpiration occur as indicated, the plant leaf will assume the temperatures shown.

In order to establish that these leaf temperatures represent the influence of these environmental conditions, it is necessary to evaluate the complete energy budget at any given time of day according to equation (3). This equation is difficult to solve for the leaf temperature, T_l, when everything else is known. In order to make this evaluation simpler, when a large number of values are involved, the energy diagram of Fig. 4 was devised (Gates, 1963b).

The energy diagram was evolved on the basis that two of the energy exchange factors, namely radiation and convection, could be expressed relative to air temperature. The air temperature is one parameter often measured by ecologists working in the field. If plant temperature relative to air temperature can be firmly established on a theoretical, as well as observational, basis then perhaps some of the interesting large scale plant geographical relationships can be better understood. It is shown in equation (5) that the strength of the convection term is proportional to the difference between leaf and air temperature. The reradiation from the leaf can also be expressed in this manner as follows:

$$R_{leaf} = \epsilon\sigma T^4{}_{leaf} \tag{9}$$

and writing

$$T_{leaf} = T_{air} + \Delta T \tag{10}$$

hence

$$R_{leaf} = \epsilon\sigma(T_{air} + \Delta T)^4 \cong \epsilon\sigma(T^4{}_{air} + 4T^3{}_{air}\Delta T) \tag{11}$$

Therefore, for a given air temperature, a single curve represents reradiation versus ΔT; a set of four such curves is shown in Fig. 4 as short dashed lines marked for air temperatures of $10°$, $20°$, $30°$, and $40°$ C respectively. For example, a leaf in air at $30°$ C absorbing 1.30 cal cm^{-2} min^{-1} would equilibrate at point A in Fig. 4, or at $55°$ C above air temperature, or at a leaf temperature of $85°$ C. Clearly, this is much warmer than a leaf ever becomes because other factors, in addition to reradiation, set in to cool a leaf. If reradiation and free convection act together to cool a leaf, then equations (5) and (11) may be represented graphically as shown by the long dashed lines in Fig. 4. The leaf of our example would then equilibrate at point B or at $28°$ C above air temperature of $58°$ C. This is still considerably warmer than most leaves become relative to air temperature, because transpiration acts to cool the leaf and photosynthesis consumes a small amount of energy. The effect of transpiration and photosynthesis is to depress the effective value of the horizontal line marked "radiation absorbed by leaf" to some lower value, such as 1.04 cal cm^{-2} min^{-1}. In still air the leaf would then equilibrate at point H or at a temperature $19°$ C above air temperature, or at a leaf temperature of $49°$ C. Leaf temperatures of this order sometimes occur, as reported by Gates (1963a). This rate of transpiration removes energy from the leaf at the rate of

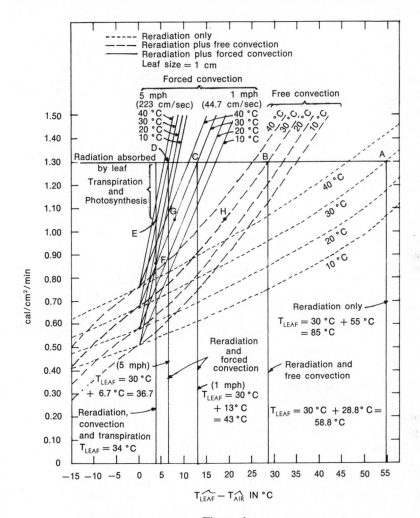

Figure 4

Energy diagram for computing a leaf temperature relative to air temperature when the radiation absorbed by the leaf is given. Energy is dissipated by reradiation from the leaf, by free convection in still air, and by forced convection in windy air, each shown as a set of curves, each curve at a constant air temperature of 10°, 20°, 30°, or 40° C. Points marked A through H represent the energy exchange for various conditions and show the resulting leaf temperature relative to air temperature.

0.26 cal cm^{-2} min^{-1}, which is a transpiration rate of 4.4×10^{-4} gm cm^{-2} min^{-1}. If the transpiration is higher, and it often is for fully sunlit leaves, the leaf temperature will be lower, perhaps 10° C above air temperature, a commonly observed value (see Gates, 1963a).

If there is wind, the cooling influence is substantial compared with the cooling by free convection. For a wind speed of 1 mph and 5 mph respectively, without transpiration, the leaf will equilibrate at point C or point D and the leaf temperature will be 43° C or at 37° C respectively. For a wind speed of 1 mph and 5 mph respectively, with transpiration, the leaf will equilibrate at point G or point E and the leaf will be at 38° C and 34° C respectively when the air temperature is 30° C. If sufficient transpiration occurs and the wind speed is 1 mph, the leaf might equilibrate at point F or again be at a temperature of 34° C. It is clear that the influence of transpiration on leaf temperature is substantial and that relatively low wind speeds also effectively influence leaf temperature. As the radiation absorbed by the leaf and the air temperature change with time of day, it is possible to follow the relationship between transpiration and leaf temperature with such an energy diagram. An example of a complete diurnal cycle is shown by Gates (1963b).

For the example of Fig. 2, where the transpiration is assumed to be as shown and the radiation absorbed as given, it is then straightforward, using the energy diagram, to determine a consistent leaf temperature relative to the air temperature. It should be noted in Fig. 2 that during the daytime with sunlight on the leaf, the wind cools the leaf below its temperature during equivalent still air conditions. During evening hours the wind adds heat to the leaf and raises the leaf temperature above the temperature it would have in still air.

For ecological purposes the establishment of leaf temperature is not an end in itself, for this is only a physical property of the leaf. It is essential to consider the physiological reactions whose rates are temperature dependent. Most biochemical reactions are rate processes which are temperature and time dependent. It is well known (Lundegårdh, 1931; Went, 1961; Galston, 1961) that the growth rate and assimilation rate of plants is temperature dependent. An optimum temperature for these processes, for example, may occur at about 28° C, with less favorable growth rate at lower and higher temperatures. An example of somewhat oversimplified rate curves is shown in Fig. 5 for the photosynthetic rate by corn leaves as a function of temperature and light intensity. The general shape of the temperature dependence is based on data by Lundegårdh (1931). The dependence of photosynthetic rate on light intensity is taken from Waggoner, Moss, and Hesketh (1963). The curves shown in Fig. 5 represent an oversimplification of the actual situation. However, sufficient information does not exist at the present time to justify further elaboration. The optimum temperature may be as low as 15° C for some arctic and alpine plants (Mooney and Billings, 1961). The optimum temperature may be different for each plant species and may depend on the conditions under which the plant developed. Bjorkmann and Holmgren (1963) show that different optima exist depending upon the light intensity during leaf development. If only the temperature dependence of the photosynthetic rate is considered at a constant light intensity and is applied to the leaf temperature curve (Fig. 2), one finds

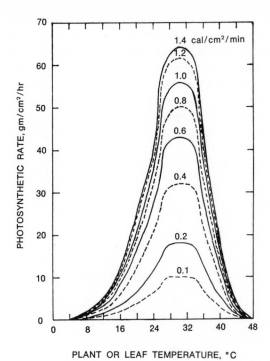

Figure 5

Photosynthetic rate curves at constant solar radiation intensity as a function of leaf temperature. These curves are based on data for maize obtained by Waggoner, Moss, and Hesketh (1963) on photosynthesis versus light intensity and the shape of the curve is based on data by Lundegårdh (1931).

that on a warm, clear, sunny summer day there may be two peaks in the growth rate or the biochemical activity of a leaf. This double peak is shown in Fig. 2. As the early morning temperature rises the most favorable temperature for the biochemical rate process is reached about 0800. During the middle portion of the day the temperature is too high for favorable biochemical activity. The temperature drops to the optimum value again during late afternoon and a second peak in leaf activity is realized about 1830. The leaf cools to less favorable temperatures during the night and leaf activity drops to a low level.

This curve is clearly a gross oversimplification of the situation and no doubt shows up the double peaks considerably stronger than they actually are in nature, where several mechanisms are acting simultaneously. Meyer and Anderson (1952) discuss the occurrence of a minimum in growth as follows: "Cyclical variations in the rate of elongation of plant organs during the course of a day can be interpreted in terms of the principle of limiting factors. During the progress of the day first one factor and then another is limiting. The rate of growth at any particular moment will be largely limited by the factor in relative minimum at that time. The three principal environmental factors influencing the daily periodicity in the rate of elongation of plant organs are temperature, the internal water relations of the plant, and light."

There are numerous examples of the occurrence of maxima and minima in the diurnal behavior of plant mechanisms. Some of these examples are plotted in Fig. 6. Various hypotheses have been invoked to explain the appearance of a midday minimum. Thut and Loomis (1944) explained the midday mini-

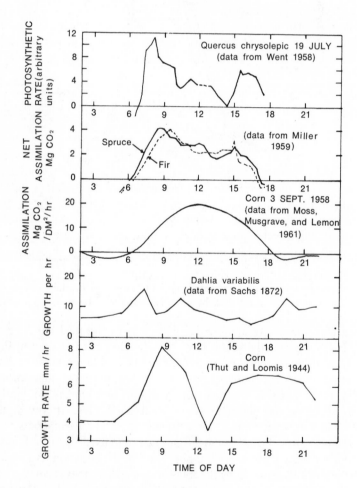

Figure 6

Examples of the diurnal behavior of photosynthesis, assimilation, and growth for various plants reported in the literature.

mum as an internal water deficit. Went (1958) discusses the possibility that translocation of the photosynthates out of the leaf cells is limiting the rate of CO_2 reduction.

It is clear that double maxima, in growth rate or in assimilation, exist on a diurnal basis for certain days. Certainly there are days during which double maxima, with midday slump, do not occur as shown for one example in Fig. 6. Probably the day during which these observations were made was not particularly warm, although the authors (Moss, Musgrave, and Lemon, 1961) do not give the air temperatures. The double maxima are not symmetrical, and the afternoon maximum is smaller than the morning maximum. The symmetrical double maxima, shown in Fig. 2, resulting from solely a temperature dependence of the photosynthetic rate process is not the complete explanation. Light and temperature together are affecting the photosynthetic rate. If the changing light intensity and the changing temperature are considered simultaneously, double maxima of photosynthetic rate appear in the diurnal cycle, but the afternoon peak is much smaller than the morning peak. An example is shown in Fig. 7, using data on air temperature and solar radiation compiled by Thut and Loomis (1944). Unfortunately, they did not measure leaf temperatures. The leaf temperatures shown were estimated for the case of the fully exposed horizontal sunlit leaf. If this diurnal cycle of radiation intensity and leaf temperature is used to estimate the photosynthetic rate from the curves of Fig. 5, the diurnal photosynthetic rate would be expected to be as shown in Fig. 7. The afternoon maximum is not as great as the morning maximum because the air temperature and the leaf temperature remain high during the early afternoon while the light intensity diminishes. Only in the late afternoon, when the light intensity is much reduced, will the leaf temperature fall to the optimum value and the second peak in photosynthetic rate will occur. This is completely borne out by the observations shown in Fig. 6.

The double peak in the diurnal behavior of photosynthesis is not adequately explained by water deficit. Water deficit will produce a midday drop in photosynthetic rate but will not account for the afternoon recovery peak. Neither will the water deficit mechanism produce as strong a change in photosynthesis as is observed or as is predicted on the basis of light intensity and temperature. The relatively small influence of water deficit is borne out by the results of Moss, Musgrave, and Lemon (1961). The water deficit mechanism will play a role and will result in stomatal closure, reduced transpiration, and decreased diffusion of carbon dioxide. This will add to and complicate the changes in the assimilation rate versus time. It will increase the midday slump and diminish the afternoon recovery.

Biochemical activity, other than photosynthesis, occurs within the leaf and the plant. Such other activity as cell enlargement or stem or leaf elongation will continue in the absence of light, but nevertheless will be temperature dependent. Hence, other biochemical processes will, of course, continue during the nighttime. If a simple rate curve as a function of plant temperature is con-

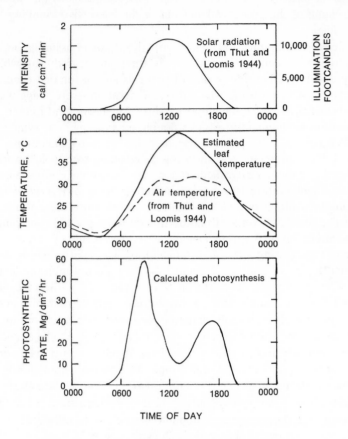

Figure 7

Calculated diurnal variation of the photosynthetic rate for maize for a clear day corresponding to the measured solar radiation and air temperature conditions reported by Thut and Loomis (1944).

sidered for these processes, it is evident that double maxima may occur during the daytime, but growth or other activity will continue during the nighttime as well. This is also borne out by the examples illustrated in Fig. 6.

Ecological Implications

The ecological implications are many concerning the influence of environment on plant temperature and the resulting photosynthesis, respiration, leaf biochemical activity, etc. The possible combinations of light and temperature which occur in nature are innumerable, and the biochemical responses of plants are probably as numerous as the number of species. Despite this overwhelming complexity of nature, however, the following examples illustrate the type of ecological investigation worthy of effort.

Two types of days will be used for illustration: a relatively cool, clear day during which the maximum temperature reaches 25° C and the minimum 12° C; and a relatively warm, clear day during which the maximum is 40° C and the minimum 20° C. Leaves in full sunlight receiving energy on a horizontal surface and leaves in shade receiving diffuse sunlight will be considered. These conditions are illustrated in Fig. 8 for a diurnal cycle. The solar radiation is given at the top, the air and leaf temperatures next for the cool day and at the bottom of the figure for the warm day. The leaf temperatures are taken relative to the air temperature, according to the experience reported by Gates (1963a) and by other workers referred to in that article. In any event, only moderate departures from the air temperature were taken for leaf temperatures, rather than the extreme possibilities. The leaf temperature curves are labelled 1 and 2 for sunlit and shaded leaves on the cool day, and 3 and 4 for sunlit and shaded leaves on the warm day respectively. If the photosynthetic curves for maize of Fig. 5 are used, one obtains the set of curves marked photosynthesis in Fig. 8. The contrasts among the different photosynthetic consequences are enormous and merit some discussion.

The curve marked 1, under photosynthesis, represents sunlit leaves on a relatively cool, clear day during which photosynthetic conditions remained near optimum for several hours and the total accumulated photosynthates might be quite substantial. For the shade leaf on the same day, one has the curve marked 2, the leaf temperature never reaching optimum and the light intensity not approaching saturation. The total accumulated photosynthates would be less than one-quarter of that for curve number 1. For the case of the warm day the photosynthetic rate of the exposed leaf, curve 3, is drastically reduced because of the high temperatures. It has a peak in the early daylight hours, photosynthesis is practically nonexistent during midday, and a very weak recovery results during the late daylight hours. The total accumulated photosynthates would be less than one-twelfth of that for the exposed leaf on the cooler day with the same amount of sunshine, and about one-third of the total photosynthates for the shaded leaves receiving diffuse light during the cool day. The accumulated photosynthates of the shaded leaves on the warm day, represented by curve 4, may be very much greater than for the sunlit leaves on that day. The total accumulated photosynthates for the shaded warm day leaves would be slightly greater than for the shaded cool day leaves.

If instead of photosynthesis, one uses a simple rate process curve, which depends only on temperature and not upon light intensity, and computes the rate of other biochemical processes within a leaf, such as cell enlargement or stem elongation, one gets the results shown in Fig. 6. Purposely, the term "leaf activity" has not been precisely defined, since many complex biochemical actions go on within the leaf simultaneously. It is desirable for the present discussion to treat them together as one process. The total accumulated leaf activity integrated over a 24-hour period, is for curves 1, 2, 3, and 4 in the

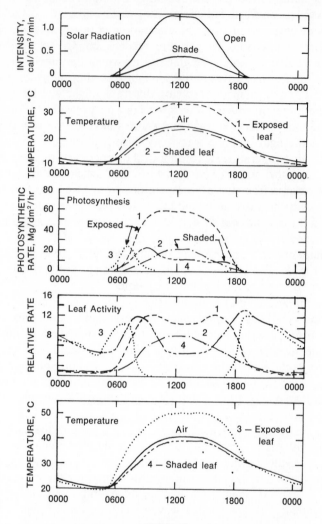

Figure 8

Illustration of the influence of a cool summer day
and a warm summer day, with the solar radiation as
shown, for sunlit and shade leaves on the photosynthetic rate and the general biochemical activity of a
leaf as a function of the time of day. Numbers 1 and
2 refer to an exposed and a shaded leaf respectively
on the cool day, and numbers 3 and 4 to the exposed
and shaded leaf on the warm day.

following ratios: 1.65/1.00/1.47/2.32. The distinctions are not as great as
for the photosynthetic curves because of the warm light activity compensating
in part for the reduced activity during the hot daytime. If one had a warm

night, e.g. 20° C minimum temperature, and a cool day, 25° C or 28° C maximum temperature, then for sunlit leaves one would follow curve 3 through the night to sunrise and then cross over in the morning to curve 1 and follow it throughout the day. Then the total integrated leaf activity would be 2.77, on the same basis as the numbers given above, a rather substantial increase. For the type of leaf activity or biochemical action defined here, wherein the optimum temperature is about 28° C, a cool night and warm day situation could be the most unfavorable as seen by following curve 1 at night and curve 3 during the day.

From an ecological standpoint, one can now visualize various contrasting situations: the upper portion of a leaf canopy in sunlight, on a cool summer day following curve 1, on a warm summer day following curve 3; the lower portion of the leaf canopy in shade following curves 2 and 4 on cool and warm summer days respectively. Cool clear summer days, of the type illustrated by curves 1 and 2, often do occur in montane and alpine environments, while the warm or hot clear summer day of curves 3 and 4 would be characteristic of lower elevations, such as the Great Plains. A subtropical mesic environment, such as Hawaii, would be characteristic of warm nights and cool or only moderately warm days, and the resulting growth and accumulated photosynthesis should be enormous in such a region. The prevalence of wind in a place such as Hawaii, where there is always available water, is also of great importance. The northwest coast of the United States is extremely mesic and also has a good deal of wind. Wind will increase transpiration and in full sunlight keep the plant temperature near or just above air temperature and the shade leaves reduced below air temperature. It is possible for fully sunlit leaves, which are transpiring freely in still air, to be below air temperature, as observed for *Mimulus cardinalis* in California by Gates et al. (1964). Generally it can be expected that under windy conditions plant temperatures will be close to air temperature.

One thing is certain: many more observations of plant temperatures should be made for a wide variety of plants and environmental conditions. Simultaneously, determinations must be made of the biochemical activity of the plant as a function of the plant temperature and light intensity for a large number of plants. Only then can one begin to sort out some of the important relationships between environment and plant physiology.

Literature Cited

Bjorkmann, O., and P. Holmgren. 1963. Adaptability of the photosynthetic apparatus to light intensity in ecotypes from exposed and shaded habitats. Physiol. Plant. 16: 889–914.

Galston, A. W. 1961. The life of the green plant. Prentice-Hall, Inc., Englewood Cliffs, N.J. 116 pp.

Gates, D. M. 1962. Energy exchange in the biosphere. Harper and Row, New York, N.Y. 151 pp.

————. 1963a. Leaf temperature and energy exchange. Archiv. Met., Geophys. Biokl. Series B, 12: 321–336.

————. 1963b. The energy environment in which we live. Am. Scientist 51: 327–348.

Gates, D. M., and C. M. Benedict. 1963. Convection phenomena from plants in still air. Am. J. Botany 50: 563–573.

Gates, D. M., W. H. Hiesey, M. A. Nobs, and H. W. Milner. 1964. Temperature and environment of mimulus in the Sierra Nevada Mountains. Carnegie Institution of Washington Year Book 1964.

Gates, D. M., H. J. Keegan, J. C. Schleter, and V. R. Weidner. 1965. Spectral properties of plants. Appl. Optics, Jan. (in press).

Gates, D. M., and W. Tantraporn. 1952. The reflectivity of deciduous trees and herbaceous plants in the infrared to 25 μ. Science 115 (2997): 613–616.

Gates, D. M., E. C. Tibbals, and F. Kreith. 1965. Radiation and convection in ponderosa pine. Am. J. Bot., Jan. (in press).

Lee, R., and D. M. Gates. 1964. Diffusion resistance in leaves as related to their stomatal anatomy and micro-structure. Am. J. Bot. (in press).

Lundegårdh, H. 1931. Environment and plant development. Edward Arnold and Co., London. 330 pp.

Meyer, B. S., and D. B. Anderson. 1952. Plant physiology. D. Van Nostrand Co., Inc., New York. 784 pp.

Mooney, H. A., and W. D. Billings. 1961. Comparative physiological ecology of arctic and alpine populations of *Oxyria digyna*. Ecol. Monogr. 31: 1–29.

Moss, D. N., R. B. Musgrave, and E. R. Lemon. 1961. Photosynthesis under field conditions. III. Some effects of light, carbon dioxide, temperature, and soil moisture on photosynthesis, respiration, and transpiration of corn. Crop Science 1: 83–87.

Thut, H. F., and W. E. Loomis. 1944. Relation of light to the growth of plants. Plant Physiol. 19: 117.

Tibbals, E. C., E. K. Carr, D. M. Gates, and F. Kreith. 1964. Radiation and convection in conifers. Am. J. Bot. 51: 529–538.

Waggoner, P. E., R. A. Moss, and J. D. Hesketh. 1963. Radiation in the plant environment and photosynthesis. Agron. J. 55. 36–39.

Went, F. W. 1958. The physiology of photosynthesis in higher plants. Preslia 30: 225–249.

————. 1961. Temperature, p. 1–23. *In* W. Ruhland [ed.] Encyclopedia of plant physiology. Springer, Berlin.

L. B. Slobodkin

Ecological Energy Relationships at the Population Level

I will be concerned with the ecologically significant energy relationships of single species populations. The theoretical analysis and data deal primarily with laboratory populations of *Daphnia pulex,* but I believe that the conclusions have significance for nature as will be indicated in the discussion.

The number and kind of organisms found in nature is variable from year to year and even from day to day. Despite this variability, it can be said that a sufficiently detailed and temporally extensive examination of any one species, or even of an isolated population of a species, will show that the number of organisms and volume of protoplasm represented by that species or population remain approximately constant. Some populations may vary in size in a cyclic way, either annually or possibly with some other period; others may vary in a random way, but in any case there is some definite mean population size, if data over a period of the order of ten times the mean generation time is considered.

Mean population size does not represent an equilibrium value in the sense that the position of a pendulum bob at rest represents an equilibrium, but rather represents a steady state. The steady state can be characterized by the fact that it requires energy for its maintenance. Just as the steady state temperature gradients in a metal bar heated at one end would disappear in the absence of an energy source, so the steady state properties of the ecological world would vanish in the absence of the radiant energy of sunlight.

It is possible to conceive of a series of metal bars in contact at their ends, with the terminal bar converting radiant energy into heat and this heat then being transmitted by conduction through the whole series of bars. Again a steady state temperature gradient would characterize each bar. Similarly in nature radiant energy is converted into potential energy by the green plants and this potential energy is transmitted through a chain of organisms. There will be various steady state values characterizing this chain of organisms. We will be concerned with some of the values that are more or less immediately recognizable as functions of energy, in particular the potential energy, contained in the various single species populations, that is, the standing crops, and

Reprinted by permission of the author and publisher from *The American Naturalist, 94:* 213–255, 1960. Research supported by the Rockefeller Foundation, the Phoenix Memorial Project of the University of Michigan, and the National Science Foundation.

with the ratios between the various steady state rates of energy transfer in the system, that is, the efficiencies (Lindeman, 1942).

I have confined myself to steady state values since a short period of very high ecological efficiency or standing crop maintenance has very little applicability to long term values that are likely to occur in nature. Non-steady state efficiencies or standing crops must eventually receive intensive study, but I feel that more immediate progress will be made by considering them as minor perturbations of the steady state values for the moment.

Examining the analogy between metal bars, electric wires, flowing water and other inanimate models on one hand and an ecological community on the other, it is seen that the analogy breaks down almost immediately. In a heat transmission system or in an electric wiring diagram the continued physical existence of the energy transmitting elements is not contingent on the maintenance of energy flow. In a biological system, if energy flow ceases there is almost immediate dissolution of the system's components.

The process of energy flow in ecological systems does not lend itself to discussion in terms of diagrams or flow diagrams, except on the most rudimentary level. Flow diagrams are primarily suitable to discussion of heat or radiant energy transport in which physical contact or simply suitable geometric distribution of the physical elements will permit energy flow to occur. In ecological interactions the energy involved is in the form of potential energy, which in general cannot be transmitted between parts of a system without displacement or distortion of the physical elements. That is, energy flows from a plant population to an animal population only when a concrete plant or piece of plant is physically removed into the body of some particular animal. It only remains for the ecologist, if he is to concern himself with energy at all, to develop his theories and concepts on a biological basis rather than by assuming the direct applicability of the laws developed for the simple systems of physics and electronics.

Even such elementary concepts as efficiency and energy, and such universal generalizations as the second law of thermodynamics, have very peculiar properties on the level of the ecological community.

I will therefore discuss the concepts of efficiency, energy and entropy as they apply to ecology. Ecological efficiency will then be shown to have at least three distinct, operationally defined meanings. These three different concepts of efficiency will be evaluated from the data on *Daphnia pulex*. I will then suggest that certain kinds of efficiency are actually constant for most populations in nature. I will finish with some speculations on the relation between energetics and the future development of a complete theory of community ecology.

An Elementary Clarification of Efficiency, Entropy and Energy in Ecological Systems

The superficial simplicity of the concept of ecological efficiency requires careful analysis.

The efficiency of an energy machine is easy to define. A machine, in general, is designed and constructed to do a particular kind of work or to produce a particular form of energy. The ratio of the output to the input (both in energy units) is the efficiency of the machine. The output of a moving locomotive is in energy used to overcome the forces that tend to stop the train; the input is in the potential energy of coal or oil burned in the process. The output of a light bulb is in visible radiation; the input in electrical energy and the ratio of the two is the efficiency. But notice that it is possible to read by the light of a coal loco-motive's fire box or to warm oneself at a cloth-draped light bulb. These do not seem particularly clever ways to read or to keep warm, but they are conceivable. From the standpoint of a moronic bookworm the efficiency of a locomotive might be measured as the ratio of visible radiant energy from the fire box to potential energy consumption. For most locomotives this efficiency is lower than our initial calculations of the efficiency of the locomotive. Our chilled illiterate in front of the draped light bulb might measure efficiency as total radiant energy output over total electrical energy input and this ratio would be higher than our original estimate of the efficiency of the bulb. I conclude from this that the magnitude of an efficiency need have nothing to do with the importance of the process to which the efficiency ratio refers, even in the case of a machine.

An organism must do many things that require energy. Movement of its internal parts, movement of itself in its environment, producing new proto-plasm to compensate for attrition of its own body, adding new protoplasm to its own body and producing offspring are all energy-utilizing processes involving single organisms. On the level of the individual we will be concerned with the efficiency of the last two of these only.

This limitation of our concern is due to a peculiar property of ecological interactions. In order to maintain an ecological community of several kinds of animals and plants at a steady state, the new protoplasm made by any population of organisms of any one species, above and beyond replacement requirements, must be consumed during the process of maintaining the steady state of one or more of the other species present. The new protoplasm produced by any population is in one sense a sum of the new growth occurring in all the individuals of that population. I will therefore consider only new protoplasm to be an ecologically useful kind of potential energy and will largely ignore other possible uses of energy on the individual level.

It is impossible to refer to *the efficiency* of a population. The term must, at all times, be qualified. We can speak only of the efficiency of producing energy in some form which we arbitrarily consider useful (the output) from some other form which we arbitrarily define as useless (the input).

The concept of energy is used rather loosely in ecological literature, and recently the concepts of entropy, negative entropy and information have been used equally loosely. We have statements in print that organisms live on order or that communities consume negative entropy, eat information, etc. It therefore seems appropriate to present a statement of the role of energy in ecology.

Radiant energy is absorbed by green plants and part of this is converted to potential energy by the process of photosynthesis. The slow conversion of this potential energy to kinetic energy permits ecological communities to survive.

Particular compounds in the plant will be converted into other compounds in the herbivore. To the extent that individual reversible chemical reactions are being considered, the various terms in the equation

$$\Delta H = \Delta F + T\Delta S \tag{1}$$

may be evaluated and the change in entropy per mole computed. An appropriate summation of the entropy contributions of all the reactions that occur in the process of incorporating plant material into the herbivore might be considered the entropy production of the herbivore, were it not that:

1. All of the reactions tend to interact with each other.
2. Phase differences and structural restrictions of complicated kinds occur in both plants and animals and the reactions producing these phase differences are, in general, not reversible in any practical sense, at least in the aggregate.

In other words, it is very difficult by simply supplying energy to get an organism to undigest a meal and thereby measure the ΔF associated with the digestion process. The entropy associated with the process of food assimilation is therefore not conveniently measurable.

It is possible to consider the state of all materials entering an organism and the state of the material leaving the organism, duplicate the degradation process in a reversible way and make the appropriate entropy calculation. To my knowledge this has never been explicitly done for all of the ingested and waste products of any particular organism. It is clear, in principle, that it could be done and if it were done we would find an increase in entropy associated with this passage through the organism as illustrated:

$$\Delta H \rightarrow \boxed{\text{organism}} \rightarrow \Delta F + T\Delta S + Q'$$

$$\Delta H = \Delta F + Q' + T\Delta S \tag{2}$$

This requires explication. ΔH can be defined as calories ingested per unit time and ΔF in this context is the calories egested which are still of use to organisms as a supply of energy. $T\Delta S + Q'$ are the caloric equivalent of the heat produced in the utilization of the energy ΔH.

$T\Delta S$ is the heat that would be produced in the various transformations occurring in the organism on the assumption that all reactions were reversible, independent, and of infinitely slow occurrence. None of these conditions is met.

Q' is the heat produced from friction within the organism and from work done by the organism on its environment. In principle, Q' can be evaluated experimentally, but the problem is technically difficult; and except for very simple systems is not likely to be done. It is possible, in an ecological steady state, to write the equation:

Caloric equivalent of the potential energy ingested = caloric equivalent of the potential energy removed from the population by egestion, predation, mortality, etc., plus the heat produced by the population.

It may be legitimate to equate this heat to entropy, but it is not clear what proportion of the potential energy ingested actually shows up as entropy. Estimates of anywhere from two to 50 percent might be offered.

The notion of entropy content of a living organism is extremely complex. Normal thermodynamic theories apply to an equilibrium state, which is equivalent in one sense to death. The theory of thermodynamics of steady states (Denbigh, 1951) is not yet capable of handling elaborate multiphasic systems. The Onsager equations which permit some development of steady state thermodynamics depend on the rigorous definition of fluxes and on their associated forces.

Any energy gradient of an appropriate sort can be considered a generalized force. This is particularly evident in the relation between a temperature gradient and heat flow. The interesting ecological energy flow is in the form of potential energy. Potential energy can have a gradient, as in the glucose gradient in a single cell. Ecologically, however, the gradient is a rather coarse histogram, of standing crop vs. trophic level. The precise procedure for the interpretation of this histogram as a generalized force seems unclear.

The fluxes can, therefore, be stated but the forces can only be dealt with on an almost metaphorical level in ecology. While metaphor leads to certain sorts of insight it does not have predictive power.

A further complication in the application of thermodynamics to steady state systems has been considered by Foster, Rappoport, and Trucco (1957) who find that Prigogine's theorem, which states that steady state systems tend to a condition of minimum entropy production, is not applicable to certain types of feedback systems. It is now generally conceded that individual organisms, populations of organisms, and natural communities must be treated as complex feedback systems and it is quite likely that Prigogine's theorem does not apply to ecological systems, or at least its validity cannot simply be assumed.

Potential energy (ΔH) can be approximately measured by direct combustion of dried tissue. A certain amount of entropy ought to be subtracted from the combustion calories but this is not practical for reasons indicated above. Some free energy is lost prior to combustion in the drying process but this has not yet been evaluated.

When I speak of the energy content of an organism I will be referring to the calories released by burning that organism under normal atmospheric conditions and measured as heat. This is equal to the difference in potential energy per gram between dried protoplasm and the various oxidation products of that protoplasm and includes both the free energy and the entropy.

When I refer to a flow of energy through a population I will be considering only the steady state in which the rate of energy accumulation is zero.

Theory of Ecological Efficiencies and Their Interactions

A population of organisms is characterized by new animals being born, by animals dying or being consumed (by other animals or by man). I will be concerned with the potential energy content of the animals removed from the population by predators or man as a useful energy output and will consider the food consumed by the population as the energy input. That is, when I speak of ecological efficiency, I am assuming the viewpoint of a predator.

In one sense, the removal of an animal by a predator can be considered a divergence of energy from the other possible roles it might play in the population. In particular, the greater the rate at which yield is removed from the population the smaller the standing crop that the population is capable of maintaining. The yield to the predator divided by the difference between the energy used in maintaining a population in the absence of predation and that used in maintaining the same population under predation will be called the population efficiency.

The ratio of the potential energy in an individual organism to the potential energy utilized in its birth and growth will be called growth efficiency, or individual growth efficiency.

The interrelation between these three concepts of efficiency is discussed below.

The gross inflow will be in units of calories per time per volume and will be designated I_F. This will be the amount of food made available to the population from some outside source. In nature food is available to an animal population as a result of the activities of some other population or populations of plants, animals or both. In the laboratory I_F is the potential energy in the food made available to the population by the experimenter. The population does not necessarily consume all of this food. In nature part of it may pass through the ecological space of a particular population without being altered at all. In the laboratory the experimenter may periodically remove excess food.

We must therefore distinguish between I_F, the food available, and I, the energy input or ingested food. $I_F \geqq I$ is always trivially valid.

I is the potential energy ingested per day per population and therefore is slightly different in concept from I_F, unless the volume considered only contains one population. In experimental situations discussed here this difference is not significant.

Population size is effectively constant at a steady state in the absence of cropping, fishing and predation. In a typical experimental study of efficiency the population is cropped and censused at regular intervals so that a plot of population size as a function of time would be saw-toothed. For our present discussion we will consider the population size as the size at the base of the saw teeth. This is equivalent to assuming that no energy must be expended in maintaining those animals which are destined to be cropped at the next census. This assumption is not dangerous so long as the ratio

$$\left(\frac{\text{yield/census interval}}{\text{population size}} \right)$$

is small (see Armstrong, 1960).

Let P' be the caloric content of the standing crop of a population subjected to some arbitrary predation process and let P be the caloric content of the appropriate control population in the absence of preda'tion. P and P' have the

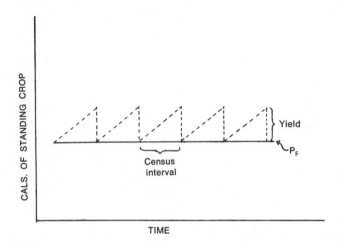

Figure 1

The term standing crop (P_F) is used as indicated in this diagram, ignoring the maintenance cost of the animals destined to constitute yield. A more precise but less convenient measure of standing crop would be the dotted line.

dimensions of calories and represent the potential energy maintained in the living protoplasm of the population. Occasionally we will use the letters P and P' as names for populations.

In order to maintain living protoplasm, energy must be expended. The greater this energy expenditure per calorie of standing crop per time the smaller will be the value of P that can be maintained by a given energy income per day (I).

In general, increase of I will imply increase of P. The precise relation between P and I is not obvious *a priori* since the maintenance cost per calorie of standing crop may be a complicated function of the interactions between individual organisms in the population.

In the most general case, since there is a unique age distribution and total number of organisms corresponding to any steady state caloric content, we can write

$$I = Pc + P^2c' + P^3c'' \ldots \qquad (3)$$

where c is the proportion of the total cost in (calories/calorie day) of maintaining one calorie of standing crop which is assignable to first-order interactions in the population, c' the proportion assignable to second-order interactions, etc.

It has been experimentally demonstrated in Daphnia that only first-order interactions are significant over a wide range of population densities (Slobodkin, 1954) so that for the present discussion (3) reduces to

$$I = Pc \qquad (3')$$

When a population is subjected to predation it either becomes extinct or it comes to a new steady state caloric content P'. If the population can survive steady predation potential energy now leaves the population at some steady state rate as yield to the predator. The ratio of yield (Y) in calories per day to I is the ecological efficiency.

The age and size of the individuals that make up the yield is determined by the interaction between the predator's method and intensity of capturing the yield animals and the population dynamics of the prey and predator.

Assuming that I is not altered by predation, we can take account of the change in maintenance cost associated with predation by writing

$$I = P'(c + \Delta c) + (P')^2(c' + \Delta c') + \ldots \qquad (4)$$

and in the case of Daphnia populations

$$I = P'c + P'\Delta c \qquad (4')$$

Assume the prey to consist only of animals of age i, taken by the predator at the rate Y_i calories/day. Then

$$P'\Delta c = \frac{Y_i}{E_{pi}} \qquad (5)$$

where E_{pi} is the efficiency, in one sense, of this predation process. An efficiency of this type will be referred to as a population efficiency. Since

$$E_{pi} = \frac{Y_i}{P'\Delta c} \qquad (5')$$

population efficiency can be interpreted as the ratio of yield of a particular kind to the increase of maintenance cost associated with the production of that yield. It will vary with the kind of organism taken as yield. It is independent of the intensity of predation so long as the linearity implicit in equation (4') holds.

The precise value of E_{pi} depends on growth and survival and their interaction with age in an intimate way which will be indicated below.

In order to clarify the meaning of E_{pi} we must examine an individual organism more closely. At the time an individual organism begins to take nourishment, say age j, it already represents the end product of a series of metabolic processes, all of which have involved the degradation of potential energy. As it grows to some arbitrary age, say i, it will consume more potential energy and may have increased its caloric content. In any case the total potential energy that must be used to replace an animal of age $i > j$ will be greater than that required to replace an animal of age j.

If we designate the total energetic cost of replacing an animal age i as S_i/E_i, in which S_i is the caloric content of the animal age i, then E_i is the growth efficiency of this animal. The caloric content (S_i) is usually proportional to the size of the animal. E_i can be evaluated as the inverse of the total calories consumed in the production of one calorie of protoplasm at age i and is the "individual growth efficiency" of an animal aged i. It varies with the age and feeding rate of the animal concerned and with the energy expended by the parents of that individual in producing it.

The concept of growth efficiency has suffered in the past from failure to specify precisely the time interval over which the growth of the animal is to be considered. Here we have taken this as the entire life span over which an energetic cost can be meaningfully associated with the individual, following the suggestion of Armstrong (1960).

The relation between E_i and E_{pi} can be clarified as follows.

Let N_0 and N_0' be the number of newborn animals produced per day in populations P and P' respectively, and let l_x and l_x' be the percent survival to age x in the two populations respectively. Define q_x as

$$q_x = \frac{l_x - l_{x+1}}{l_x}$$

and correspondingly define q_x'

Also let

$$d_x = q_x l_x \text{ and similarly for } d_x' \tag{6}$$

and

$$D_x = d_x N_0 \text{ and similarly for } D_x'. \tag{7}$$

The deaths per day in population P is

$$\sum_0^\infty D_x$$

and in population P',

$$\sum_0^\infty D_x'.$$

The primary characteristic of a steady state population is that births and deaths are equal and there is no change in mean total biomass with time.

The caloric cost per day of replacing the dying individuals and maintaining biomass constancy is

$$\sum \frac{D_x S_x}{E_x}$$

in population P and assuming that caloric content as a function of age and growth efficiency are both dependent on predation

$$\sum \frac{D'_x S'_x}{E'_x}$$

in population P'.

In other words

$$I = \sum_0^\infty \frac{D_x S_x}{E_x} = Pc \tag{8}$$

$$= \sum_0^\infty \frac{D'_x S'_x}{E'_x} = P'(c + \Delta c)$$

whence

$$c = \frac{1}{P} \sum_0^\infty \frac{D_x S_x}{E_x} \tag{9}$$

and

$$\Delta c = \frac{1}{P'} \left(\sum_0^\infty \frac{D'_x S'_x}{E'_x} \right) - \frac{1}{P} \left(\sum_0^\infty \frac{D_x S_x}{E_x} \right) \tag{10}$$

and substituting (10) in (5') we define the population efficiency of animals age i as

$$E_{pi} = \frac{Y_i}{\left(\sum_0^\infty \frac{D'_x S'_x}{E'_x} \right) - \frac{P'}{P} \left(\sum_0^\infty \frac{D_x S_x}{E_x} \right)} \tag{11}$$

or if food ingestion is constant under predation simply:

$$E_{pi} = \frac{Y_i}{I \left(1 - \frac{P'}{P} \right)} \tag{11'}$$

From equation (11) it can be seen that population efficiency varies inversely with the depletion of standing crop population size associated with the removal of the yield. Decrease in life expectancy with predation also lowers population efficiency. A predator would be acting with maximum prudence if he removed yield from his prey in such a way as to maximize population efficiency.

We will return to this concept after we have considered ecological efficiency. The commonest usage of the term efficiency in ecological literature is the ratio of the energy per unit time taken from some population (the prey) as yield by some other population (the predator) to the energy per unit time ingested by the prey population. I am deliberately ignoring the often made distinction between ingestion and assimilation, since the meaning of ingestion seems fairly clear while it is an almost arbitrary matter to decide when, or what portion of, a particular mouthful of food is assimilated.

Food chain efficiency (a term borrowed from LaMont Cole) is similar to ecological efficiency except that the denominator is the food available (I_F) rather than the food ingested (I).

Ecological efficiency (E) is therefore defined by Y/I. Since population efficiency is defined for any constant predation method, if I is not changed by predation

$$E = E_p \left(1 - \frac{P'}{P} \right), \tag{12}$$

from which it is clear that for any predation method

$$E \leqq E_p. \tag{13}$$

The relation $E = E_p$ will hold only for a scavenger or for a predator which replaces some other source of mortality. If there is any selective advantage in maintaining a large standing crop, a predator population will tend to maximize yield from its prey. This is equivalent to maximizing food chain efficiency Y/I_F. As predation becomes more intense, the food consuming capacity and standing crop of the prey population will decrease. The decrease of prey standing crop associated with a given yield can be minimized by the predator if he chooses his yield in such a way as to maximize population efficiency. This can generally be accomplished by taking yield animals which are about to die in any case, so that their replacement cost would have to be paid even in the absence of the predator.

Application of the Theory

First order evaluations of the various concepts of efficiency have been made in laboratory populations of *Daphnia pulex* by Richman (1958), Armstrong (1960) and Slobodkin (1959). All three workers have depended on the caloric determinations of *D. pulex* and *Chlamydomonas reinhardi* made by Richman.

Richman (1958) analyzed the growth and feeding of *Daphnia pulex*.

Slobodkin provided an initial theoretical analysis of laboratory predation experiments (1959) and that analysis has been considerably amplified and modified in the present paper.

Armstrong has reconsidered certain of the theoretical assumptions of both

Richman and Slobodkin and has amplified their calculations, in addition to providing new data on growth and predation.

All three workers dealt with a system consisting of *Daphnia pulex* and *Chlamydomonas reinhardi* in which the Daphnia were maintained in conditioned tap water and the algae were grown on sterile agar. Algae was fed to the Daphnia by washing it off the agar, measuring its optical density with a photometer and adding an aliquot of suspension to the Daphnia. Any of the three above cited papers will provide more detailed information on culture techniques.

Richman collected 50 mg. dry samples of Chlamydomonas. These were combined with 250 mg. of benzoic acid and burned in a semi-micro calorimeter bomb. Twelve determinations gave a mean of 5289 cal./gm. on a dry weight basis or 5506 on an ash-free dry weight basis. These figures are very close to those for other Chlorophyceae. The mean of 17 analysis of five species reported by Ketchum and Redfield (1949) is 5340 cal./gm. dry weight and 6154 cal./gm. ash-free dry weight. The caloric content of one Chlamydomonas cell is given by Richman as 1.308×10^{-6} cal.

He sorted *Daphnia pulex* into three size categories. Dried samples of 10–25 mg. were combined with c. 275 mg. of benzoic acid and burned. Mean caloric contents per gram were 4059 ± 203, 4124 ± 229 and 5075 ± 235 respectively for animals of mean length 0.7, 1.3, and 1.8 mm.

Trama found from 5295 to 5975 cal./gm. in the may fly *Stenonema pulchellum* (Trama, 1957). Golley (undated mimeographed sheets) reports cal./gm. determinations for a variety of animals. The extremes are 1780 for the mud crab *Panopius herbsti* and 6223 for *Mus musculus*. Presumably the cal./gm. ash-free dry weight would be somewhat higher since all his reported values for whole Malacostraca seem low, indicating possible inclusion of the mineralized exoskeletons in the samples.

There is sufficiently close agreement between Richman's analyses and the various values reported by Golley and Ketchum and Redfield, to indicate that neither *Daphnia pulex* nor Chlamydomonas are at all extraordinary in caloric content. This point is of some importance since I will later make the claim that ecological efficiencies are quite likely as similar as caloric contents.

Using Richman's caloric content data Slobodkin (1959) assumed three conversion constants which were used to translate numerical census and yield data, derived from 22 laboratory populations, into terms of calories. In addition, the number of Chlamydomonas cells provided for these populations was estimated and translated into calories by using Richman's value for calories per algal cell. This provides a direct estimate of I_F.

From I_F and the calories of yield the food chain efficiency could be evaluated directly for each population. This is presented as a function of the intensity of the predation process (Fig. 2). This measure of fishing intensity is defined elsewhere (Slobodkin, 1957, 1959) and for present purposes we need simply indicate that it is a fishing rate set as a percent of the births occurring in the population.

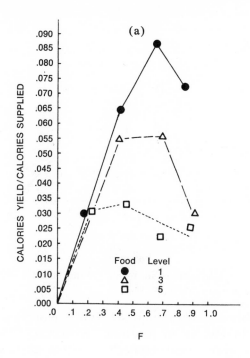

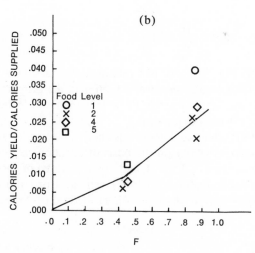

Figure 2

(a) Food chain efficiency on the ordinate vs. F on the abscissa for populations in which adult animals were preferentially removed as yield. (b) Identical with 2(a) except that young animals were preferentially removed as yield.

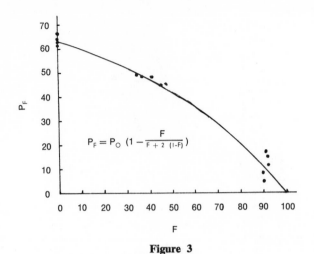

Figure 3

P_F, for populations in which young animals were preferentially removed, vs. F.

Daphnia population standing crops are linearly proportional to their food consumption in the absence of predation (Slobodkin, 1954). There is a simple relation between F and standing crop when all food is consumed, namely

$$\frac{P_F}{P_O} = \left(1 - \frac{F}{2 - F}\right) \qquad (14)$$

(Slobodkin, 1957), Fig. 3. These two relations were assumed generally valid for Daphnia populations and were used to estimate the proportion of the food provided (I_F) that was actually eaten. From this, values of I, the food ingested, could be computed for each population.

Armstrong (1960) computed food ingestion for some of the populations discussed by Slobodkin (1959) on the basis of filtration rate estimates. Comparative values are shown in Table 1 and are seen to be of the same order of magnitude, but in general somewhat lower estimates of I are derived by the method of Slobodkin than by the more direct method of Armstrong.

Table 1

Population	Armstrong (1960)	Slobodkin (1959) I	I'
1.25 A	8.1	8.3	8.6
1.50 A	8.1	7.1	7.9
1.75 A	8.1	8.1	7.7
1.90 A	7.7	6.2	4.9
1.50 Y	8.1	8.1	9.0
1.90 Y	8.0	7.3	9.5

Having estimates of I/four days, standing crop calories and also yield/four days of small animals, large animals and eggs, for 22 experimental populations, an equation of the form

$$I = P'c + \sum \frac{Y_i}{E_{pi}} \tag{15}$$

was set up for each population. The subscript i can take the values A for large animals, S for small animals and E for eggs.

This system of 22 equations was then reduced to a set of four equations:

$$\sum_1^{22} P' I = (c) \sum (P')^2 + \frac{\sum P'Y_A}{E_{pA}} + \frac{\sum P'Y_Y}{E_{pY}} + \frac{\sum P'Y_E}{E_{pE}}$$

$$\sum Y_A I = (c) \sum Y_A P' + \frac{\sum Y_A{}^2}{E_{pA}} + \frac{\sum Y_A Y_Y}{E_{pY}} + \frac{\sum Y_A Y_E}{E_{pE}}$$

$$\sum Y_Y I = (c) \sum Y_Y P' + \frac{\sum Y_Y Y_A}{E_{pA}} + \frac{\sum Y_Y{}^2}{E_{pA}} + \frac{\sum Y_Y Y_E}{E_{pE}} \tag{16}$$

$$\sum Y_E I = (c) \sum Y_E P' + \frac{\sum Y_E Y_A}{E_{pA}} + \frac{\sum Y_E Y_Y}{E_{pY}} + \frac{\sum Y_E{}^2}{E_{pE}}$$

This set of equations was then solved for c, and the three E_{pi},

$$c = 1.68 \text{ cal./cal. day}, \quad E_{pA} = .48, \quad E_{pY} = .036, \quad E_{pE} = .062.$$

We have implicitly assumed that the increments in standing crop maintenance cost associated with the various kinds of yield are additive. This assumption probably does not hold at high rates of yield production but precise analysis of the interaction has not yet been made. The E_{pi} are dimensionless, while c has the dimensions

$$\frac{\text{cal.}}{\text{cal.} \times \text{days}}.$$

The values E_{pi} found from equation (16) are the population efficiencies that would presumably be associated with predation that took only one category of organism as yield. The calculated value of c successfully predicted the mean standing crop of five control populations which did not enter directly into the analysis of equation (15). (Observed 4.8, calculated 4.7). The control populations were used in computing I for each population by means of the relation shown in Fig. 3.

There also exists a population efficiency for any distribution of the age and size of yield organisms at a steady state in a particular population.

From our previous assumptions and equations (11) and (14) this can be determined for each population, as

$$E_p = \frac{\dfrac{2Y}{F} - Y}{I}. \tag{17}$$

The only explicit free variables in this equation are Y and F, since I has already been adjusted in value by the use of (14). In addition, the age and size distribution of the yield are free to vary from population to population, thereby permitting the estimation of E_p from the composition of the yield and the E_{pi} as

$$\frac{1}{E_p} = \sum \frac{Y_i / \sum Y_i}{E_{pi}} \tag{18}$$

The relation between population efficiency estimated from (17) and from the relative composition of the yield (18) is shown in Fig. 4.

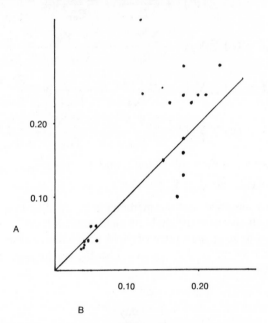

Figure 4

The ordinate (A) is given by $E_p = \dfrac{\dfrac{2Y}{F} - Y}{I}$

The abscissa (B) is $E_p = \sum \dfrac{Y_i / \sum Y_i}{E_{pi}}$. The line assumes $A = B$.

The I' values listed in Table 1 are the result of substituting c and the E_{pi} from the solution of equation (16) back into equation (15) for each population and solving for the input. The fact that the individual values I' tend to diverge from Armstrong's estimates more than do the values of I must be attributed to nonlinear effects. Ecological efficiency, expressed as Y/I', is presented in Fig. 5 as a maximum estimate of ecological efficiency. The maximum

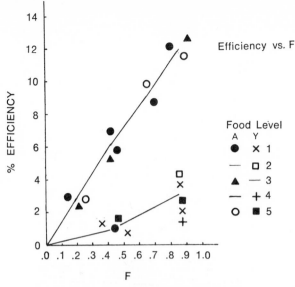

Figure 5

A maximum estimate of ecological efficiency in the
Daphnia populations. Ordinate: Y/I'; abscissa: F.

estimate obtained is 12.5 percent and it seems clear that ecological efficiency
would not exceed 14 percent under any conceivable experimental circumstances.

Values for ecological efficiency of animals in the field, summarized by
Patten (1959) include a value of 75 percent from Teal (1957) which seems
almost impossible, a rather high value of 21 percent (Lindeman, 1942) and
eight other non-zero values ranging from 5.5 percent to 13.3 percent. There
is no significant relation between trophic level and efficiency in these eight
values. Top trophic levels have zero ecological efficiency by definition.

The Daphnia experimental maximum is therefore in good accord with other
data. It seems likely on general grounds that any population in nature will be
producing yield at close to its maximum steady state efficiency.

Combining life table data with growth data Armstrong could compute a
table of E_i for the age categories "eggs," "young," "small," "large" and
"adult." The process of solution was remarkably ingenious but would involve
excessive digression to present here. These efficiencies are presented dia-
grammatically in Fig. 6, with the omission of the data for eggs.

In excessively low concentrations of algae, growth efficiency is low, since
the effort involved in feeding is not compensated adequately by the food ac-
quired. As algal concentrations increase, individual efficiencies increase and
then decrease as the rate of ingestion of food exceeds the capacity of the gut
to digest the food.

Individual growth efficiencies in Daphnia are somewhat higher in maximum

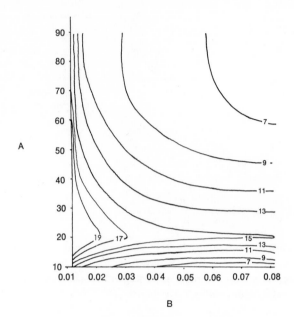

Figure 6

Individual growth efficiency × 100 of *Daphnia pulex*
as a function of Chlamydomonas concentration in
thousands of cells per ml. (ordinate) and the caloric
content of the animals (abscissa). (Using data from
Armstrong, 1960).

value then ecological efficiencies. They are dependent on the food consumption
and growth of individual animals as a function of time and on the energetic
cost of producing an egg. (See Armstrong, 1960; Slobodkin, 1959, Appendix B.)

The rather startling difference in age dependence between population efficiency and growth efficiency is explicable in terms of the distribution of life
expectancy and food consumption as a function of age. Frank, Boll and Kelly
(1957) and Pratt (1943) have shown that Daphnia life expectancy decreases
as a function of age, after the first week of life. Various workers (Richman,
1958; Ryther, 1954) have shown the rate of filtration to be considerably
greater for an adult Daphnia than for a small Daphnia. Removal of an adult
Daphnia will therefore be expected to make relatively little difference in the
mean life expectancy of the animals in the population, not only because the
adult animals' probability of survival in the absence of predation is not particularly high but also because its removal results in a food increase for the survivors which tends to lengthen their life expectancy. This, in effect, decreases
the denominator of equation (11). At the same time the large size of an adult

tends to increase the numerator. The older and bigger an animals gets, the greater this effect. To remove animals that are growing slowly, have lived most of their time and have a low reproductive value (see Fisher, 1958) is the epitome of prudent predation and therefore has a high population efficiency. The consumption of old sows will do little to deplete a pig population, while consuming suckling pig in equal quantity will be disastrous, despite the high growth efficiency of the piglet and the low growth efficiency of the sow. This may be verified at any meat market.

Conclusions

Three types of efficiency have been defined. These are:

1. Ecological efficiency, the steady state ratio of yield to food ingested. This is of primary interest in analysis of natural community interactions. There is some reason to believe that ecological efficiency, at least in aquatic environments, will always have values of from five to 15 percent.

2. Population efficiency, the steady state ratio of yield to the alteration in population maintenance produced by the removal process. The precise value of population efficiency will depend on the age distribution of the animals removed and the population and growth dynamics of the population in question. It may have values greater than one, under some circumstances. In Daphnia it varies from 4 percent for the removal of young animals to 48 percent for old animals. It is of primary interest in establishing criteria for the removal of yield, by relating efficiency to standing crop size.

3. Growth efficiency, the ratio of the calories in an individual organism to the calories expended in the course of its development. This is dependent on a variety of physiological responses of the organism to its immediate environment and has no direct relation to community dynamics. In Daphnia the extreme values found by Armstrong (1960) are 37 percent for eggs at 20,000 algal cells per ml. and 6 percent for adults at algal concentrations of 70,000 cells per ml.

The Daphnia values for all three types of efficiency may be considered typical, at least until more data are available for other species, since the ecological efficiences determined from Daphnia seem of the same order as those determined from various natural situations.

Speculation

A single laboratory population requires approximately two to five hours of work per week for a year, not counting data reduction time or effort. A significant number of populations must be run in any one experiment.

Field studies are even more time consuming and expensive. The laboratory suffers from a lack of reality and the field from a lack of repeatability. At those points where concepts are comparable, the Daphnia laboratory studies agree with various field studies, enhancing my faith in the applicability of the laboratory and the reliaiblity of the field.

As the phenomena that cry for explanation by the physiologist and biochemist are the simple observational facts of animal life, so the phenomena that must be predictable from any ecological theory are the facts of natural history and species abundance distributions. So far we are a long way from explaining these facts. The hope is raised by the present study that just as the metabolism of all organisms turned out to be essentially the same, so the economy of all populations may turn out to be roughly the same. The only way to tell is to repeat these rather painful studies on as many organisms as possible in the laboratory, if possible with considerable increase in precision. I expect to find that ecological efficiency will have approximately the same maximum throughout the animal kingdom, that growth efficiency will vary as a function of age to the same degree as growth rate and that population efficiency as a function of age will vary somewhat more widely, just as population growth curves are more variable than individual growth curves.

In further field studies, it is more difficult to make clear predictions of the pattern that future data will show. I can, however, make a guess. Sampling errors and errors in the conversion of animals to energy units and errors due to failure to have steady state data will all diminish.

In my own laboratory, Richman and I are getting equipment in operating order which will permit us to measure the calories released on combustion of tissue samples weighing as little as four mg. Golley, in Georgia, is now collecting data on larger animals. In a few years it should be possible to convert biomass data from field studies directly into energetic units, not only for large animal studies but for studies of terrestrial and aquatic microfauna. I expect that the use of direct conversion constants for each species will considerably increase the precision of field studies of energetics.

Concurrently, the laboratory predation studies are now being repeated on two species of Hydra and on Chlorohydra. I hope that this will test the applicability of the efficiency values determined for Daphnia to carnivorous animals.

The apparent differences between the estimates of food chain efficiency of corresponding trophic levels in different communities will also tend to vanish. I would guess that herbivores in general will have an efficiency of from 10 to 13 percent. Higher trophic levels may quite likely have slightly lower efficiencies. The presently accepted order of magnitude for food chain efficiencies of from c. 6 to c. 15 percent is almost certainly correct.

In the absence of yield removal, the corpses in a laboratory Daphnia population represent 5 percent of the energy input. Even on high trophic levels, in which predation in the normal sense is not occurring, an efficiency of conversion to decomposer of the same order as the other efficiencies in the system might be expected.

Assuming that we do find constancy of the food chain efficiencies in a steady state community, what type of theoretical structure can be built with this information? By itself, it tells us relatively little that would not have been predictable from elementary thermodynamics or elementary biochemistry. In combination with other ecological information it may provide a set of restrictions that will severely limit the range of possible ecological speculation.

The basic theoretical problem of community ecology is to construct a model or metamodel (Slobodkin, 1958) based on a simple set of assumptions that will generate not only the steady state conditions of the biosphere at a particular instant but the responses of these steady states to various climatic and geologic perturbations. These responses will constitute a theoretical reconstruction of evolution and almost incidentally will be a guide to exploitation of the natural world by man.

It seems possible that the following ecological generalizations are valid.

1. Food chain efficiencies can only have a narrow range of values.

2. Species abundance distribution patterns can only take the form of distributions generated from the theory of interspecific competition (Hairston, 1959; MacArthur, 1957).

3. Pairs of competing species must have a certain minimum of ecological difference if they are to coexist in a steady state (Hutchinson, 1959).

If we now demand that all models of the ecological world that make any pretense to reality must meet all of these conditions simultaneously we will be saved from unbridled speculations and misleading metaphors.

To the degree that these and other generalizations hold we may eventually be able to turn to the mathematician or even to his idiot cousin, the IBM machine, and ask him, or it, to build us all the theoretical models which will meet our restrictions and still maintain steady states and evolve properly under perturbation. At that time, community and population ecology will enter the company of the exact sciences.

In the interim we must increase the precision of those measurements which we know must be made and test the range of applicability of those generalizations which now seem valid.

Summary

The energetic relation between different trophic levels and populations in a community involves primarily potential energy transfer in complex feedback systems, making the applicability of existing steady state thermodynamic theory questionable, since the requirements for direct evaluation of entropy are not met by ecological systems. The only form of energy considered here was potential energy.

The efficiency of a population does not have a unique meaning. Three different concepts of efficiency were defined and evaluated for *Daphnia pulex*. Two of these, the ecological efficiency and population efficiency, refer to the population level. The growth efficiency refers to individual organisms.

Ecological efficiency is a function of the rate of removal of yield and of the kind of yield animals removed. Population efficiency is a function of the kind of animals removed as yield and the interaction between these animals and the population. Growth efficiency does not depend on the removal of yield at all. It is a function of individual food consumption, growth rate and the energetic cost of reproduction.

These three are interrelated. In general, for a particular system of predation ecological efficiency is proportional to population efficiency. Population efficiency is related to the individual growth efficiency through the effect of the removal of animals on the maintenance cost per calorie of standing crop, which in turn is a function of growth efficiency.

The maximum ecological efficiencies found in the Daphnia experiments are of the same order as ecological efficiencies found in nature, implying that ecological efficiency is effectively constant. Presumably the observed value of c. 10 percent has selective significance.

In speculating on the future development of community ecology, I suggested that certain generalizations now available, including the approximate constancy of ecological efficiency, restrict the development of possible theories. When a sufficient number of these generalizations have been stated and tested a comprehensive predictive general theory of community ecology will appear, if only by the elimination of all conceivable theories whose predictions do not conform to the generalizations.

GLOSSARY OF SYMBOLS

Symbol	Units	Meaning
c	calories/(calories $\times$ days)	Maintenance cost of one calorie of standing crop for one unit of time
Δ c	calories/(calories $\times$ days)	Increment in maintenance cost per calorie of standing crop attributable to the removal of yield.
d_x	animals/animals	The fraction of animals born at time 0 that die during the age interval x.
D_x	animals/days	The number of animals that die during the age interval x.
E	$\dfrac{\text{calories/time}}{\text{calories/time}}$	Yield calories divided by input calories. Ecological efficiency.
E_i	$\dfrac{\text{calories}}{\text{calories}}$	Potential energy in an individual of age i, divided by the potential energy needed to replace that individual. Growth efficiency.
E_p	$\dfrac{\text{calories/time}}{\text{calories/time}}$	Yield calories divided by the difference in maintenance cost between the population producing the yield and a corresponding control population. Population efficiency.
E_{pi}	$\dfrac{\text{calories/time}}{\text{calories/time}}$	Population efficiency for the situation in which the yield consists exclusively of animals age i.
i and j	days	Age categories.
l_x	animals/animals	The fraction of animals born at time 0 that survive to time x.

N_o	animals/days	Number of newborn animals produced in a population during one time interval.
P	calories	Steady state standing crop caloric content of a population.
q_x	animals/animals	The proportion of animals that survive up to an age interval that die during that interval.
S_x	calories	The calories of potential energy contained in an animal of age x.
Σ		Summation sign.
x	days	An age category. (Occasionally used as a size category.)
Y	calories/time	Total steady state yield removed from a population per unit time.
Y_i	calories/time	Steady state yield of animals age i removed from a population per unit time.

Note: Except for c' and Δ c', in equations (3) and (4), a symbol with a prime (that is, P' or S_x') refers to a property of a population subject to predation, but is otherwise understood to have the same meaning as the corresponding symbol without the prime (that is, P or S_x).

In the discussion of entropy the symbols all have their conventional meanings.

Symbol	*Meaning*
Δ F	Change in free energy
Δ H	Change in enthalpy
Q'	Non-entropic heat
Δ S	Change in entropy
T	Absolute temperature

ACKNOWLEDGMENTS

I am grateful to the staff and graduate students that have participated in the community ecology seminar at the University of Michigan for their discussion of this work. Doctors Armstrong and Richman have been particularly helpful. Dr. Peter Ovenburg has criticized the mathematical presentation. Professors G. E. Hutchinson, Anatol Rappoport and Karl Guthe have been liberal with their knowledge and encouragement.

Literature Cited

Armstrong, J. T., 1960, Ph.D. dissertation, Department of Zoology. University of Michigan, Ann Arbor, Mich.

Cole, L. C., 1959, Personal communication.

Denbigh, K. G., 1951, The thermodynamics of the steady state. 103 pp. Methuen & Co., London, England.

Fisher, R. A., 1958, The genetical theory of natural selection. Pp. 27–30. Dover Publications, Inc., New York, N.Y.

Foster, C., A. Rappoport and E. Trucco, 1957, Some unsolved problems in the theory of non-isolated systems. General Systems 3: 9–29.

Frank, P. W., C. D. Boll and R. W. Kelly, 1957, Vital statistics of laboratory cultures of *Daphnia pulex* DeGeer as related to density. Physiol. Zool. 30: 287–305.

Golley, F. B., 1959, Table of caloric equivalents. Mimeographed, 7 pp. Available from the author. Department of Zoology, University of Georgia, Athens, Ga.

Hairston, N. G., 1959, Species abundance and community organization. Ecology 40: 404–416.

Hutchinson, G. E., 1959, Homage to Santa Rosalia or why there are so many kinds of animals. Amer. Nat. 93: 145–159.

Ketchum, B. H., and A. C. Redfield, 1949, Some physical and chemical characteristics of algae grown in mass culture. J. Cell and Comp. Physiol. 33: 281–300.

Lindeman, R. L., 1942, The trophic-dynamic aspect of ecology. Ecology 23: 399–418.

MacArthur, R. H., 1957, On the relative abundance of bird species. Proc. Nat. Acad. Sci. U.S. 43: 293–295.

Patten, B. C., 1959, An introduction to the cybernetics of the ecosystem: the tropic-dynamic aspect. Ecology 40: 221–231.

Pratt, D. M., 1943, Analysis of population development in Daphnia at different temperatures. Biol. Bull. 85: 116–140.

Richman, S., 1958, The transformation of energy by Daphnia pulex. Ecol. Monogr. 28: 273–291.

Ryther, J. H., 1954, Inhibitory effects of phytoplankton upon the feeding of Daphnia magna with reference to growth, reproduction, and survival. Ecology 35: 522–533.

Slobodkin, L. B., 1954, Population dynamics in Daphnia obtusa Kurz. Ecol. Monogr. 24: 69–88.

1957, A laboratory study of the effect of removal of newborn animals from a population. Proc. Nat. Acad. Sci. U. S. 43: 780–782.

1958, Meta-models in theoretical ecology. Ecology 39: 550–551.

1959, Energetics in Daphnia pulex populations. Ecology 40: 232–243.

Teal, J. M., 1957, Community metabolism in a temperate cold spring. Ecol. Monogr. 27: 283–302.

Trama, F. B., 1957, The transformation of energy by an aquatic herbivore, Stenonema pulchellum (Ephemeroptera). Ph.D. dissertation, Department of Zoology, University of Michigan, Ann Arbor, Mich.

4

Community Ecology

Evolution, as remarked earlier, affects communities and ecosystems to no lesser an extent than it does species populations. A short paper by H. G. Baker opening this last section describes certain of the concepts of evolutionary ecology that were discussed in the second section as they relate to adaptation in ecosystems. Dr. Baker, Director of the University of California Botanic Garden at Berkeley, has published numerous works in the fields of biosystematics and evolutionary ecology. The paper reproduced here underlines the fact noted earlier, and reiterated by Dr. Ehrlich and Dr. Holm, that the science of ecology is indivisible. In this paper, Dr. Baker traces the developing philosophy of ecosystem adaptation from the Clementsian concept of the organismic community, and the individualistic concept of Gleason.

Such considerations are inseparable from those of other basic concepts, such as dominance and diversity in communities. R. H. Whittaker has long been concerned with the theoretical implications of such concepts, and with the analysis of community structure. In the paper reproduced here, Dr. Whittaker presents a critical review of dominance and diversity in terrestrial communities.

The questions raised in this second paper are pursued further by M. F. Buell and his associates from Rutgers University. This ecological group, one of the largest in the country, has been working for a number of years on the mixed deciduous forests of northeastern America. In this study they have confirmed the validity of the application of the Curtis multidimensional concept to the forest vegetation of northern New Jersey. One major result of this application is the conclusion that the present oak-dominated vegetation is successional to a maple-dominated forest.

In plants, as in animals and microbes, the question of dominance is related to that of energy transfer in ecosystems. J. S. Olson discusses the question of energy storage, balance, and transfer in populations—questions that are inseparable from those of ecosystem analysis.

The subject of bioenergetics is taken up in an exhaustive review, reproduced in full, by M. D. Engelman. In this major statement, Dr. Engelman follows the development of studies in terrestrial energetics from the physics of combustion by animals, through physiological work on maintenance metabolism, to trophic-dynamic modelling. He considers available information on terrestrial communities in regard to the Lindeman trophic-dynamic model, and suggests equations for the further analysis of communities.

In the sixth and last paper, R. Margalef presents suggestions as to general ecological theory. He provides two general conclusions. One is that the energy required to maintain an ecosystem is inversely related to its complexity; the other is that in adjacent systems there is a flow of energy toward the more mature system. If, as is sometimes maintained, bioenergetics represents the ultimate expression of the discipline, ecology can be considered to have come to maturity only when such principles as these have been presented, established, and accepted.

Herbert G. Baker

Reasoning About Adaptations in Ecosystems

The term ecosystem was introduced 30 years ago by A. G. Tansley, although the concept itself is much older. In Tansley's [1] view an ecosystem consists of all the living organisms together with the physical and chemical components of their immediate environment interacting together in a system. Use of the word system [2] implies that there is "a set of elements or objects together with relationships between the objects and between their attributes."

In the investigation of ecosystems, most controversy has centered upon the relations between the biotic components. Here, two extreme arguments, propounded in pre-ecosystem days, still have their supporters. One, based on the "biome as an organism" concept of F. E. Clements [3, 4, 5], contends that the degree of organization in a biotic community is so great that the analogy with an organism is properly drawn. Ecological succession leading to the steady state of the climax is looked upon as the equivalent of the development of an individual organism to adulthood.

In complete contrast is the "individualistic" theory of the plant community put forward in detail in 1926 by H. A. Gleason [6] (and recently extended to biotic communities in general by P. R. Ehrlich and R. W. Holm [7]).

Gleason points out that environments vary both in space and in time, consequently in no two places will the vegetation be exactly alike. Furthermore, when a new area is opened up for colonization, species whose populations could flourish in the new area will tend to arrive, but each species migrates independently and at a different rate. Some will fail to arrive at all. The "individualistic" theory goes to the limit in implying that organization, as such, is absent or quite unimprotant in a community which, in Gleason's words, [8] is a *"coincidence"* resulting from chance immigration followed by environmental sorting. Elsewhere, Gleason has indicated his belief that the sorting takes place at the level of the individual by writing [9] "Phenomena of vegetation depend completely upon the phenomena of the individual."

A definition of the verb "to organize" is needed here and the following seems applicable [10]: "To form as or into a whole consisting of interdependent or coordinated parts, especially for united or harmonious action." "Organization" is "the state or manner of being organized."

Reprinted by permission of the author and publisher from *BioScience, 16:* 35–37, 1966. Research supported by the National Science Foundation.

Most holders of the "individualistic" theory are botanists—taxonomists and plant geographers who have encountered "vegetational continua" rather than spatially circumscribed, floristically discrete plant communities when attempting to classify or map vegetation. However, the existence in nature of continua does not necessarily mean that organization is missing from naturally occurring biotic communities (nor does it mean that discrete communities will not occur as well as continua).

In fact, most demonstrations of vegetational continua have been made from the sampling of stands within a single plant formation. This is to be expected because when two communities differ markedly in physiognomy there is usually a marked change in species composition on passing from one to the other. No doubt this results largely from the effect of the ecological dominants in modifying the conditions for the plants growing beneath them, thereby differentially selecting which may survive.

Raunkiaer's demonstration [12], through his "biological spectra," of physiognomic similarities of floras and vegetation in corresponding climates in different parts of the world has been paralleled in my own research [13] by the determination of "spectra" based on seed-dispersal mechanisms, pollination-relations, and other features of reproductive biology. From this we may deduce that in each one of these plant communities there is a kind of structure which indicates by its constant repetition a more efficient exploitation of natural resources on a long-term basis than would be produced by other combinations of plant forms. At least one of the criteria of "organization" is met here—there is coordination, at any rate. Because plants of more than one species are capable of filling each of the roles, however, the successful substitution of one species for another (as in a continuum)can occur without loss of coordination.

If whole biotic communities (or ecosystems containing them) are studied, structuring is clearly visible and the cycling of energy and nutrients in the ecosystem emphasizes the interdependence (another of our criteria of "organization") between the occupants of different trophic levels. Mutualism of other kinds than the directly nutritional (mostly cases of protocooperation, where the relationships are mutually beneficial without being completely obligate) also involves populations operating at different trophic levels. As a consequence, it will be the student of the ecosystem, or at least of the biotic community within it, who will be most likely to see and appreciate mutualistic interactions if and when they occur. One cannot extrapolate arguments from plant communities taken separately to total biotic communities; even the alleged random dispersal of seeds and spores which so impressed Gleason cannot be applied unhesitatingly to animals which, to varying degrees, move preferentially into certain environments.

If, in addition to coordination and interdependence, it can be demonstrated that a significant measure of homeostasis resides in a community, the existence of "organization" in that community should be unchallengeable. In fact, since 1877, when Möbius [14] published his study of an oyster bank in the North Sea, evidence has been brought forward repeatedly of the resistance of natural communities to change, including resistance to invasion by new kinds of organisms reaching the locality. Weeds and other exotics do not usually replace indigenous species unless the natural vegetation is disturbed by man [15]. According to Howard [16], reduction in numbers of predators in an ecosystem does not usually permanently increase the numbers of animals in the prey populations because other control mechanisms come into play; it takes really drastic alterations, usually by man, such as logging, burning, or the introduction of radically different herbivores in artificially maintained excess numbers, to produce devastating changes in the ecosystem.

Homeostasis appears also to be involved in cases of secondary succession and in the cyclic events which take place in climax communities [17]. The subject of homeostasis in large ecological systems is discussed in general fashion with positive conclusions in a recent paper by C. F. A. Pantin [18], but it does need more attention from students working at first hand with smaller, more particular ecosystems.

Altogether, however, although the amount of organization occurring in communities may vary from example to example, its presence can hardly be denied.

Ecology and Evolution—A Synthesis

We are only now beginning to assemble the necessary background information, equipment, and techniques to investigate how coordination, interdependence, and homeostatic mechanisms come into being and operate. We are only just beginning to appreciate how complex are the relationships between, for example, flowers and anthophilous insects, between trees and the microbiota of the soil, and between many other interactants. Nevertheless, we are also beginning to find out how to analyze and appreciate these relationships. Thus, even if recent evidence [19] that exudates into the air of the soil from one kind of plant are selectively toxic to other kinds of plants does show that interactions between plants in nature are more complex than just competition for resources which are in short supply, it also shows us that they are of a sort susceptible to analysis and experimental modification.

Mutualistic interactions need not necessarily involve only one pair of populations at a time. Thus, several plant species may be linked in a community by their common dependence upon a single kind of pollinator [20]. Evidence of this in relation to "humming bird flowers" in California, Mexico, and Central America is being collected and other examples, such as the concentration of bat-pollinated trees in tropical African savannas, may be quoted [21].

Much of the study which is needed before we can hope to properly appreciate the coordination and interdependence of populations of plants and animals in ecosystems (and the homeostasis of the latter) is going to be both ecological and evolutionary. I believe it is most important that ecologists should develop and keep such an evolutionary outlook, recognizing that directional, disruptive, and stabilizing evolution are going on continuously, now as well as in the past. Although any original association of plants and animals *may* have been fortuitous, character-displacement, race-formation, and other local adjustments may be expected to be continually improving and maintaining coordination, interdependence, and community homeostasis. Evolutionists, on the other hand, might, with advantage, increase their awareness that the organisms which they study have not evolved in biological vacua, responding only to the climatic features of past environments.

In the century which has passed since Charles Darwin and Alfred Russel Wallace first put evolution on a sound selectionist basis, it has become progressively more ecological. Characters, individuals, and populations have followed each other as the units upon which natural selection is deemed to act. Now, the stage is set for the next step in synthetic evolutionism, the study of the evolution of biotic communities, even of ecosystems.

There may be at least as many evolutionary processes involved here as are involved in evolution at the population level. Chance probably plays a greater role than it does in the evolution of species populations, but the end-product, the biotic community, has its own order of organization. This is hardly surprising when the cells, the organs, the individuals, and the populations which compose it are, themselves, highly organized. The closeness of the organization may decrease continuously in this progression from cell to ecosystem, but it is there for the evolutionist-ecologist to study. I believe that this marriage of ecology and evolutionism should be a highly fertile one.

References

1. Tansley, A. G. 1935. The use and abuse of vegetational concepts and terms. *Ecology,* 16: 284–307.
2. Schultz, A. M. 1964. The ecosystem approach. Paper presented to the American Society of Range Management, Ukiah, California, Nov. 12, 1964.
3. Clements, F. E. 1916. Plant succession. *Carnegie Inst. Wash. Publ. No. 242.*
4. Clements, F. E., J. E. Weaver, and H. C. Hanson. 1929. Plant competition. *Carnegie Inst. Wash. Publ. No. 398.*
5. Phillips, J. 1931. The biotic community. *J. Ecol.,* 19: 1–24.
6. Gleason, H. A. 1917. The structure and development of the plant association. *Bull. Torrey Bot. Club,* 44: 463–481. 1926. The individualistic concept of the plant association. *Bull. Torrey Bot. Club,* 53: 7–26.
7. Ehrlich, P. R., and R. W. Holm. 1963. *The Process of Evolution.* McGraw Hill Book Co., New York.
8. Gleason, H. A. 1926. The individualistic concept of plant association. *Bull. Torrey Bot. Club,* 53: 16.
9. Gleason, H. A. 1917. The structure and development of the plant association. *Bull. Torrey Bot. Club,* 44: 464.
10. Barnhart, C. L. (ed.). 1961. *The American College Dictionary.* Random House, New York.
11. Curtis, J. T. 1959. *The Vegetation of Wisconsin. An Ordination of Plant Communities.* University of Wisconsin Press, Madison.
12. Raunkiaer, C. 1934. *The Life Form of Plants and Statistical Plant Geography.* Collected papers translated by H. Gilbert-Carter. Clarendon Press, Oxford, England.

13. Assisted by N.S.F. Research Grant No. G21821.

14. Möbius, K. 1877. *Die Austern und die Austernwirtschaft.* Berlin.

15. Baker, H. G. 1965. Characteristics and modes of origin of weeds. In *The Genetics of Colonizing Species* (H. G. Baker and G. L. Stebbins, eds.), Academic Press, Inc., New York.

16. Howard, W. E. 1965. Interaction of behavior, ecology, and genetics of introduced mammals. In *The Genetics of Colonizing Species* (H. G. Baker and G. L. Stebbins, eds.), Academic Press, Inc., New York.

17. Watt, A. S. 1947. Pattern and process in the plant community. *J. Ecol.,* 35: 1–22.

18. Pantin, C. F. A. 1964. Homeostasis and the environment, in Symp. Soc. Exp. Biol., no. 18, *Homeostasis and Feedback Mechanisms.* Cambridge.

19. Muller, C. H., W. H. Muller, and B. L. Haines. 1964. Volatile growth inhibitors produced by aromatic shrubs. *Science,* 143: 471–473.

20. This matter was dealt with at some length in the verbal presentation of this paper. As far as I can tell, the idea was advanced first by L. van der Pijl, Fledermäuse und Blumen. *Flora,* 131: 1–40. See Baker, H. G., 1963. Evolutionary mechanisms in pollination biology, *Science,* 139: 877–883, for a more extended consideration of the subject.

21. Baker, H. G. 1961. The adaptation of flowering plants to nocturnal and crepuscular pollinators, *Quart. Rev. Biol.,* 36: 64–73.

R. H. Whittaker

Dominance and Diversity in Land Plant Communities

Natural communities are mixtures of species which are unequally successful. In a given community one or a few species, the dominants, overshadow all others in their mass and biological activity and may strongly affect conditions of environment for other species. The community also includes other species which are of intermediate abundance or rare, and it is the number of these less conspicuously successful species which primarily determines the community's diversity—its richness in species. When species are arranged in a sequence from most to least important, they form a continuous progression from dominants through intermediates to rare species. This article is an inquiry into the form and meaning of these progressions in plant communities on land, based on field data from Great Smoky Mountains National Park. A number of "laws," interpretations, and models to fit such progressions have been offered [1–10]; curves expressing four major hypotheses are shown in Fig. 1. Much of the discussion that follows concerns the fact that the relations are less lawful, orderly, and consistent than ecologists might wish. They are no less significant for all that, in relation to both ecology and evolution.

Two approaches to measurement need to be distinguished, although they are often closely related. (i) Species-diversity may be measured on the basis of numbers of species in sample units large enough to include some minor species. In terrestrial communities relations of species numbers to sample areas are complex; but, within limits, numbers of species increase approximately as the logarithm of sample area [11]. It is not feasible in most cases to obtain all the species from the community, and comparing numbers of species in sample quadrats of equal area is the most convenient way to compare diversities in different communities. Measurements which are based on relations of numbers of species to numbers of individuals have been suggested by Fisher, Corbet, and Williams [4], who propose the relationship

Reprinted by permission of the author and publisher from *Science, 147*: 250–260, 1965. Copyright 1965 by the American Association for the Advancement of Science. Research was supported by the National Science Foundation and the State of Washington (Initiative Measure No. 171). The author thanks R. W. Becking, J. S. Olson, and W. A. Niering for collaboration in part of the field work and J. E. Cantlon, D. M. Hurst, and W. A. Niering for comments on the manuscript.

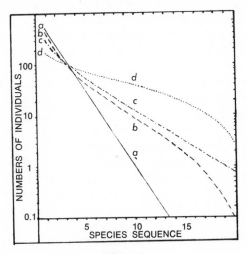

Figure 1

Curves to fit dominance-diversity relations—four major hypotheses: (curve *a*) geometric series of Motomura [1], $c = 0.5$; (curve *b*) lognormal distribution of Preston [6], $a = 0.2$, $n_o = 2.26$; (curve *c*) logarithmic series of Fisher, Corbet, and Williams [4], $a = 3.542$; (curve *d*) random niche hypothesis of MacArthur [10]. Numbers of individuals in the species, on the ordinate, are plotted against species number in the sequence of species from most to least abundant, on the abscissa. The curves are all computed for a hypothetical sample of 1000 individuals in 20 species.

$$S = \alpha \ln(1 + N/\alpha),$$

and Margalef [9], who proposes

$$d = (S - 1)/\ln N.$$

(In these equations S is the total number of species in the sample, α and d are diversity measurements, and N is the sum of the "importance values" for all species in the sample.) (ii) Other measurements, based on quantitative relations of species, include Simpson's [12] index,

$$c = \Sigma \, (y/N)^2;$$

the slope of the geometric progression [13],

$$y = Ac^{(x-1)};$$

and the measurement used by MacArthur [14; see 9],

$$c = -\Sigma \, (y/N) \log \, (y/N).$$

[Here c is a measurement of concentration of dominance (in the last equation c decreases with increasing concentration of dominance); y is the "importance" of a given species (number of individuals, biomass, productivity, coverage, and so on); A is the importance value for the most important species; and x is the number of a species in the sequence from most important to least important.] Although measurements of the group ii type have been used as diversity measurements, their magnitudes are determined primarily by the extent to which importance values are concentrated in one or a few major species; they express concentration of dominance.

It is difficult to apply some of these measures to plant communities because it is uncertain what constitutes a plant individual in some vegetation [15]. It also seems inappropriate to compare on the same scale individuals as disparate in size as trees and herbs. Terrestrial plant species are best ranked by scales —of productivity, biomass, or coverage—which are independent of the concept of "individual" and more directly expressive of importance than are numbers of individuals. "Success" and "importance," words derived from human affairs, must be given meaning by the ecologist if they are to be used in discussing species in natural communities. Probably the best single measure of the species' importance in the community is its productivity (dry weight of organic matter produced or energy bound per unit area per unit time), which both expresses the species' biological activity and indicates the share of the community's environmental resources that it utilizes.

Table 1 gives the numbers of species in quadrats and the Simpson indexes [12] of dominance concentration for plant communities in the Great Smoky Mountains. The species numbers are numbers of tree and shrub species in a 0.1-hectare (20 × 50 m) quadrat and numbers of herb species within, and outside, 20 randomly selected quadrats, of 1 square meter each, within the 0.1-hectare quadrats. The Simpson indexes are computed from measurements [16] which indicate relative net annual primary production (dry weight of organic matter produced by green plants, after respiration by these plants, per unit area per year) of species [17].

Ranges of Dominance and Diversity Values

Species-diversities in the Great Smoky Mountains show a wide range of values. The "quadrat totals" (of tree and shrub species in the 0.1-hectare quadrats plus herbs in the 20 1-square-meter quadrats) may be compared with data for the Siskiyou Mountains of Oregon [18] and the Santa Catalina Mountains of Arizona [19]. The poorest communities are high-elevation heath balds with 2 to 4 vascular plant species. (Some stands consist of a single-vascular plant species, but several lichen and moss species are also present.) Floristically poor forests, including many high-elevation stands of spruce and fir in all three mountain ranges and western yellow pine (*Pinus ponderosa*) forest in the Santa Catalinas, have quadrat totals of 5 to 15 species. The creosote bush (*Larrea divaricata*) desert below the Santa Catalina Mountains has an average quadrat total of 9.3 species, exclusive of winter herbs. Many plant communities have quadrat totals of 15 to 35; these communities include a wide range of forests and woodlands in all three ranges, as well as desert grasslands and most types of desert in the Santa Catalina Mountains. The richest communities have quadrat totals of 40 or more; these are the deciduous cove forests, or mixed mesophytic forests, and one oak forest in the Great Smoky Mountains, certain rich grasslands and open woodlands in the Santa Catalina Mountains, and the north-slope, shrub-phase Sonoran desert of mountain slopes in the Santa Catalina Mountains. The species-diversity of vascular plants in this desert actually exceeds that of the rich cove forests if the many winter annual herbs of the desert, excluded from its quadrat total of 43 species, are considered [19]. Diversities of varied communities in Norway [20] and Wisconsin [21], though not directly comparable because they are based on samples of different sizes, show similar wide ranges.

Variations in species-diversity do not simply parallel variations in community production. In the Great Smoky Mountains, production and diversity are not significantly correlated either in vegetation samples or in samples of foliage insects [22]. The magnificent redwood forests of the California and Oregon coasts, probably among the most productive of temperate-zone climax forests [16], have low species-diversity [18]. So far as the data can be interpreted in relation to community development or succession [see 9, 23] they suggest that diversities may both increase during successions and decrease during parts of successions [as from open to closed heaths (in Table 1, from sample 1 to sample 2 and from 5 to 6) and from some mixed heaths (samples 5 and 7) to climax spruce heath (sample 17)]. Diversity is as high in the disturbed, immature forests (samples 15, 19, 22) as in mature, stable forests of corresponding environments. Tree-stratum diversities increase from high elevations toward low [24]. Diversities of herb and shrub species show no clear relation to elevation below 1400 meters in the Smokies. In both the Siskiyou and Santa Catalina Mountains herb diversities increase from low to middle elevations, and decrease from these to high elevations (Fig. 2) [18, 19]. Along the moisture gradient in the Smokies, the highest tree diversities are in intermediate sites, the highest shrub diversities are in intermediate-to-dry sites, and the highest herb divisities are in moist sites. Diversities of the three strata are scarcely correlated (Table 1), and numbers of insect and bird species are not simply correlated with numbers of plant species [14, 22].

Simpson indexes of concentration of dominance in the tree stratum range from over 0.9 in forests with a single species strongly dominant, through values of 0.3 to 0.7 in a variety of other forests in which one species is less strongly dominant or in which two species share dominance, to values of 0.1 to 0.3 in stands with dominance shared among a number of important species. Stands of the last group include, from opposite ends of the moisture gradient, the moist deciduous cove forests and the dry oak heath and low-elevation pine forests. Those shrub and herb strata for which significant measurements can be obtained show similar ranges of values. No marked positive or inverse corre-

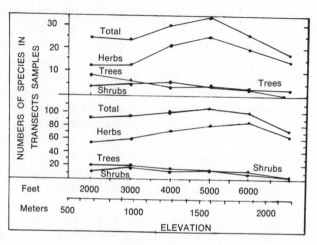

Figure 2

Species diversities of vascular plants in relation to
elevation in the Siskiyou Mountains, Oregon, based
on data of Whittaker [18]. (Top) Average numbers
of trees and shrub species in 0.1-hectare quadrats
and of herb species in 25 quadrats of 1 square meter
each, and totals of these averages for all three strata.
The averages are based on the 50 vegetation samples
of a transect for each 300-meter elevation belt.
(Bottom) Total numbers of herb, shrub, tree, and all
vascular plant species occurring more than once in
the 50 samples of a transect.

lations among dominance concentrations for the three strata appear. An inverse
relation between dominance concentration and species-diversity can be observed, but it is weak. Results from measurements of both diversity and concentration of dominance reinforce previous observations [18, 22, 24] on the
lack of simple pattern and lack of strong correlation in the relations of these
community characteristics to environment and to each other.

Dominance-Diversity Curves

The data from the Great Smoky Mountains make it possible to rank most
of the vascular plant species in a community by relative amounts of net annual
production [16, 17]. Dominance-diversity curves for a number of communities
are shown in Fig. 3, with species arranged in sequence by estimated above-
ground net annual production. A range of forms may be observed in these
curves and in curves for other samples from the Smokies. The numbers in the
following paragraph refer to production samples listed in Table 1 and tabulated
elsewhere [16]; the numbers are given to indicate the relative frequency of
occurrence of different types of curves among the 37 samples.

Steeply oblique curves approximating geometric series occur in some communities of low species-diversity—in Fraser fir forest [No. 33 (illustrated in Fig. 3) and No. 32], hemlock forest (No. 16), California coast redwood forest (No. 43), and some heath balds (Nos. 4, 8, 9). At one extreme the slopes are nearly vertical; in certain heath balds (Nos. 2, 3) the production of the second most productive vascular plant species is lower by several orders of magnitude, and there is no third species in the samples. In contrast to these communities, certain communities of intermediate species-diversity [Nos. 10 (illustrated) and 28] have moderate slopes approximating geometric series. The majority of the curves are of the sigmoid form illustrated for a spruce heath (No. 17) and pine heath (No. 12) and appearing in forests of low (Nos. 17, 29–31), intermediate (Nos. 11–13, 20–22, 24), and high (Nos. 15, 18, 23, 27) species-diversity, as well as in some heath balds (Nos. 6, 7) and grassy balds (Nos. 34–36). In a number of the curves [Nos. 6 (illustrated) and 19, 24, 31, 35, 49], the curve from the first to the second (or second and third) species is less steep than the apparently geometric slope from these major species down to the less steep middle slope of the curve. A few curves (Nos. 5, 19, 25, 26, 30) have two separate middle portions of less steep slope. The floristically rich cove forests [Nos. 15, 18, 23 (all illustrated)] have sigmoid curves of moderate slope throughout. The rich oak forest (No. 27, illustrated) combines a steep initial slope, indicating strong dominance concentration, with a moderate middle slope expressing high herb-stratum diversity.

Several considerations bear on the confidence with which the curves can be interpreted.

1) Species are plotted by values for above-ground net production which are based on three different types of field measurements, and on conversion of these measurements to give above-ground net annual productions [17]. Root production is omitted, but use of reasonable estimates for root production does not change the shape of the curves, though it changes the sequence of some species. The curves do not include all the vascular plant species in the communities. The species omitted (including the "additional herbs present" listed in Table 1) are of very low productivity and are believed to fit into the steep lower slopes of the curves, with production values scattered through orders of magnitude below 0.01 gram per square meter.

2) Curves have been plotted also by biomass and coverage. In forests the fraction of the community's biomass contributed by the dominant trees is even larger than the fraction of community production contributed by these trees. Use of biomass values steepens the initial slopes of the curves for the dominant trees but does not otherwise change their shapes. Coverage, being a lower power function than biomass and production, produces curves which are less steep throughout but which retain their essential geometric or sigmoid form. Coverage curves of similar forms have been obtained for a wide range of communities, from forest to desert, in the Santa Catalina Mountains [25].

3) In the sigmoid curves the initial slopes include mostly trees, but in some cases major shrub and herb species; the middle slopes include mainly herbs,

Table 1

Numbers of Vascular Plant Species in Quadrats, and Dominance Concentration Values Based on Net Production Measurements, for Communities in the Great Smoky Mountains

Sample No.	Community	Elevation (m)	Exposure (Direction, Inclination)	Number of Species					Dominance Concentration		
				Trees, per 0.1 ha	Shrubs, per 0.1 ha	Herbs, per 20 m²	Additional herbs present*	Quadrat total	Tree	Shrub	Herb
	HEATH BALDS										
1	Rock succession	2110	SW, 30°		2	2	3	4		0.76	0.98
2	Leiophyllum lyoni mat	2110	SW, 20°		2			2		1.00	
3	Rhododendron carolinianum	2110	S, 32°		2			2		0.99	
4	Rhododendron catawbiense	2110	NE, 20°		4		1	4		.98	
5	Open mixed heath	1500	SE, 15°		7	5	1	12		.30	.48
6	Mixed heath, Peregrine Peak	1430	SW, 35°		5	2		7		.45	
7	Mixed heath, Brushy Mountain	1500	NE, 15°		7	3		10		.46	
8	Mixed heath, Rocky Spur	1560	SW, 20°		5			5		.54	
9	High mixed heath	1490	SE, 14°		8		1	8		.29	
	FOREST HEATHS										
10	Pine forest, Cades Cove	610	SW, 15°	12	10	5	2	27	0.24	.37	.51
11	Pine forest, Pittman Center	550	SW, 26°	13	7	12	10	32	.30	.40	.29
12	Pine heath, Brushy Mountain	1070	S, 30°	6	10	7	4	23	.92	.43	.58
13	Pine heath, Greenbrier Pinnacle	1340	SW, 22°	7	9	4	1	20	.51	.39	.75
14	Chestnut oak heath	970	W, 32°	9	9	5	2	23	.16	.24	.81
15	Hemlock-beech cove forest	430	Ravine	18	9	13	13	40	.21	.45	.81
16	Hemlock-rhododendron forest	1280	NNE, 30°	3	2		1	5	.74		.15

272

No.	Stand										
17	Spruce-rhododendron forest	1740	ESE, 40°	3	4			7	.69	.66	.12
						FORESTS					
18	Deciduous cove forest	730	NW, 17°	10	3	30	18	43	.18	.18	.23
19	Cove forest transition	820	N, 17°	18	10	16	24	44	.12	.82	.56
20	Oak-hickory forest†	300	W, 8°	17	5	4	4	26	.40	.84	.83
21	Chestnut oak forest	820	ENE, 10°	13	8	6	1	27	.37	.35	.15
22	Successional tulip forest	760	NE, 10°	9	9	17	9	35	.73		.27
23	Upper deciduous forest	1310	NNW, 25°	9	4	26	7	39	.26		.38
24	Hemlock mixed cove forest	870	N, 7°	8	3	20	5	31	.34		.37
25	Gray beech forest	1580	N, 25°	6	1	22	10	29	.65		.22
26	Gray beech forest	1580	S, 32°	4	3	14	7	21	.59		.27
27	Northern red oak forest	1450	E, 16°	9	5	27	4	41	.65		.23
28	Red oak, white oak forest	1390	SW, 15°	7	8	17	14	32	.36	.32	.41
29	Spruce-fir forest	1800	NE, 7°	4	3	10	2	17	.47		.46
30	Spruce-fir forest	1620	SW, 25°	5	5	4	7	14	.56		.29
31	Spruce-fir forest	1620	SW, 24°	4	1	9	8	14	.54		.52
32	Fraser fir forest	1920	NNW, 11°	3	5	6	2	14	.93		
33	Fraser fir forest	1900*	SSW, 35°	3	2	1	2	6	.64		.27
43	Coast redwood forest‡	100	Flats	4	1	15	2	20	.99		
						GRASSY BALDS					
34	Silers	1700			2	19	5	21			.79
35	Gregory	1670			1	9	6	10			.42
36	Thunderhead	1500			1	7	2	8			.97

* Additional herb species observed outside the 20-m² clipping quadrats, within the 0.1-hectare stand quadrat, which are excluded from the quadrat totals.

† From Oak Ridge National Laboratory, Oak Ridge, Tenn.　　‡ From Humboldt Redwoods State Park, Calif.

but usually some minor tree and shrub species; and the final steep slopes are predominantly minor herbs. When the tree and shrub stratum and the herb stratum are plotted separately, geometric slopes in some cases result for one or both strata. In other cases curves for both strata have the sigmoid form, as do many of the curves for the single-stratum balds. The sigmoid curves are not simply products of different geometric slopes for canopy and undergrowth communities.

4) It is not possible to make statistical tests in most cases. Five replicate samples were taken, however, from a spruce-fir forest. The five gave somewhat different slopes and arrangements of species in the middle of the curves, but generally similar slopes and patterns for the curves as wholes. An indication of reliability results from superimposition of the curves for the three cove forest samples from different environments (Fig. 3, Nos. 15, 18, 23): curves representing different species sequences have remarkable identity of form. It is believed that, while individual points are affected by sampling error, the forms of the curves are reliable.

Models for Dominance-Diversity Curves

The geometric series was originally suggested as a fit for such curves by Motomura [1], but it fits only a minority of them. Both geometric and sigmoid curves may be generated, however, by quite modest models.

It may be assumed that productivity and species composition of the plant community are determined by environmental factors such as light, moisture, temperature, and nutrients. Intensities of these factors in the soil and microclimate within the community are strongly affected by the character of the community, and most of the factors vary horizontally in a small-scale pattern or mosaic determined by microrelief and by root, shade, and leaf-fall effects of the plants themselves. Different species are differently adapted to various intensities of these factors, to different levels of above-ground vertical space and below-ground root space, and to different seasonal times of foliage production, flowering, and fruiting. A species' specialization in the community— its particular way of relating to other species and to intracommunity conditions of environment, space, and time (diurnal and seasonal)—is termed its "niche." Ranges of environmental factors, of space, and of time to which different species within a community are adapted represent axes of a "niche space," or hypervolume, in the sense in which the term is used by Hutchinson [26]. The niche space is an arena in which the species populations compete and evolve in competition with each other. The word *competition* here denotes the situation in which (i) environmental resources are limited in amount, (ii) each species population increases to a maximum determined by the resources available to it, (iii) amounts available to a given species are affected or determined by the use of these resources by other species of the community, and (iv) species populations are consequently limited by the presence of other species, a

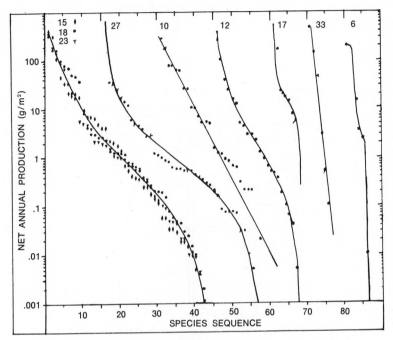

Figure 3

Dominance-diversity curves for vascular plant communities in the Great Smoky Mountains. Points represent species, plotted by net annual above-ground production (on the ordinate) against the species' number in the sequence of species from most to least productive (on the abscissa). In each curve the highest point represents the most productive species (species number 1 in the sequence) and the lowest point the least productive species. For the sake of graphic clarity, however, the curves have been arbitrarily spaced out, their origins being separated by 10 or 15 units along the abscissa. Positions of their origins on the abscissa are indicated by the vertical ticks along the top border of the figure.

limitation which is often mutual. Each species occupies the part of niche space to which it is best adapted—the part in which it has competitive advantage over other species—and each species occupies as large an area, and occupies it as densely, as competition and other limitations permit.

The multidimensional niche space is represented in the model by a two-dimensional square in which species occupy rectangular niches (Fig. 4a). The size of a species' rectangle represents the fraction of the community's niche space which that species occupies. It is assumed that the fraction of environ-

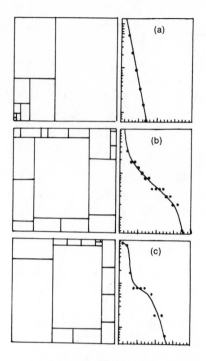

Figure 4

Models for species and niche relations which may
underlie dominance-diversity curves. The squares in
each case represent a niche space which is divided
among the species of the community, represented by
rectangles. Sizes of the rectangles for species represent their share of niche space and environmental
resources, as expressed in their population density,
productivity, or other "importance" measurement. In
the curves to the right of each model, species are
plotted (on the ordinate) on a logarithmic scale by
areas of their rectangles against species number in the
sequence of species from most to least important (on
the abscissa).

mental resources utilized and the fraction of total community production
realized by the species will be closely related to (though not identical with)
the fraction of niche space occupied. If the community has a total green plant
production N and the most successful species is able to appropriate a fraction
k of the niche space and environmental resources with a production kN, if the
second most successful species utilizes the same fraction of the remainder, and
if each succeeding species utilizes the same fraction of the space not appropri-
ated by more successful species, then,

$$y = N(1 - k)^{x-1} k = Ac^{x-1}, k = 1 - c,$$

—the familiar geometric series. With random variation in k, series closely resembling the data for some communities result. Although the model greatly simplifies relations in the community, as a model must, it may be a plausible representation of competitive relations, and their expression in production, in some communities with few species.

In many communities evolution has produced a larger number of competing species, among which no one has so great a competitive advantage over all the others. If the first species occupies a smaller, "central" area of the niche space, there may be several "peripheral" niches to be occupied, each representing a different pattern of adaptive specialization—adaptation to low intensities of light and other environmental factors; timing different from that of the dominants, as in the case of spring and late-summer herbs; and so on. For the model it has been assumed that each species will occupy a rectangle of somewhat flexible shape (the ratio of the sides being between 1.5 and 2.0) and will occupy, within the limits set by these ratios and by prior occupation of niche space by other species, the largest niche space available to it. There results the sigmoid curve of Fig. 4b, with three slopes: (i) an upper slope, representing a few dominant species, each appropriating a substantial fraction of niche space, with numerical relations between them approaching a geometric series; (ii) a middle, less steep slope representing a larger number of subordinate species, each adapted to some special portion of niche space, less widely separated from one another in productivity than the dominants; (iii) a terminal slope representing a few rare species occupying the remnants of space; since their number is small and the range of their production values is wide, the terminal portion of the curve slopes steeply to the last, rarest, species.

There is one further consideration relative to the forms of some of the curves. In many communities two species share dominance. The subarctic-subalpine forests (or taiga) which occur around the Northern Hemisphere in cool climates, below the tundra, and extend southward in mountain chains are such communities. In many areas, including the Great Smoky Mountains, the pair of dominants includes a spruce (*Picea* sp.) and a fir (*Abies* sp.). The two dominants have different optimum environments, where their populations reach maximum densities. Generally the fir population is centered in the higher, cooler, and moister part of the spruce-fir forest, the spruce population in the lower, warmer, and drier part. Along environmental gradients between the environments where spruce is most strongly dominant and those where fir is most strongly dominant, the population balance between the two shifts gradually and continuously. In some environments the two dominants are of equal importance; in many environments they are too nearly alike in importance to fit a geometric series. It is assumed that, because of differentiation between the environmental requirements of these species, they share the central niche space in the model. If the first species occupies a niche area to one side of the center and the rest of the niche space is assigned to the second and the remaining species in accordance with the rules discussed for Fig. 4*b*, there results a sigmoid curve with a flattened uppermost slope (Fig. 4*c*), resembling the curves for several of the field samples (for example, sample 6 in Fig. 3).

Types of Dominance-Diversity Curves

Dominance-diversity curves are thus not of a single form but represent a range of intergrading types. The variations observed in data for the Great Smoky Mountains and the curves produced by the models permit us to interpret the various mathematical relationships proposed to fit these curves (Fig. 1).

1) Curves approximating geometric series [1, 2] are of fairly wide occurrence. They appear for some communities which have rigorous environments and only a few species, widely scattered along the logarithmic scale of relative importance. Less steep geometric slopes appear also for some communities with less severe environments and moderate species-diversity. Small samples from communities for which the curves are sigmoid (for example, samples limited to the first few species of sample Nos. 12, and 15, 18, and 23 of Fig. 3) will often have curves approaching geometric form [27].

2) Most communities, including many of those in relatively rigorous environments, have a small group of dominants, a larger middle class of moderately important species, and a smaller number of rare species, many of them ecological specialists. The curves are sigmoid on the semilogarithmic plot of Figs. 1 and 3, but various departures from simple sigmoid form result from the competitive relations among species in particular communities. Although competition is assumed to have a major role in determining species abundance of vascular plants, at least two other factors should be allowed for. (i) The importance of some species may be controlled in part by animal consumption. Control of populations of plant species by different consumer species may represent a further aspect of niche differentiation, increasing the number of species which can occupy the niche space of the community beyond the number made possible by their niche differentiation in relation to factors of environment other than animal consumption. This and other forms of niche differentiation involving relations between species populations may affect the slope of the intermediate and lower portions of the curves and the species-diversity of the community. (ii) Because of the internal pattern of the community, which is affected by microrelief and other factors, only in scattered places in the community may niche requirements of some species be met. The importance of these species, and the number of species successfully occupying such niches, may be determined in part by balances of seed dispersal into, and mortality in, these scattered niche locations, analogous to the balances of immigration and extinction that affect island floras [28]. The importance of rarer species, especially, and the slopes of the lower parts of curves, may be affected by this balance, for seed dispersal in some species may be inadequate to fill more than a fraction of the suitable niche locations in the community.

3) Some samples from communities of high species-diversity, among them the cove forests, have sigmoid distributions of moderate slope throughout. These same communities have "lognormal" distributions when plotted by Preston's method [6, 7, 29] (Fig. 5). The numbers of species in octaves of im-

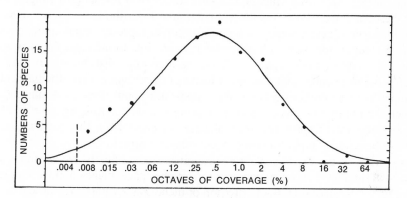

Figure 5

The lognormal distribution of Preston [6], applied to rich north-slope, shrub-phase Sonoran desert communities on lower mountain slopes of the Santa Catalina Mountains, Arizona [19]. Points are numbers of species (on the ordinate) plotted against their coverage values within the octaves of coverage (on the abscissa). The coverage values indicated in the abscissa are upper limits of octaves. Coverage values (for 122 species) are averages of measurements for ten similar stands [19]. The fitted curve is described by $y = 17.5e^{-(0.245\,R)^2}$, where y is the number of species in an octave R octaves distant from the modal octave (which contains $n_0 = 17.5$ species). The dashed vertical line is the "veil line," to the left of which no data on species numbers and importances are available. (Field methods did not measure coverages below 0.004 to 0.008 percent.) The data form a sigmoid curve of gentle slope in a plot of the type of Figs. 1 and 3.

portance measurements (production of 1-2, 2-4, 4-8 . . . g/m², and so on) are determined, and these numbers of species, on the ordinate, are plotted against the octaves (hence, according to a logarithmic scale of importance values) on the abscissa. Species numbers then form a binomial curve on a logarithmic base, a lognormal distribution fitted by the relation.

$$n = n_0 e^{-(aR)^2}, \ \Sigma n = S = n_0(\pi)^{1/2}/a,$$

in which n is the number of species in an octave R octaves distant from the modal octave containing n_0 species, and a is a constant which often approximates 0.2. Here, as in the treatment in terms of geometric series, it is assumed that importance values of species are best compared on a logarithmic scale, and the results indicate that this is the case. The lognormal distribution implies that there are many species of intermediate importance, and that numbers of species decrease according to a probability curve with increasing departure from the modal importance value. Incomplete data for tropical forests [30] suggest that for these, as for the cove forests, geometric and logarithmic plots give sigmoid and lognormal curves, respectively, but the curves represent many more species than the curves for the cove forests do. It is possible to interpret the curves of Fig. 3 as small-sample departures from the lognormal distribution. It may be preferable to consider that the varied forms of the curves express the particular competitive (and other) relationships of species populations in communities. When the number of species is large and the factors determining their relative importance are complex and multiplicative in effect [31], the distribution of species by relative importance approaches the lognormal.

4) None of the vascular plant communities studied fits the MacArthur [10] curve a (random division of constant total niche space, niches nonoverlapping, see Fig. 1) or curve b (random division of niche space without reciprocal competitive limitation, niches overlapping). Data for animal communities also generally fail to fit these curves [32, 33]; curve a is fitted by some small samples of bird [10] and snail [34] populations. The bird samples compiled by Udvardy [35] show, on the semilogarithmic plot of Figs. 1 and 3, a range of forms from geometric slopes to sigmoid curves approximating the MacArthur curve a. MacArthur's studies [14, 36] of niche relationships in birds are among the most significant contributions to the species-diversity problem. It is probably not the case, however, that division of niche space is in general random in the sense assumed in MacArthur's models [see 29, 32]. Species of singing birds combine self-limitation of population density (by territoriality) with self-limitation of niche space, each species having behavior which limits the fraction of community space in which it nests and takes food: they "cartelize" niche space. Consequently, no species reaches the degree of dominance which might be possible with unrestricted competition, and the relative importance of species are much less widely divergent than is the case with vascular plants and may fit the MacArthur curve a. The steep geometric series and the MacArthur curve may thus represent different limiting cases in organisms with widely different kinds of interaction and modes of population limitation.

5) Samples which are not taken from a single community of interacting species (for example, collections of insects caught in light-traps) will often approximate a geometric series because (i) a small number of species, not competitively related, will tend to have their relative abundances widely scattered along the logarithmic scale; (ii) such samples may include mainly major species, among which geometric relations are frequent; and (iii) hierarchial relations (in which one secondary predator feeds on n_1 individuals of a primary predator species and each of these feeds on n_2 individuals of a herbiv-

orous species) may be involved when more than one trophic level is represented [37].

6) Larger samples which are not from a given, integrated community will often approximate lognormal distributions [6, 7, 38, 39]; these distributions imply that there are many species of intermediate abundance and fewer rare and common species. The logarithmic series [4, 38, 40] often fits the steep upper and flatter middle parts of such curves but predicts an excessive number of rare species. The lognormal distribution seems to be the most satisfactory interpretation of the relative abundances of species in nature in general, as distinguished from sets of interacting species in particular communities.

Diversity in Relation to Environment

These observations may also place in perspective the results on species-diversity and concentration of dominance. The inverse relation of these is weak. In temperate-zone communities, at least, no strong and consistent relationship should be expected between the steep initial slopes of curves, which relate the dominant species, and the middle slopes, which primarily affect species-diversity. There is no reason why species-diversity relations for different strata or fractions of the community, subject to different environmental factors and modes of population limitation, should parallel one another; and they often do not [18, 22, 24]. Species-diversities of vascular plant communities are affected most strongly by richness in subordinate species; in temperate-zone forests these subordinate species are mainly the herbs. High species-diversities consequently occur under such divergent conditions (all favoring the growth of subordinate species) as those of the southern Appalachian cove forests, open woodlands of drier environments and woodlands on serpentine soils in the Siskiyou Mountains [18], and certain deserts of less severely arid environments [19]. In contrast to these, eastern hemlock (*Tsuga canadensis*) forests, in favorable moist sites intermediate to the rich upper cove forests and the red oak (*Quercus borealis*) forests (samples No. 16, 23, 27), are of very low species-diversity—as low as the diversities of some communities of highest elevations.

Although the external, topographic environment of the hemlock forest is as favorable as that of the cove and red oak forests, the needle-litter and root relations of the dominant hemlocks render the environment *within* the community, affecting subordinate species, unfavorable [24, 41]. The deciduous cove forest and serpentine woodland offer, for very different reasons, more favorable conditions for undergrowth plants. In the deciduous cove forest, although the intensity of the light reaching the herb stratum in the summer is low, soil nutrients and moisture conditions are favorable. The serpentine woodland is believed to offer undergrowth plants relatively favorable conditions of light, soil moisture, and some nutrients, because the special nutrient conditions of serpentine soil permit the development of only an open tree stratum [18, 42]. An intensity of one of these environmental factors that is more favorable for the community as a whole may imply a wider range of tolerable variations in that factor, from place to place within the community, to which different species are adapted. The serpentine woodland, for example, offers herb species a wide range of light intensities, from sunlight to shade, beneath its open tree and shrub strata, in contrast to the more uniform shade beneath canopies of evergreen forests of lower species-diversities on other soils nearby. The factors are also variously interrelated in their effects on plants. The favorable moisture conditions of the cove forest permit spring herbs to grow and fruit rapidly before trees are in leaf; these spring herbs are largely absent from the drier forests of the area. The greater soil moisture of the cove forest makes possible wider niche differentiation in relation to season than that which occurs among herbs in drier forests. It is suggested that the effect of environmental "favorableness" on undergrowth diversity results from the fact that favorable conditions for a given environmental factor permit a wider range of adaptations, by different species, to different intensities of that and other environmental factors within the community.

Two broad geographic trends in species-diversity have been observed.

1) One of the major generalizations of biogeography is the increase in numbers of species in many plant and animal groups from high latitudes into the tropics. Numbers of tree species in forests, for example, increase from high elevations downward and from high latitudes equatorward—from one to three species in many subarctic-subalpine forests to more than 100 species in some tropical forests [30, 43]. The effects of glaciation in northern latitudes are one source of contrast, as illustrated in the low diversity and distinctiveness of serpentine-soil floras of glaciated areas compared with serpentine floras of non-glaciated areas [42]. There has been less time, in the younger communities which have developed on surfaces exposed by the retreat of glaciers, for numerous species to evolve while interacting with one another in these communities and to evolve niche differentiation. To state this more generally, tropical environments have changed less during evolutionary time than temperate and arctic ones, and have been freer from severe environmental conditions of catastrophic consequence to natural populations. Evolution under tropical conditions may consequently be more strongly influenced by selection for survival relative to other organisms than by selection for survival in a severe environment. Over longer periods of evolutionary time larger numbers of species evolve in accommodation to each other in the tropics, and they evolve with smaller differences in niche requirements; because of this they are able to exist together in communities of high species-diversity [44].

2) Paradoxically, species-diversities have been found to increase from maritime climates inland to continental climates which have apparently less favorable, more widely fluctuating present climates, which one would expect to be less favorable to species-diversity (Fig. 6) [18, 19]. The increase occurs on three levels, distinguished as "alpha" diversities (diversities within indi-

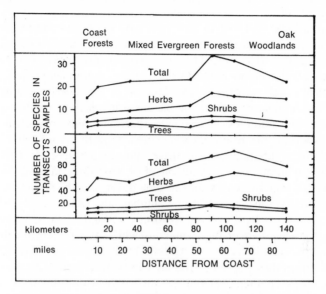

Figure 6

Species-diversities of vascular plants in relation to the climatic gradient from maritime climates inland to continental climates at low elevations in the Siskiyou Mountains, Oregon and California, based on data of Whittaker [18]. (Top) Average numbers of tree and shrub species in 0.1-hectare quadrats and of herb species in 25 quadrats of 1 square meter each, and totals of these averages for all three strata. The averages are based on six samples representing the topographic moisture gradient in each study area (ravine, lower north-facing slope and open north-, east-, southeast-, and southwest-facing slopes). (Bottom) Total numbers of herbs, of shrubs, of trees, and of all vascular plant species occurring in the six samples of a study area. The diversities in the plot at top are alpha diversities of individual plant communities; those in the plot at bottom are gamma diversities of vegetation patterns in relation to topography. The points at far left are for the coastal redwood forests. The lower diversities of the points at far right may result from grazing disturbance.

vidual communities), "beta" diversities (or relative extents of differentiation of communities along topographic gradients), and "gamma" diversities (diversities of vegetation patterns, resulting from both alpha and beta diversities). It is not known whether these trends are worldwide. Possible bases for them have been discussed [18, 19]; it is likely that during the dry summers of temperate maritime climates most of the limited available soil moisture is used by dominant plants and soil drought limits the growth and diversification of subordinate plants.

Various interpretations of these trends may be suggested. (i) Severe, unstable, and recent environments limit the numbers of species which have evolved to maintain themselves in those environments. In older and less severe environments larger numbers of species tolerate environmental conditions and maintain themselves with finer differentiation of their environmental requirements. (ii) In both severe and favorable environments species-diversity results mainly from utilization by subordinate species of environmental resources "left over" beyond the resources requisitioned by the dominant species and from niche differentiation among these subordinate species. (iii) Species-diversity of a community is a resultant of at least three interrelated determinants—characteristics of environment, time during which species have evolved niche differentiation in relation to one another, and characteristics of the particular species which have evolved to form communities in that environment, especially characteristics of the dominants which affect environmental conditions for subordinate species. (iv) Certain broad trends in relation to climate exist. Apart from these, species diversity can be interpreted, but is not simply predictable, from characteristics of the environment or from such community characteristics as dominance, productivity, maturity, and structure or physiognomy.

Conclusion

Dominance and diversity form an area of complex and often obscure relationships, not subject to neat, unitary formulation. The preceding discussion may illustrate, in this area of ecological study, the "loosely ordered complexity" of natural communities [45], and the consequent need for sufficiently wide observations to allow one to judge which observations are of general and which are of exceptional phenomena. In this, as in other areas, the ecologist needs to seek a balanced perspective in which he neither loses sight of complexities in his fondness for theory, model, and generalization nor loses sight of significant general relationships in his fondness for the professional's knowledge of details, complexities, and exceptions. Recognition that dominance-diversity relations lack neatness is essential to a realistic understanding of these relations; this lack of neatness does not reduce their significance or the fascination of the suggestions about community organization which they offer.

The interpretations suggested follow Hutchinson [8, 26, 46] in applying the concepts of "niche" and "niche space" to diversity problems and assume that the principle of Gause applies to vascular plant species. According to the principle of Gause (and Volterra), or the principle of competitive exclusion [26, 47], no two species in a stable community occupy the same niche and compete for the same environmental requirements in the same part of intra-community space at the same time. The idea may suggest another idea from across the sciences—the principle of Pauli, that no two electrons occupy the same atomic "niche." Theory of population dynamics, experiments with laboratory populations, and some observations of competitive relations of species in the field support the belief that if two species are in direct competition, one or the other must become extinct or one or both must so evolve that their requirements are no longer identical. Competition among vascular plants has been investigated [48], and aspects of niche differentiation in plant communities observed [49]; but the application of the principle of Gause to vascular plants is often obscure. It must for the present be assumed that differences of degree in the requirements for different environmental resources exist among the vascular plant species in a community. These differences of degree among plants would be analogous to the phenomenon of character displacement [46, 50] among animals—quantitative differences in dimensions (of the order of 1.2 to 1.0 or 1.3 to 1.0) between related species, differences which permit them to occur together in communities as partial competitors in those parts of their geographic areas in which both species occur. Some differences in environmental requirements of plant species are expressed in morphology, but others which result from physiological differences and are not expressed in morphology are likely to be unknown to us.

Such marginal differentiation in environmental requirements may also permit competing plant species to have widely overlapping distributions. Cases are observed in which two animal species in direct competition replace one another abruptly along an environmental gradient [26, 51). The principle of Gause may imply, for these direct competitors, a sharp boundary of competitive exclusion at the point along a gradient where the competitive advantage shifts from one to the other. Such population discontinuities are, though of much theoretical significance, of rare occurrence in relation to the immense number of cases in which distributions of competing species overlap broadly [24, 52, 53]. Because plant species populations in general overlap broadly along an environmental gradient and population densities of the species change gradually along the gradient, composition of the communities changes gradually and continuously along the gradient (Fig. 7) [18, 24, 54, 55]. Some relatively steep transitions or "zonal" boundaries between communities occur, but these appear to be of exceptional rather than general significance and are apparently not based on competitive exclusion [24]. Green plant species are undoubted competitors for light, water, and nutrients, but they must be partial competitors with small differences in requirements which make possible their occurrence together in communities, their broad distributional overlap, and the continuity along environmental gradients of the communities they form.

The environmental gradients of a landscape may be conceived as forming a multidimensional habitat-space, to which there corresponds a multidimensional pattern of populations and communities. In this pattern each species has its own population center and distribution, differing from those of all other species according to the principle of species individuality [56]. Along a given environmental gradient, and probably in habitat-space, the centers or modes of species populations are scattered, as if randomly located (Fig. 7) [24, 54]. It has been thought that species evolution in communities might produce clusters of species with distributional centers close together in habitat-space and separated from the clusters of other species [18, 24, 52, 57]. It is probable, however, that if such clusters exist they are exceptional [18, 24]. It is suggested that, rather than evolving to form clusters of associates, green plant species predominantly evolve toward dissociation (in the sense of scattering of distributional centers in habitat-space and in geographic areas), by which means they escape direct competition within their population centers.

Niche differentiation and habitat differentiation may thus be very closely related aspects of the same tendency to evolve away from direct competition. Alpha diversities of communities and gamma diversities of landscapes are ex-

---

Figure 7

Plant populations along an environmental gradient. The gradient is the topographic moisture gradient from mesic (moist) ravines (at left) to xeric (dry) southwest-facing slopes (at right), between elevations of 460 and 760 meters in the Great Smoky Mountains. Populations of major tree species are plotted by percentages of the total numbers of tree stems over 1 centimeter in diameter 1.4 meters above the ground; the curves are smoothed from data summarized in Table 1 of Whittaker [54]. All the species illustrated are part of the same vegetation gradient, but they are separated into four panels for the sake of clarity. Although, with 28 species and 13 steps of the gradient, some species must have their modes in the same step, the modes of species populations appear to be scattered along the gradient. Pairs of species having their modes in the same step of the moisture gradient may be shown to be differently distributed in relation to the elevation gradient [24]. Some species are bimodal, with two ecotypes having different population centers [24]. Plant communities intergrade continuously, from cove forests (transect steps 1–4), through oak forests (steps 6–8), to pine forests (steps 10–13). The species are as follows: 1, *Halesia monticola;* 2, *Acer saccharum;* 3, *Hamamelis virginiana;* 4, *Carya tomentosa;* 5, *Nyssa sylvatica;* 6, *Pinus strobus;* 7, *P. rigida;* 8, *Quercus borealis;* 9, *Tsuga canadensis;* 10, *Fagus grandifolia;* 11, *Acer rubrum;* 12, *Qu. alba;* 13, *P. echinata;* 14, *Aesculus octandra;* 15, *Betula alleghaniensis;* 16, *B. lenta;* 17, *Cornus florida;* 18, *Carya glabra;* 19, *C. ovalis;* 20, *Qu. marilandica;* 21, *P. virginiana;* 22, *Tilia heterophylla;* 23, *Cladrastis lutea;* 24, *Liriodendron tulipfera;* 25, *Qu. prinus;* 26, *Qu. velutina;* 27, *Oxydendrum arboreum;* 28, *Qu. coccinea.*

pressions on different levels of the same evolutionary processes. The evolution of differences in environmental requirements permits many species to exist together in the landscape, broadly and continuously overlapping in varied combinations to form the landscape's many, intergrading communities. A common principle of evolutionary diversification in environmental relations and interrelations of species, by which direct competition is avoided, may thus relate such varied ideas and observations as the principle of Gause and the phenomenon of character displacement, adaptive radiation and the richness in species of the living world, the rare occurrence of discontinuities of competitive exclusion and the more general broad overlap of partial competitors, the principle of species individuality, and the continuity of natural communities.

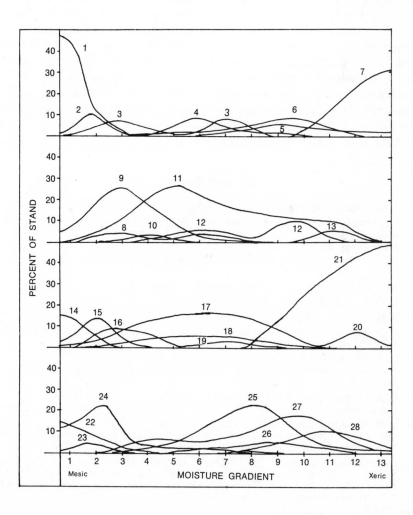

Summary

Most plant communities consist of several or many species which compete for light, water, and nutrients. Species in a given community may be ranked by their relative success in competition; productivity seems to be the best measure of their success or importance in the community. Curves of decreasing productivity connect the few most important species (the dominants) with a larger number of species of intermediate importance (whose number primarily determines the community's diversity or richness in species) and a smaller number of rare species. These curves are of varied forms and are believed to express different patterns of competition and niche differentiation in communities. It is probably true of plants, as of animals, that no two species in a stable community occupy the same niche. Evolution of niche differentiation makes possible the occurrence together of many plant species which are partial, rather than direct, competitors. Species tend to evolve also toward habitat differentiation, toward scattering of their centers of maximum population density in relation to environmental gradients, so that few species are competing with one another in their population centers. Evolution of both niche and habitat differentiation permits many species to exist together in communities as partial competitors, with distributions broadly and continuously overlapping, forming the landscape's many intergrading communities.

References and Notes

1. I. Motomura, *Japan. J. Zool.* 44: 379 (1932).
2. M. Numata, H. Nobuhara, K. Suzuki, *Bull. Soc. Plant Ecol.* 3: 89 (1953); H. Nobuhara and M. Numata, *ibid.* 3: 180 (1954); K. Shinozaki and N. Urata, *Res. Population Ecol.* 2: 8 (1953).
3. A. S. Corbet, *Proc. Roy. Entomol. Soc. London* A16: 101 (1942); M. V. Brian, *J. Animal Ecol.* 22: 57 (1953).
4. R. A. Fisher, A. S. Corbet, C. B. Williams, *J. Animal Ecol.* 12: 42 (1943).
5. D. G. Kendall, *Biometrika* 35: 6 (1948).
6. F. W. Preston, *Ecology* 29: 254 (1948).
7. R. E. Beschel and P. J. Webber, *Ber. Naturwiss. Med. Vereins Innsbruck* (1963), vol. 53 (Festschrift Gams), p. 9.
8. G. E. Hutchinson, *Proc. Acad. Nat. Sci. Phila.* 105: 1 (1953); ———, in *Readings in Population and Community Ecology*, W. E. Hazen, Ed. (Saunders, Philadelphia, 1964), p. 2.
9. D. R. Margalef, *Gen. Systems* 3: 36 (1958) [translated from *Mem. Real Acad. Cienc. Arts Barcelona* 32: 373 (1957)].
10. R. H. MacArthur, *Proc. Natl. Acad. Sci. U.S.* 43: 293 (1957); ———, *Am. Naturalist* 94: 25 (1960); ———, in *Readings in Population and Community Ecology*, W. E. Hazen, Ed. (Saunders, Philadelphia, 1964), p. 307.
11. H. A. Gleason, *Ecology* 3: 158 (1922); A. G. Vestal, *Illinois Biol. Monographs* 20: No. 3, 1 (1949); E. E. A. Archibald, *J. Ecol.* 37: 274 (1949); D. W. Goodall, *Biol. Rev. Cambridge Phil. Soc.* 27: 194 (1952); B. Hopkins, *J. Ecol.* 43: 409 (1955); P. D. Kilburn, *Science* 141: 1276 (1963).
12. E. H. Simpson, *Nature* 163: 688 (1949).

13. R. H. Whittaker, *Ecology* 42: 177 (1961).

14. R. H. MacArthur and J. W. MacArthur, *ibid.,* p. 594.

15. C. B. Williams, *J. Ecol.* 38: 107 (1950); P. Greig-Smith, *Quantitative Plant Ecology* (Butterworths, London, 1964).

16. R. H. Whittaker, *Ecology* 44: 176 (1963); ———, "Estimated net production of forests in the Great Smoky Mountains," unpublished.

17. Measurements used to compute Simpson indexes for the tree stratum are estimated volume increments (apparent volume growth of wood, computed from half the area of wood growth per year at 1.4 meters above the ground times tree height, summed for all individuals of the species of trees and arborescent shrubs in the 0.1-hectare quadrats). Simpson indexes for the shrub stratum are based on dry weights of current twigs with leaves, clipped in the 20 1-square-meter undergrowth quadrats; those for herbs are based on dry weights of clippings at ground level in the same quadrats. The curves of Fig. 3 are based on multiplication of the same field data by conversion factors to obtain estimated above-ground net annual production [R. H. Whittaker, *Ecology* 43: 357 (1962); ———, N. Cohen, J. S. Olson, *ibid.* 44: 806 (1963)]. Although conversion factors vary with plant species, plant size, and environment, the reader can obtain curves similar to those of Fig. 3 for the other published samples [16] by using average conversion factors for strata: above-ground net annual production of trees per unit of estimated volume increment $= 2.0$ g/cm³; above-ground net annual production of shrubs per weight of current-twig clipping $= 3.0$ g/g; above-ground net annual production of herbs per weight of clipping $= 1.0$ g/g.

18. R. H. Whittaker, *Ecol. Monographs* 30: 279 (1960).

19. ——— and W. A. Niering, *Ecology,* in press.

20. E. Dahl, *Skrifter Norske Videnskaps-Akad. Oslo, I: Mat-Naturv. Kl.* 1956, No. 3, 1 (1957). ·

21. J. T. Curtis, *The Vegetation of Wisconsin* (Univ. of Wisconsin Press, Madison, 1959), p. 517.

22. R. H. Whittaker, *Ecol. Monographs* 22: 1 (1952).

23. J. L. Yount, *Limnol. Oceanog.* 1: 286 (1956); E. P. Odum, *Ecology* 41: 34 (1960); D. R. Margalef, *Am. Naturalist* 97: 357 (1963).

24. R. H. Whittaker, *Ecol. Monographs* 26: 1 (1956).

25. ———, unpublished data.

26. G. E. Hutchinson, *Cold Spring Harbor Symp. Quant. Biol.* 22: 415 (1957).

27. K. Shinozaki, *Physiol. Ecol. Kyoto* 6: 127 (1955).

28. R. H. MacArthur and E. O. Wilson, *Evolution* 17: 373 (1963).

29. F. W. Preston, *Ecology* 43: 185, 410 (1962).

30. P. W. Richards, *The Tropical Rain Forest* (Cambridge Univ. Press, Cambridge, 1952); S. A. Cain, G. M. O. Castro, J. M. Pires, N. T. da Silva, *Am. J. Botany* 43: 911 (1956); ———, in *Fifty Years of Botany,* W. C. Steere, ed. (McGraw-Hill, New York, 1958), p. 261; S. A. Cain and G. M. O. Castro, *Manual of Vegetation Analysis* (Harper, New York, 1959); D. J. Greenland and J. M. L. Kowal, *Plant Soil* 12: 154 (1960).

31. P. J. Clark, P. T. Eckstrom, L. C. Linden, *Ecology* 45: 367 (1964).

32. N. G. Hairston, *ibid.* 40: 404 (1959); ———, in *Readings in Population and Community Ecology,* W. E. Hazen, Ed. (Saunders, Philadelphia, 1964), p. 319; ———, *J. Ecol.* 52: suppl., 227 (1964).

33. M. D. Engelmann, *Ecol. Monographs* 31: 221 (1961); ———, in *Readings in Population and Community Ecology,* W. E. Hazen, Ed. (Saunders, Philadelphia, 1964), p. 332; F. B. Turner, *Ecology* 42: 600 (1961); C. E. King, *ibid.* 43: 515 (1962).

34. A. J. Kohn, *Ecol. Monographs* 29: 47 (1959).

35. M. D. F. Udvardy, *Cold Spring Harbor Symp. Quant. Biol.* 22: 301 (1957).

36. R. H. MacArthur, *Ecology* 39: 599 (1958); ———, J. W. MacArthur, J. Preer, *Am. Naturalist* 96: 167 (1962).

37. H. T. Odum, J. E. Cantlon, L. S. Kornicker, *Ecology* 41: 395 (1960).

38. C. B. Williams, *J. Animal Ecol.* 22: 14 (1953); *Patterns in the Balance of Nature* (Academic Press, London, 1964).

39. R. Patrick, M. H. Hohn, J. H. Wallace, *Notulae Naturae Acad. Nat. Sci. Phila.* 259: 1 (1954); R. Patrick and D. Strawbridge, *Am. Naturalist* 97: 51 (1963).

40. C. B. Williams, *J. Ecol.* 34: 253 (1947).

41. R. F. Daubenmire, *Butler Univ. Botan. Studies* 1: 61 (1930); *ibid.* 2: 29 (1931).

42. R. H. Whittaker, *Ecology* 35: 275 (1954).

43. G. A. Black, T. Dobzhansky, C. Pavan, *Botan. Gaz.* 111: 413 (1950); J. M. Pires, T. Dobzhansky, G. A. Black, *ibid.* 114: 467 (1953); H. Ogawa, K. Yoda, T. Kira, in *Nature and Life in Southeast Asia,* T. Kira and T. Umesao, Eds. (Fauna and Flora Research Society, Kyoto, 1961), p. 21; M. E. D. Poore, *J. Ecol.* 52: suppl., 213 (1964).

44. T. Dobzhansky, *Am. Scientist* 38: 209 (1950); A. G. Fischer, *Evolution* 14: 64 (1960); P. H. Klopfer and R. H. MacArthur, *Am. Naturalist* 94: 293 (1960); ———, *ibid.* 95: 223 (1961).

45. R. H. Whittaker, *Am. J. Botany* 44: 197 (1957); ———, in *Fifty Years of Botany,* W. C. Steere, Ed. (McGraw-Hill, New York, 1958), p. 340.

46. G. E. Hutchinson, *Am. Naturalist* 93: 145 (1959); ———, in *Readings in Population and Community Ecology,* W. E. Hazen, Ed. (Saunders, Philadelphia, 1964), p. 293.

47. V. Volterra, *Mem. Reale Accad. Nazl. Lincei, Cl. Sci. Fis. Mat. Nat. Ser. 6* 2: 31 (1926); ———, in R. N. Chapman, *Animal Ecology with Especial Reference to Insects* (McGraw-Hill, New York, 1931), p. 409; A. J. Lotka, *J. Wash. Acad. Sci.* 22: 461 (1932); G. F. Gause, *The Struggle for Existence* (Williams and Wilkins, Baltimore, 1934); ———, *Quart. Rev. Biol.* 11: 320 (1936); ——— and A. A. Witt, *Am. Naturalist* 69: 596 (1935); A. C. Crombie, *J. Animal Ecol.* 16: 44 (1947); G. E. Hutchinson and E. S. Deevey, *Surv. Biol. Progr.* 1: 325 (1949); E. P. Odum and H. T. Odum, *Fundamentals of Ecology* (Saunders, Philadelphia, 1959); G. Hardin, *Science* 131: 1292 (1960); B. Wallace and A. M. Sub, *Adaptation* (Prentice-Hall, Englewood Cliffs, N.J., 1964). Limitations of the principle of Gause, especially for unstable communities, are discussed by J. G. Skellam, *Biometrika* 38: 196 (1951); L. C. Cole, *Science* 132: 348 (1960); and G. E. Hutchinson (see 8, 26).

48. F. E. Clements, J. E. Weaver, H. C. Hanson, *Carnegie Inst. Wash. Publ. 398* (1929), p. 1; R.. Knapp, *Experimentelle Soziologie der höheren Pflanzen* (Ulmer, Stuttgart, 1954); J. L. Harper, *Symp. Soc. Exptl. Biol.* 15: 1 (1961); C. T. de Wit, *ibid.,* p. 314; F. L. Milthorpe, *ibid.,* p. 330.

49. W. W. Alechin, *Repertorium Specierum Novarum Regni Vegetabilis Beih.* 37: 1 (1926); J. L. Harper, J. N. Clatworthy, I. H. McNaughton, G. R. Sagar, *Evolution* 15: 209 (1961).

50. D. Lack, *Darwin's Finches* (Cambridge Univ. Press, Cambridge, 1947); W. L. Brown and E. O. Wilson, *Systematic Zool.* 5: 49 (1956); E. Mayr, *Animal Species and Evolution* (Harvard Univ. Press, Cambridge, Mass., 1963), p. 82.

51. R. S. A. Beauchamp and P. Ullyott, *J. Ecol.* 20: 200 (1932); N. G. Hairston, *Ecology* 32: 266 (1951); E. Mayr, *Advan. Genet.* 2: 205 (1948).

52. R. H. Whittaker, *Botan. Rev.* 28: 1 (1962).

53. B. C. Patten, *Science* 134: 1599 (1961).

54. R. H. Whittaker, *Northwest Sci.* 25: 17 (1951).

55. J. T. Curtis and R. P. MacIntosh, *Ecology* 32: 476 (1951); R. T. Brown and J. T. Curtis, *Ecol. Monographs* 22: 217 (1952); J. R. Bray and J. T. Curtis, *ibid.* 27: 325 (1957); R. P. MacIntosh, *Am. Scientist* 51: 246 (1963); D. W. Goodall, *Angew. Pflanzensoziologie (Wien), Festchr. Aichinger* 1: 168 (1954).

56. L. G. Ramensky, *Wjestn. opytn. djela Woronesch* (1924), abstracted in *Botan. Centr. N.F.* 7: 453 (1926); H. A. Gleason, *Bull. Torrey Botan. Club* 53: 7 (1926).

57. D. W. Goodall, *Vegetatio* 11: 297 (1963).

Murray F. Buell
Arthur N. Langford
Donald W. Davidson
Lewis F. Ohmann

The Upland Forest Continuum in
Northern New Jersey

Introduction

The forest vegetation of northern New Jersey, primarily broadleaf summer-green forest, defies any simple designation. Maps have failed to convey the true situation. Braun (.1950) mapped it as "oak-chestnut" with the boundary of the hemlock-northern hardwood forest close enough to suggest local presence. Hawley and Hawes (1912) called it "sprout hardwoods" forest. These terms are perhaps the best that small scale maps permit. Certainly oak predominates over much of the forested areas of today, chestnut used to be abundant, and both oak and chestnut produce stump sprouts freely.

The designations of these authors fail, however, to describe the present vegetation of the area. The principal reason for this failure is that northern New Jersey is comparatively rugged typographically and complicated geologically. Physiographically it lies in part on the piedmont, a rolling plain underlain by shales and interrupted by low residual hills of basalt (Fig. 1). In part it consists of highlands underlain predominantly by resistant pre-Cambrian rocks of gneiss and schist. The northwesternmost part of the state is in the ridge and valley province, which is formed mostly on Paleozoic rocks. The valleys there are underlain by shales and limestones, and the ridges are formed of more resistant rocks, several kinds of conglomerate, sandstone, and gneiss. The general trend of the ridges throughout is northeast to southwest. In addition to the broader physiographic features, erosion has produced many narrow valleys and ravines trending in various directions. Pleistocene glaciation covered the northern portion of the state. Since the direction of movement of the ice in general followed the strike of the rock, the till is essentially of the same material as the geological substratum. The Wisconsin terminal moraine more or less bisects the area. The relief is about 700–800 ft. It is the vegetational blanket of this geologically and topographically heterogeneous area that has been mapped in the simple terms set forth in the introductory paragraph.

There is great diversity of local climate—among ridge tops and valleys, north and south slopes, and ravines. Except for Cantlon's (1953) work, such microclimates in this area have not been measured and the magnitude of their

Reprinted by permission of the authors and publisher from *Ecology, 47:* 416–432, 1966.

differences can only be presumed. That such differences may be pronounced and significant has been shown by Wolfe and his associates working in southern Ohio (Wolfe, Wareham, and Scofield, 1949, Wolfe and Gilbert, 1956).

Man's influence has been considerable. Forests have been cut and recut, although in the last half century such cutting has been greatly curtailed. The best agricultural lands were cleared and farmed and are still farmed. Much of the area has been burned repeatedly. Perhaps the designations of sprout hardwoods or oak-chestnut derive from the fact that a large part of the land—the fertile valleys—is farmed, the forests of the valleys having been largely decimated while the less fertile hillsides and ridges bear the prevailing forests that fit the simple designations. Had the broad, fertile valleys also been left in forests the regional generalizations might have been different.

A few quantitative studies have been made on the vegetation of northern New Jersey, mostly on the resistant rocks of the uplands. Niering (1953) studied the vegetation of High Point State Park near the northwest corner of of the state. The area is almost entirely on sandstone and conglomerate. He described a mosaic of vegetation in which *Quercus prinus* (chestnut oak) and *Q. rubra* (red oak) predominate, forming the continuous phase. In broad upland valleys he found Quercus alba (white oak) predominating, and in ravines *Acer saccharum* (sugar maple), *Fraxinus americana* (white ash), *Betula lutea* and *B. lenta* (yellow and sweet birch), and sometimes *Tsuga canadensis* (hemlock). McDonough and Buell (1956) reported on the vegetation of Voorhees State Park where the ridge of gneiss is primarily clothed with an oak forest, the narrow valleys with various combinations of *Acer saccharum, Fagus grandifolia* (beech), *Tsuga canadensis, Franxinus americana, Betula lutea,* and *B. lenta.* Cantlon (1953) described the vegetation on contrasting north- and south-facing slopes of Cushetunk Mountain, a diabase ridge in central New Jersey. The two slopes were occupied by oak-dominated forests of distinctly different compositions. Baird (1956) worked in the Watchung Reservation, an extensive natural area extending from the top of one basalt ridge across a narrow valley to a parallel basalt ridge to the northwest. Narrow ravines cut deeply into the northwest-facing slope of the valley. The Wisconsin terminal moraine crosses the north part of the reservation. It is not surprising, then, that Baird found that the reservation included a diversified forest vegetation, which he sampled in some detail. With each soil depth, soil type, and exposure, the composition of the forest changed, from oak forest at one extreme, for example xeric ridge tops, to hemlock and northern hardwoods at the other extreme in ravine bottoms. Collins (1956) found similar diversity in Greenbrook Sanctuary on the Palisades across from New York City. The extremes in that area were from the ridge top oak forests to mesic ravine forests with an increasing importance of hemlock, sugar maple, and sweet birch along this gradient.

On the fertile, broad valleys underlain by shale and limestone, forests are fragmentary and are usually found in areas not suitable for agriculture. There are few published vegetational studies of these areas. Pearson (1960*a*, 1960*b*,

1962) studied the forest remnants on limestone and found that they were either dominated by combinations of sugar maple and hemlock or, if dominated by oaks, the latter were yielding to hemlock and sugar maple.

Thus, on the basis of scattered vegetational studies, a general concept of the vegetation of the region emerges. On the extreme ridge tops are chestnut oak and sometimes pitch pine, and on the slopes and high valleys of the hard rock substrata are oak forests of varying species composition. In the narrow ravines in these hills are the mesic hemlock and sugar maple with their associates. In the broad low valleys of shale and limestone are mesic stands dominated or partially dominated by sugar maple and hemlock, but the forests of which they are the remnants have largely given way to agriculture.

We decided that a broad survey of northern New Jersey upland forests would augment the existing fragmentary information on the vegetation. The variety of environments favored the use of a system of analysis that could be adapted to wide habitat diversity. There are many places where the vegetational gradients and parallel environmental gradients can be clearly seen on mountain slopes. However, the common spatial discontinuity of forest stands suitable for study suggested the use of the methods (including continuum analysis) developed by Wisconsin ecologists (McIntosh, 1958, Curtis, 1959). In fact, one of the objectives of this study was to determine whether or not the continuum concept could be applied successfully to the vegetation of an area having such a heterogeneous environmental complex as that of northern New Jersey.

Field Methods

The criteria used for the selection of stands were: (1) that all stands be on sites affording the ready removal of rain water by surface run-off or by internal drainage; (2) that the stands be representative of as many as possible of the upland habitats of northern New Jersey, both as to geological and soil substrata and to physiography; (3) that all stands be naturally established, and free for at least 60 years from pronounced disturbances such as fire, cutting, grazing by domestic animals, and severe windstorm damage; and (4) that the stands not represent early forest stages of old field succession.

Stands were located through the assistance of foresters and local residents, through stereoscopic study of air-photo pairs, through the examination of published studies of New Jersey vegetation, and through searching on the ground. All stands were extensively examined before final acceptance for study. In two cases our study was a re-analysis of data collected by Cantlon (1953). The distribution of 60 stands on the major geological formations of the area is shown in Fig. 1.

There are few discrete, uniform stands of forest vegetation in northern New Jersey but, rather, there are continuous forest units, sometimes extensive, with altitudinal gradients in composition and also with diversification resulting from

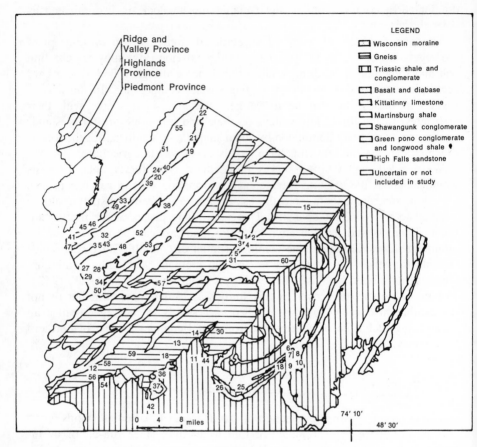

Figure 1

Map of northern New Jersey showing the physiographic provinces (upper left), the surface distribution of the geological substrata on which the forest
stands were located, and the location of the 60 stands
included in the study.

past differences in fire experience and treatment, including cutting. Ridge tops
differ from slopes, ravines from open areas. On ridge tops we considered a
stand as a narrow rectangular strip of forest that appeared homogeneous upon
reconnaissance. On the flanks of the hills and mountains we delimited more
compact stands, disposed along a contour belt at a limited altitudinal range.
The range in altitude included in any one stand was such that we could not,
during reconnaissance, detect any appreciable gradient in the composition
of the vegetation from the upper edge to the lower edge of the "stand." Since
stands were to be analyzed numerically, data were not pooled from parts of
larger areas with obvious diversity along any kind of gradient. We were not

concerned with the investigation of extensive forests but rather with areas that satisfied our primary criteria and appeared homogeneous to the eye during thorough reconnaissance.

In 51 of the 60 stands, trees of 4.0 inches dbh and over (all diameter readings were taken to the nearest 0.1 inch) were sampled by means of the quarter method (Cottam and Curtis, 1956). Where possible, 40 points were used in the early stages of the study, 48 in the later stages. In stands on hillsides two lines of 24, four lines of 12, or even six lines of 8 points each were laid out, according to the dictates of our reconnaissance. A few stands too small for sampling by the quarter method were included in order to represent particular habitats. In these stands a complete count was made in contiguous quadrats, usually 1 chain square.

Data were obtained on sapling density in several different ways. Saplings of tree species (individuals 1.0–3.9 inches dbh) were recorded, in most cases in rectangular quadrats. In most of the stands the size of the quadrat was 6.0 by 29.0 ft (1/250 acre), but in some of the earlier stands the quadrat was half this size (1/500 acre). In other stands the quarter method was used precisely as it was used for tree sampling, and this method proved to be more satisfactory. Whenever the quarter method was used to sample trees, the saplings were sampled at each point by one of the above methods. When small stands were sampled by the complete count, a complete sapling count was also made.

Percentage cover of seedlings (individuals of tree species less than 1.0 inch dbh) was estimated in ½- by 2-m quadrats placed in a uniform fashion at each point or in small stands laid down uniformly and systematically according to a predetermined pattern.

Voucher specimens were collected for species difficult to identify. *Amelanchier laevis* and *A. arborea* are not separated in the field data, being recorded as *Amelanchier* spp. Because of the uncertainty of identification without fruits, no distinction was made between *Carya glabra* and *C. ovalis* (Manning 1950). Nomenclature follows Fernald (1950).

Laboratory Methods

Importance values of trees were determined by a modification of the methods of Curtis and McIntosh (1951), Brown and Curtis (1952), Cottam and Curtis (1956), and Curtis (1959). Since frequency values determined by the quarter method in the larger stands and by quadrat methods in the smaller stands are not equivalent, they were omitted from the calculation of importance value of trees in the present study. This decision is in keeping with the findings of Penfound (1945). Relative dominance (percentage of total dominance) is the percentage of the basal area of any species in terms of the total basal area for all species in any sample. Relative density is the number of trees of any species, relative to the total number of trees in any sample, expressed as percentage. Our importance values for trees were obtained by adding relative dominance and relative density and dividing by two. For example, in a pure stand of *Tsuga canadensis, Tsuga* would have an importance value of 100. Our importance values for saplings (individuals with dbh of 1.0–3.9 inches) represented a compromise, since in the early part of the field work we recorded the numbers and species only, in quadrats. In these cases we used half the sum of the relative density and relative frequency. Relative frequency was determined by summing the frequency percentages for all species and then expressing the frequency of each species as the percentage of this sum. When the saplings were sampled by the quarter method, the importance values were determined as for trees.

Importance values for seedlings were arrived at by summing relative cover and relative frequency and dividing by two. The total importance value was again 100.

A chi-square test (Snedecor, 1956) of homogeneity was applied to each stand. For this purpose data from a number of points (4, 5, 6, or even 8, according to the geographical distribution of these points and the number of points available) were pooled in geographically compact groups and these groups treated as units in making the test. The recommendation of Cochran (1954) that the test be applied where expected values are 2 or more was accepted, but in nearly all cases the expected values were above 5. We rejected any stand in which the heterogeneity of the leading dominant was beyond that expected at the 5% level of confidence and applied the less* rigorous rejection level of 1% to species of secondary importance value. As a result of these procedures one stand only was rejected, suggesting that reconnaissance had been quite successful. Another index of homogeneity of the accepted stands is the fact that in 35 of the 36 stands sampled by the quarter method the species indicating homogeneity at the 5% level of confidence accounted on the average for 75% of the total importance values. In the single remaining stand the species indicating homogeneity at the 1% level accounted for 71% of the total importance values.

In comparable studies in Wisconsin, "climax adaptation numbers" ranging from 1 to 10 were assigned to the various constituent species (Curtis and McIntosh 1951). The word "climax" was later dropped from this designation, without comment (Curtis 1959, p. 94), and the resulting "adaptation numbers" were "interpreted as a measure of the biological adaptation of a species toward successful survival in the complex of environmental conditions found

---

* Since the use of the adjective "less" at this point has been questioned, explanation is in order. If a stand were, in fact, highly homogeneous then heterogeneity values due to the chances of sampling would be generally very low, as evidenced by low chi-square values and high P values. In applying a stricture for stand acceptance, based on homogeneity, the lower the P value (expressing the degree of heterogeneity) the weaker is the stricture. If, for instance, we accepted for further analysis only those stands in which a degree of heterogeneity as great as or greater than that actually observed might be expected, on the basis of chance alone, once in five times ($P = 0.2$) we would accept very few stands. If, on the other hand, we allowed heterogeneity so great that it or a greater heterogeneity would not be expected more frequently than once in 1,000 cases, our stricture would indeed be a light one. We have chosen the more rigorous rejection level of $P = .05$ rather than the less rigorous rejection level of $P = .01$. We are not rejecting a null hypothesis; we are accepting relatively homogeneous stands of forest, rejecting relatively heterogeneous stands.

in a forest dominated by sugar maple. The higher the number, the greater is the possibility that the species will be able to exist in company with sugar maple."

In our study of *Tsuga canadensis,* the species most characteristic of ravines and cool slope exposures, was assigned a "habitat adaptation number" of 10, *Acer saccharum,* also viewed as occupying a terminal position in forest development, was assigned the number 9, while *Pinus rigida* (pitch pine), the species most restricted to high exposed ridges, was assigned the number 1. The habitat range represented by these numbers is from the most mesic to the most xeric in the study area. Adaptation numbers for the principal intermediate species were assigned essentially by the method of leading dominants (Curtis and McIntosh, 1951), as elaborated by Brown and Curtis (1952). For this purpose alone, data from a large number of additional stands on gneiss, stands from which this paper does not otherwise include data (Ohmann, 1964), were used. Six leading dominants, each dominant in at least four stands, were used for this determination (Table 1). The average importance value of *Quercus*

Table 1

The Most Symmetrical Array of the Average Importance Values of Six Species of Trees in 73 Stands, Where Members of this Group of Species Are the Leading Dominants

Number of Stands	Leading Dominant	*Tsuga can- adensis*	*Acer saccha- rum*	*Quercus velutina*	*Quercus alba*	*Quercus rubra*	*Quercus prinus*
15	*Tsuga canadensis*	67.9	0.6	1.6	1.7	6.0	10.1
4	*Acer saccharum*	0.8	44.9	8.0	6.9	11.1	3.5
13	*Quercus velutina*	0.0	1.3	33.6	8.8	10.5	4.8
8	*Quercus alba*	3.7	5.0	10.1	36.7	11.3	4.3
14	*Quercus rubra*	0.4	3.2	7.3	11.1	32.6	11.4
19	*Quercus prinus*	1.3	0.8	4.8	2.9	13.2	54.9

rubra, for example, in the 13 stands dominated by *Q. velutina,* was 11, while *Tsuga* was absent from these stands. With *Q. prinus* belonging at one end of the array and *Acer saccharum* and *Tsuga canadensis* at the other, the remaining three species were placed between *Acer saccharum* and *Quercus prinus* on a trial and error basis. The sequence of species shown in Table 1 is the sequence which yielded the closest approach to a series of smooth, one-peak curves when the figures in both rows and columns were plotted (Fig. 2).

Using the results set forth in Table 1, adaptation numbers were assigned to the six leading dominants as follows: *Tsuga canadensis,* 10; *Acer saccharum,* 9; *Quercus velutina,* 7; *Q. alba,* 6; *Q. rubra,* 4; *Q. prinus,* 2. The objective method of placing these leading dominants used by Wisconsin workers was nevertheless maintained.

None of the leading dominants has been given an adaptation number of 1. *Pinus rigida* is by far the most characteristic "pioneer" species of high, dry, exposed ridge tops. Its presence as a dominant in New Jersey forests is dependent on fire, and one stand only was sampled where it was the leading domi-

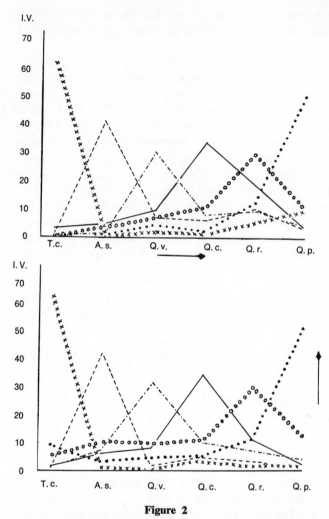

Figure 2

Above: Average importance values of the six leading dominants plotted from rows of Table 1. Below: Same, plotted from columns of Table 1. Species symbols below curve peaks are: T.c. = *Tsuga canadensis,* A.s. = *Acer saccharum,* Q.a. = *Quercus alba,* Q.v. = *Quercus velutina,* Q.r. = *Quercus rubra,* Q.p. = *Quercus prinus.*

nant. *Quercus prinus,* a species less restricted to ridge tops, is nonetheless very widely found on dry, exposed ridge tops. It occurred as the leading dominant in far more than the established minimum of four stands and hence qualified in the initial assignment of adaptation numbers. Having a somewhat less pioneer status than *Pinus rigida,* it was assigned the number 2.

Assignment of adaptation numbers (Table 2) to all other species was made

Table 2

Habitat Adaptation Numbers of all Tree Species Occurring in the Sampled Stands,[a] and Average Importance Values for the Species on Various Geological Substrata (The Six Leading Dominants Used in Table 1 Are in Bold Face)

		Geological Substrata and Number of Stands							
Species	Habitat Adaptation Number	Conglomerate (11)	Sandstone (8)	Gneiss (10)	Longwood shale (3)	Basalt (11)	Brunswick formation (3)	Martinsburg shale (10)	Limestone (4)
Tsuga canadensis	10	7.0	16.2	17.6	x	8.8		23.5	16.6
Acer saccharum	9		1.7	1.5	2.4	3.8	x	8.2	26.5
Fagus grandifolia	9	x[c]	.4	1.4	.1	1.2	25.8	4.0	
Ostrya virginiana	9		.2	.4	x	.3	x	1.5	3.4
Tilia americana	9			.1	x	.2		x	2.5
Acer pennsylvanicum	8	.2	x						
Betula lutea	8		1.1	.6					
Carya cordiformis	8			x	x	.5	x	·.1	.1
Fraxinus americana	8	x	.3	4.0	x	1.3	.1	2.0	3.3
Acer rubrum	7	.8	9.4	5.1	15.5	2.3	10.5	5.7	.4
Carpinus caroliniana	7		.1			1.0	x	x	x
Cornus florida	7	x	3.0	1.8	.5	1.5	.6	2.3	4.3
Quercus velutina	7	3.1	7.5	8.8	1.0	20.4	7.0	4.3	13.0
Liriodendron tulipifera	6		.5	4.5	1.6	5.4	1.0	2.5	2.1
Quercus alba	6	4.0	10.4	10.6		15.5	17.1	14.1	4.9
Ulmus americana*	6		1.5			.1			.4
Ulmus rubra*	6					.1			.1
Betula lenta	5	11.4	4.8	5.1	1.6	1.9	1.0	3.8	5.1
Castanea dentata	5	x	x	x	x	x	x	x	x
Carya spp.[b]	5	2.1	2.0	3.8	x	2.0	1.5	1.8	7.1
Celtis occidentalis*	5			x		x			
Pinus strobus	5	1.2	.5						.9
Quercus palustris*	5			.2				.1	
Ailanthus altissima*	4					x			
Juglans cinerea*	4			.5		.1			.1
Juglans nigra*	4			1.8					.3
Nyssa sylvatica	4	x	2.8	1.4	.5	1.3	.8	1.0	
Prunus serotina	4	.2	.1	.1	x	x	.3	.6	x
Quercus rubra	4	7.4	3.2	20.1	18.6	11.9	8.6	18.9	6.1
Sassafras albidum	4	.2	.6	2.1	.1	2.1	7.5	.5	.5
Prunus avium	3			.1		.1	.2	x	.3
Amelanchier spp.	2	.2	.4	.3	x	2.0	x		x
Quercus coccinea	2	5.6	13.4	.5	.5	.3	12.1	.5	
Quercus prinus	2	48.7	26.4	8.5	57.3	1.5	4.8	15.7	.8
Betula populifolia*	1	.4					.2		
Crataegus sp.*	1			x				x	
Juniperus virginiana*	1		x			x	x	x	x
Pinus rigida	1	7.6	4.1						
Populus grandidentata*	1	.1	.3		x				.1

[a] With the exception of *Magnolia tripetala*, which occurred in one stand, though not at a sample point.

[b] *Carya* spp. includes *C. glabra, C. ovalis, C. ovata,* and *C. tomentosa,* of which the *C. glabra-ovalis* complex is the most important.

[c] The symbol "x" indicates a species found on a substratum but not recorded at the sample points.

* Species of scattered occurrence whose adaptation numbers were assigned mainly on the basis of judgment.

through their association with the leading dominants. This was done as far as possible by plotting graphs of their importance values in relation to those of the leading dominants. *Ostrya virginiana* (hop hornbean), for example, showed its highest importance values in stands where *Acer saccharum* was the leading dominant. Hence it was assigned an adaptation number of 9. Numbers for the species of low, scattered occurrence were assigned as much as possible on the basis of association with dominants but also on the basis of field knowledge of the species. Their designations could not, then, be considered as entirely objective or precise. However, the contributions of these species to stand importance values were low and their quantitative influence on the results slight.

The importance value of each species was multiplied by its adaptation number and the products for all species totaled for the stand to give a stand continuum index. In Wisconsin studies, with importance values totaling 300 and climax adaptation numbers ranging from 1 to 10, the resulting continuum index numbers fell within the maximum range of 300–3000. In our analysis total importance value in a stand was reduced to 100 and the sum of products of individual importance values by "adaptation numbers" (ranging from 1 to 10, as above) was divided by 10, bringing the New Jersey continuum index numbers within the range 10–100.

Results

Distribution of Continuum Index Numbers

In relation to Geological Substrata   Geological substrata are noticeably related to the distribution of the continuum index numbers. In the 60 stands continuum indices ranged from a low of 16, a pitch pine-dominated stand on the Shawangunk conglomerate, to a high of 89, a hemlock-dominated stand on basalt (Fig. 3). Between these extremes the continuum index numbers, when plotted against substrata, fell into groupings that were more or less distinctive. On some substrata the range was much narrower than on others. Although this difference may result from the number of stands sampled, the four on Green Pond conglomerate ranged from 22 to 28 and the four on limestone from 64 to 82. The widest range (32 to 87) was found on gneiss. Furthermore the groups from each substratum can be arranged in order from a low average continuum index number of 34 on the more resistant, highly siliceous conglomerates to a high average index number of 75 on limestone (Fig. 3). Stands on the High Falls sandstone, with an average index number of 51, fall next to the conglomerates. Stands on gneiss, basalt, and Martinsburg shale show a wide range of continuum indices but lack representation at the low end of the continuum spectrum. They yield average indices of 61, 65, and 65 respectively.

In Relation to Altitude and Exposure   There is an even more striking correlation between continuum index numbers and altitude (Fig. 4) than between continuum index and substratum. With the exception of a few scattered stands continuum index number increases with decrease in altitude ($r = -0.58$ and $p_{(0.99)} = -0.33$ to -0.77). The stand with the lowest number, 16, is the pitch pine-dominated stand on the Kittatinny ridge at 1600 ft, the highest elevation at which a stand was sampled. The stand with the highest number, 88, is at an elevation of only 300 ft; only one stand was sampled at a lower elevation. Those few stands at high elevation with high index numbers receive their position in the continuum by virtue of a high contribution by hemlock. Hemlock is a strongly dominant species in special habitats such as ravines and steep northerly slopes, at any altitude and on any substratum.

It is difficult to separate the influence of substratum from altitude in northern New Jersey because the more resistant rocks have been left behind in erosion, leaving high ridges, while the less resistant shales and limestones have been eroded, forming valleys. More fertile soils have developed from the limestones and shales of the valleys. The poorest soils occur on the highest ridges formed by the Shawangunk and Green Pond conglomerates. Soil processes characteristic of rugged topography have had their influence on the vegetation. Whereas podsolization predominates on the ridges and upper slopes, the lower slopes may be enriched by "flushing" (Ratcliffe, 1959) and probably by other processes. At the same time the thinner soil mantle on ridges and upper slopes, contrasting with the deeper soils accumulated at the lower slopes, means a considerable difference in the available water reservoir.

In addition to its influence upon soil character, altitude has an influence upon climate through varying degress of exposure to winds and to such environmental extremes as high winds and frequent ice storms. The higher ridge tops experience a comparatively severe climate. Consequently the trees on the ridges are low and badly broken in their tops, producing a relatively thin canopy, with all its secondary effects.

We attempted to assess the influence of exposure by assigning a series of index values for combinations of exposure and altitude from most xeric sites (ridge top and upper, southwest-facing slopes) to most mesic sites (lower, northeast-facing slopes). Instead of increasing the correlation between physiography and continuum indices, the new sample correlation coefficient ($r = -0.59$) was almost precisely the same as that using altitude alone ($r = -0.58$) and the 99% limits of confidence for the parameter, p, identical (-0.33 to -0.77) (Fig. 4). Our selection of altitude-exposure indices was obviously not meaningful in the context of our stands, even though logical. It probably failed because the majority of the sampled stands were on northwest- or southeast-facing slopes, a result of the general trend of the ridges and valleys of the area. It is, however, worthwhile to turn to the example of the forests of two contrasting slopes of Cushetunk Mountain sampled by Cantlon (1953). His stands were at equal elevations, one on the north-facing slope and one on the south-facing slope. The two stands were very different from each other, a difference in the tree layer of about 45%, based on composite of quantitative data. However, converted to continuum index numbers, the resulting figures

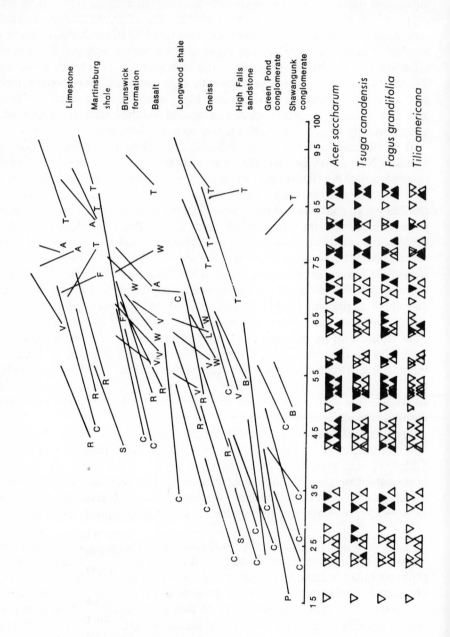

are 43 for the north slope and 45 for the south slope, a minor difference. When the subcanopy species such as flowering dogwood (*Cornus florida*) are excluded, the figures are 42.0 for the north slope and 42.2 for the south slope, an insignificant difference. So even when different forests of two very different exposures on the same substratum are compared, the continuum index numbers may fail to reflect the compositional difference. These computations help to explain why the addition of exposure to make an altitude-exposure index contributed nothing to our correlations.

Diversity of Canopy Tree Species

Although certain substrata are less represented than others and although there is considerable variation in the species diversity of individual stands, even on one substratum, some interesting relationships between diversity and substratum and between diversity and continuum index numbers have been found. In 11 stands on conglomerate substrata 17 canopy species were sampled as seedlings, saplings, or trees. For other substrata represented by 8 or more stands the corresponding figures are: 23 for 8 stands on High Falls sandstone, 28 for 10 stands on gneiss, 28 for 11 stands on basalt, and 26 for 10 stands on Martinsburg shale. The sequence of geological substrata shown in Fig. 3 was drawn up quite independently of the present assessment of species diversity on the various substrata. Although no significant differences in diversity are indicated by the figures of 28, 28, and 26 species for gneiss, basalt, and Martinsburg shale, respectively, the above diversity figures conform well to the substratum sequence established for Fig. 3. Species numbers from substrata less extensively sampled are: 16 for three stands on Longwood shale, 17 for three on the Brunswick formation, and 27 for four stands on limestone. This small series also fits smoothly into the array of Fig. 3, although these figures have less signficance than those from the remaining 50 stands. Further

---

Figure 3

Continuum index numbers (horizontal scale) of stands based on trees (lower end of each graph line) and saplings (upper end of each graph line) plotted according to substratum. The order of arrangement of substrata was established, before continuum indices were calculated, on the basis of familiarity with the characteristics of the various substrata, the soils derived therefrom, and the performance of these soils in agriculture and forestry. Solid triangles indicate the presence, open triangles the absence of the four species with high adaptation numbers. Letters at lower ends of stand lines designate the leading dominant in each stand: A = *Acer saccharum*, B = *Betula lenta*, C = *Quercus prinus*, F = *Fagus grandifolia*, L = *Liriodendron tulipifera*, P = *Pinus rigida*, R = *Quercus rubra*, S = *Quercus coccinea*, T = *Tsuga canadensis*, V = *Quercus velutina*, W = *Quercus alba*.

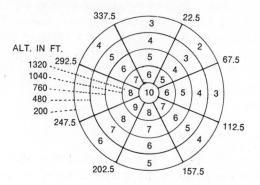

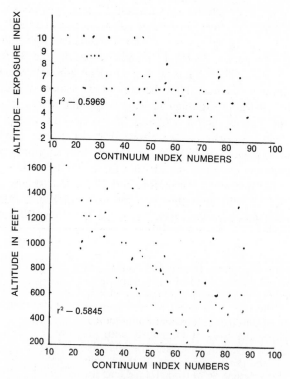

Figure 4

Below: Distribution when continuum index numbers are plotted against altitude. Above: Distribution of stands when continuum indices are plotted against altitude-exposure indices ranging from 10 for xeric ridge tops to 2 for the most mesic northeast-facing slopes at low altitudes. Scale of indices is shown at top.

sampling would probably increase the diversity, since when four stands were chosen randomly from each of the five main substrata and the species diversity calculated, the smaller number of stands resulted in an average decrease of 4.5 species per substratum.

Thus the diversity of canopy species is relatively low in stands on conglomerate, Longwood shale, and the Brunswick formation, intermediate in stands on High Falls sandstone, and relatively high in stands on gneiss, basalt, Martinsburg shale, and limestone. The increase in species represented with increased sampling, suggested by the immediately preceding calculations with the stands on more extensively sampled substrata, suggests that, of all substrata studied, limestone may support the greatest diversity of tree species. Indeed the more extensive studies of Pearson (1960b) at this laboratory showed 32 species occurring in 17 stands on limestone.

When species diversity in individual stands is plotted against continuum index numbers, the greatest diversity is clearly associated with the central range of continuum index numbers. In contrast, stands with the highest continuum index numbers show generally lower diversity, and stands with the lowest continuum indices show decidedly lower diversity. Low diversity is commonly associated with poor soils and unfavorable climatic conditions of the ridge tops; but it may be related, on the other hand, to the overwhelming and restrictive influence of *Tsuga* on the habitat (Moore et al., 1942). Even where it occurs on limestone, *Tsuga* tends to be associated with a depauperization of the aborescent flora of the stand.

Influence of Succession on Continuum Index

There is little doubt that the stage of succession influences the continuum indices of all stands, and in nearly all stands this influence is pronounced. Cutting and fire and in some cases grazing, even though absent for 60 years or more, have left their mark on the vegetation.

The successional status of the stands sampled is dramatically demonstrated by comparing continuum indices of saplings with those for trees (Fig. 3) and importance values of dominant trees with those of saplings. In only five of the 60 stands does the sapling class have a significantly lower continuum index. In the majority of stands the continuum index based on trees is impressively smaller than that based on saplings. For example, the stand with the lowest tree continuum index, 16, has a sapling index of 43, and another stand with a low 26 for trees, has a sapling index of 50. Even quite mesic stands show this same phenomenon. One stand on limestone has a continuum index for trees of 82, for saplings, 86; and a stand on gneiss an index for trees of 79, for saplings, 98.

Seventy-five percent of the continuum indices for seedlings are greater than for trees in the same stands, although a large proportion of these are less than the sapling numbers. Although sampling methods were necessarily different for seedlings and the presence of seedlings or even saplings does not inevitably mean the success of the species, seedling-sapling-tree relationships strongly indicate a successional trend to species with higher adaptation numbers. The overall relation between continuum index numbers of the three classes (trees, saplings, and seedlings) in the forests of northern New Jersey suggests increasing continuum indices with time. This relationship could be interpreted as a successional development progressing everywhere toward forests of more mesic composition.

Three points deserve further attention:

1) Oak importance is in general inversely related to the continuum index except in the single *Pinus rigida*–dominated stand. At low continuum index numbers, oak is of much greater importance than at the high numbers. Oak saplings show comparatively high importance values only where the continuum index numbers of stands are low (Fig. 5).

2) Perhaps the most striking illustration of the successional status of the stands in general is revealed by the ratios of importance value of trees/importance value of saplings. Considering the four species of highest importance in each of five representative stands selected from the complete range of geological substrata, we find that none of the oaks involved shows an increased importance of saplings relative to trees and in five instances the oaks are not even represented as saplings. In these stands *Tsuga, Cornus florida,* and *Acer rubrum* show some increase in sapling importance, and elsewhere various other species show a relative sapling increase. Only on conglomerate do the oaks not seem to face reduction to a minor role in the forest. It is true that it does not take many saplings to replace the trees that are lost, and also that some species, such as white ash, are prolific producers of seed. But it is the consistently overwhelming proportion of species other than oaks in most stands that points toward a decreasing importance of *Quercus* if cutting and fire, processes favoring regeneration by stump sprouting, are not active. Where species with high adaptation numbers are among the leading dominants, the sapling figures are typically high, suggesting increasing importance of these species. An examination of the density, by size classes, of various species reveals, in the majority of stands, a general decline in oaks, accompanied by an increase in other species.

3) Fifty-five of the total of 60 stands show a trend toward higher continuum index numbers with the passage of time (Fig. 3), as evidenced by tree-sapling comparisons. Stands on typical ridge sites on conglomerate, however, would never be expected to support forests of continuum index values as high as those possible on limestone and basalt. Some species, such as *Carya cordiformis* and *Tilia americana,* appear to be limited more to sites that favor high continuum index numbers, and *Acer saccharum,* though less restricted, is unlikely to be a prominent member of forests that succeed those with the lowest continuum indices.

Thus, successional trends are all in the direction of greater continuum index numbers, but on different sites and substrata the ultimate continuum index numbers will differ.

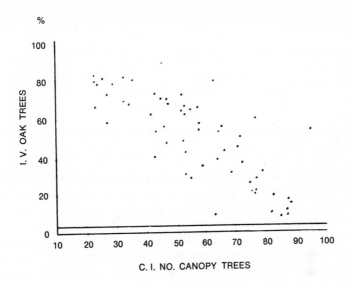

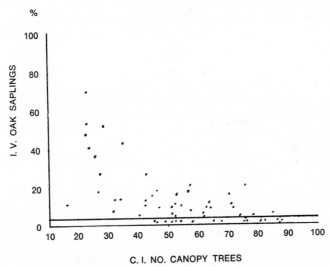

Figure 5

Above: Percentages of total importance values due to all oak species at tree sample points (vertical scale) plotted against continuum index numbers, based on canopy species (horizontal scale). Below: Percentages of total importance values due to all oak species in sapling plots and points (vertical scale) plotted against continuum index numbers (horizontal scale), based on canopy trees. Stands plotted below the zero in the lower graph indicate no oak reproduction.

Relationship Between Paired Like Continuum Indices and Coefficients of Vegetative Difference

Strong evidence against the uni-dimensional continuum emerged from a consideration of the "degree of vegetative difference" (Cantlon, 1953) of 52 pairs of stands, the members of each pair differing by 1.0 continuum index unit or less. Cantlon's "degree of vegetative difference," i.e.,

$$\frac{\text{sum of the differences in the character between stands for all species}}{\text{sum of the values for the character in both stands for all species}} \times 100$$

is the complement of Kulczynski's (1937, fide Oosting, 1956) coefficient of community and should be interpreted in the light of the findings of Bray and Curtis (1957). These authors sampled each of two stands seven times, obtaining an average coefficient of community of 82, which they interpreted as a mean error of coefficient reproducibility of about 20 units. They therefore considered a coefficient of community of 80 to represent the maximum—the value for two identical stands. In general, then, a vegetative difference of 20 may be considered as insignificant, while additions to this figure add to the significance of a difference. Table 3 summarizes the data and shows clearly the tremendous

Table 3

Coefficients of Vegetative Difference (Based on Importance Values of Canopy and Subcanopy Trees) Between Pairs of Stands with Continuum Index Numbers Differing by 1.0 Continuum Unit or Less

Number of Pairs	Average of Continuum Index Numbers of Pairs of Stands	Range of Coefficients	Average of Coefficients
7	20.1–30.0	24 to 71	42
3	30.1–40.0	37 to 44	41
13	40.1–50.0	38 to 97	63
11	50.1–60.0	21 to 75	54
6	60.1–70.0	48 to 97	75
5	70.1–80.0	11 to 88	60
7	80.1–90.0	14 to 97	45
52	22.4–88.3	11 to 97	56

compositional diversity among stands of almost identical continuum index. It is noteworthy that only two pairs of stands showed a vegetative difference of less than 20 and, further, that five of the seven indices greater than 80 were found in pairs of stands with continuum indices greater than 68. In other words, stands of high continuum indices may be very similar in composition or exceedingly diverse. The most striking case of diversity concerns our stands no. 11 on the Brunswick formation (continuum index 69.2), no. 49 on sandstone (continuum index 68.3), and stand no. 50 on limestone (continuum index 67.7). The coefficients of vegetative difference are: for stands 49 and 50 coefficient = 97; for stands 11 and 49 coefficient = 96; for stands 11 and 50 coefficient = 73. Importance values in these stands were found as follows: stand 11—*Quercus alba* 36, *Fagus grandifolia* 28, *Quercus velutina* 15, and *Acer rubrum* 10; stand 49—*Tsuga canadensis* 60 and *Quercus prinus* 38; stand 50—*Q. velutina* 44, *Cornus florida* 11, *Acer saccharum* 9, and *Fraxinus americana* 7. Clearly these stands have little in common except their continuum indices. Just as clearly, there can be no application of a linear continuum concept to the forests of northern New Jersey.

Relationship of *Acer saccharum* and *Tsuga canadensis* in the continuum

An analysis of 37 stands in which *Tsuga* and *Acer saccharum* were present as trees and/or saplings indicated clearly that, in our area, the amounts of *Acer saccharum* present in homogeneous stands dominated by *Tsuga canadensis* and vice versa are very low (Table 4, items 1 and 2). For example, the

Table 4

The Relationships of Tsuga canadensis *and* Acer saccharum *Found as Trees and/or Saplings in 37 Stands (Subcanopy Species Are Included in the Calculations of Importance Values (I.V.).)*

Stand Characterization	Number of Stands	Average Total Importance Values of all Species with Higher I.V.'S in Each Stand Than Those of:	
		Tsuga	Acer
1. *Tsuga* a leading dominant (Average I.V.–59.9)			
a. *Acer* absent	5	0	100
b. *Acer* present (Av. I.V.–1.0)	8	13.5*	95.3
2. *Acer* the leading dominant (Average I.V.–48.4)			
a. *Tsuga* absent	2	100	0
b. *Tsuga* present (Av. I.V.–2.5)	2	93.7	0

		Average Importance Values of:			
		Tsuga		Acer	
		Trees	Saplings	Trees	Saplings
3. Neither *Tsuga* nor *Acer* a leading dominant					
a. *Tsuga* present	3	0.7	4.0	—	—
b. *Acer* present	12	—	—	3.3	6.0
c. *Tsuga* and *Acer* present	5	1.1	3.8	1.2	6.8

* In two stands only, *Tsuga* had the second highest importance value.

total of importance values greater than that of *Acer saccharum* in the stands dominated by *Tsuga* ranged from 90 to 99 (average 95.3), expressing consistently the minor position of sugar maple. Inasfar as we may place confidence in the small importance values calculated, the majority of the remaining

20 stands (Table 4, item 3) have been and are continuing to be colonized slowly by hemlock or sugar maple but not by both species. In the case of the five stands with representation of both species, even the low figures presented as averages are accounted for very considerably by one stand (the only one of this sort in our study) with appreciable hemlock and sugar maple importance values, 3.5 and 4.5, respectively, for trees and 5.5 and 11.0 for saplings. Both species are far too infrequent in this instance to have been involved in homogeneity testing. These figures do not indicate a future stand with large quantities of these two species, but rather they indicate a near-exclusiveness of *Tsuga canadensis* and *Acer saccharum* in our sampled areas, particularly where one or the other of the pair is now dominant. The hemlock-dominated stands are found on steep north- and northwest-facing slopes, in deep valley bottoms and in situations combining these two attributes in less extreme fashion (e.g. less steep north-facing slopes in more open valleys). The sugar maple-dominated stands are found on broad low ridges, e.g., of limestone, and on other sites quite distinct from the hemlock sites. We found no stand in which *Tsuga* and *Acer saccharum* were in competition. On the other hand we found abundant evidence of succession from oaks to hemlock or to sugar maple.

Discussion

Interpretation of the Vegetation of Northern New Jersey

The attempt to test the applicability of a linear continuum, following the methods of Curtis and McIntosh (1951) and Brown and Curtis (1952), has shown the continuum to have difficulties as well as certain values in connection with the interpretation of the vegetation of northern New Jersey. One problem encountered was the assignment of adaptation numbers. The initial studies in Wisconsin used the term "climax adaptation number" in assigning weights to various species. The highest number was assigned to *Acer saccharum*, which was known to be the species most able to compete with all others and hence the species capable of attaining dominance when succession might proceed to climax on favorable sites. The lowest number was assigned to the characteristic pioneer species least able to exist in company with the climax species. In southern Wisconsin this species was *Quercus macrocarpa* (Curtis and McIntosh, 1951) and in northern Wisconsin, *Pinus banksiana* (Brown and Curtis, 1952). Relative numbers were assigned to most other species by quite objective methods, using association with other species as revealed by field data. Thus the "climax adaptation" numbers express the degree to which each species is adapted to exist under the conditions of the climax community. The higher the number given to a species, the more successful it is in competition.

In Northern New Jersey a comparable assignment of the terminal species was more of a problem. In many situations sugar maple could well be classed as the climax species and assigned a number of 10; under other circumstances hemlock fits this position. Furthermore, there is no single, clearly pioneer species related successionally to all upland vegetation. Instead, the great influence of physiography led to the designation of terminal species on the basis of habitat. Thus our data showed that *Quercus prinus* was a leading dominant most often in the extreme xeric sites, such as ridge tops, and *Tsuga canadensis* not only the leading dominant but competitively the most successful tree in the especially mesic sites, such as steep-sided ravines and northerly-facing slopes. Hence the adaptation numbers assigned to these two were essentially "habitat adaptation numbers" based on association with site. *Quercus prinus* is not as restricted to dry ridge tops as is *Pinus rigida* nor is it as much a pioneer; hence *Quercus prinus* was given an adaptation number of 2 and *Pinus rigida* 1. *Pinus rigida* is rarely a leading dominant in forests of this area. It occupied this position in only one stand, on the Shawangunk conglomerate. Old field stands of *Populus grandidentata, Betula populifolia,* or *Juniperus virginiana* illustrate early successional stages, and all these species have been assigned an adaptation number of 1.

All other species occurring as leading dominants in several stands were objectively assigned relative adaptation numbers by the method of leading dominants (Curtis and McIntosh, 1951). The remaining common species were assigned numbers objectively by their associations. A number of less common, sporadically occurring species were assigned numbers based on our knowledge of their ecology. Such methods result in a series that is related at each end to habitat. The assumption is made, correctly or incorrectly, that the series from 1 to 10 reflects progressively increasing adaptation to more mesic habitat. Superimposed on this is a certain "climax adaptation." During the study it became evident that there could be no simple segregation of the climax concept from the habitat association concept. Where the microclimate of ravines and northerly slopes favors hemlock, hemlock is the terminal species. In all other mesic habitats on "favorable" geological substrata, sugar maple is more correctly considered the terminal species and could be given a number of 10, but since it apparently thrives in less restricted habitats than hemlock, we gave it an adaptation number of 9. Apparently sugar maple and hemlock are somewhat mutually exclusive, and hence the continuum could perhaps have been represented more correctly by a bifurcating structure with hemlock at the end of one branch and sugar maple at the end of the other.

All species are distributed along a series relative to the extremes which were selected. The weighted numbers so obtained are used, together with the importance values, to establish the relative position of all of the stands. Thus, hemlock in a pure stand of hemlock would have an importance value of 100 and the stand would have a continuum index number of 100. That the continuum index number is not a precise measure and the continuum not a linear relationship is suggested by a stand dominated by hemlock but with considerable *Quercus prinus* and two other minor species, resulting in a continuum index number of 68, while the stand nearest to it in number, 70, was obviously very different, with neither hemlock nor chestnut oak but a fairly rich mixture of 11 species.

In assessing the adequacy of the continuum approach our primary concern must be with the six species that were the leading dominants in stand after stand. It has been made abundantly clear that three of them, *Quercus prinus, Tsuga canadensis,* and *Acer saccharum,* were assigned their terminal or near terminal position on the basis of qualitative observations, supported, however, by the quantitative data gathered. The other three were assigned objectively, strictly in accordance with the Wisconsin "method of leading dominants." When graphs of the possible arrays of species were made, that array finally selected (*Quercus rubra, Q. alba, Q. velutina*) was selected by eye as the most suitable, its nearest competitor being *Quercus rubra, Q. velutina, Q. alba.* A quantitative assessment of the various curves clearly confirmed the preliminary choice. Nonetheless we and others who have considered the forests of New Jersey have been dissatisfied with the final selection, feeling that *Quercus rubra* should have been higher on the scale, *Q. velutina* lower. Curtis d McIntosh (1951), using identical objective methods, assigned ada   .mbers of 2 for *Q. velutina,* 4 for *Q. alba,* and 6 for *Q. rubra,* in contra   our assignments of 7, 6, and 4, respectively. The secondary species were selected through their association with the major leading dominants, but here again there is cause for subjective dissatisfaction with the results.

Parmelee (1953) found that when he used the methods of Curtis and McIntosh (1951) the species in the data taken from the Michigan forests did not align themselves exactly as they did in the data taken from the Wisconsin forests. His positions for *Quercus alba* and *Q. rubra* turned out to be different, being higher on the scale (*Q. alba* 5 and *Q. rubra* 6.5), although the relative positions of the three oaks, *Q. velutina, Q. alba,* and *Q. rubra,* was the same as that assigned them in the Wisconsin study.

In spite of lack of precision in the meaning of continuum index numbers, and in spite of the difficulties and our dissatisfaction with the array of adaptation numbers, continuum analysis proved useful in arriving at our interpretation of the vegetation of northern New Jersey.

The forests of the region today are dominated overwhelmingly by oaks. The leading dominants in 33 of 60 stands and the second leading dominants in all but six of the others are species of *Quercus.* In contrast, *Quercus* saplings are much reduced in importance or even absent, except perhaps in the most generally unfavorable sites on ridge tops. However, several canopy species are important in the sapling class in these forests. They are *Tsuga canadensis, Acer saccharum, Tilia americana, Fagus grandifolia, Carya* spp., *Acer rubrum, Betula lenta, Fraxinus americana,* and *Prunus serotina.* Except for habitats especially favorable for *Tsuga canadensis, Acer saccharum* is the most generally successful in reproduction wherever it has become established. If the ability to reach sapling stage indicates a reasonable chance of a place in the canopy of the next generation, then the forests of the future will be dominated by mixtures of the above species. All of them occur together on limestone; fewer than the full complement occur on basalt, gneiss, and shales; and still fewer occur on the sandstone and conglomerates. Red maple, sweet birch, and black cherry persists on the upper slopes, and oaks have an increasing better chance of survival toward the ridge tops.

Sprout hardwoods decrease continually as natural succession proceeds. What influence *Castanea dentata* (chestnut) may have had is debatable. It is unreasonable to expect that the disappearance of the chestnut has had any influence on the current decline of the oaks. Just as the oaks have persisted in these forests in the face of fire and cutting, so, before the chestnut blight, the chestnut may have survived. In other words, the vegetation of northern New Jersey has been designated as "oak-chestnut" forest or "sprout hardwoods" because of the prevailing forest in the recent past and not because of what it might be were succession to proceed unrestrained. Such a practice is logical and useful, but designation on the basis of climax potential is of considerable academic and practical interest.

Two past influences, cutting and fire, have probably been responsible for the present oak dominance. An enormous demand for wood existed from the time of settlement to the late 19th century (Collins, 1956). According to Vermeule et al. (1900) the maximum deforestation was about 1850 when large areas of the Highlands appeared bare. The oaks have a capacity to sprout vigorously when cut, and this may well have aided in their persistence. Other species not so well endowed would be at a disadvantage. Likewise, fire has been a factor in determining the nature of the forests of New Jersey, especially during Indian days (Day, 1953, Buell, Buell, and Small, 1954). Oaks are rather fire tolerant and capable of sprouting when killed back by fire. With present and recent efforts at fire prevention, aided by greater discontinuity of forest units, extensive destruction by fire is relatively rare. The less fire-resistant species are now able to assert themselves.

Hence we may consider northern New Jersey as generally capable of supporting mixed hardwoods with hemlock. The richest of these forests will develop at the lower altitudes, less rich ones with increasing altitude, while oak-hickory forests may persist on the most exposed ridges.

One of the more interesting aspects of the continuum study in northern New Jersey is the application of its results to the concept of monoclimax (Clements, 1936) and physiographic succession as emphasized by Cowles (1901). Clements, in his enthusiam for pigeonholing vegetation, spoke in terms of successional communities more or less as specific steps to a climax. Though the continuum concept recognizes diverse non-successional differences in communities, it certainly also views a progression to climax as a continuous, merging phenomenon without distinct successional communities. The climax concept is not basically altered thereby nor is the process.

To exemplify this, in northern New Jersey the physiographic processes of erosion are gradually eliminating the extreme habitats—high ridges, steep mountain slopes, and deep ravines. The habitats favoring oak-hickory forests on the one hand and hemlock forests on the other are in process of disappearing. In terms of process (i.e., the direction in which the trend of succession is pointing today) it does not matter that these physiographic changes are slow.

Presuming peneplanation were to be accomplished under the existing macro-climate and with the existing flora, the resulting climax forest, if allowed to develop, would be dominated by sugar maple, with some residual diversity from substratum to substratum, e.g., from conglomerate to limestone. With microclimatic differences minimized there would eventually be a much more nearly unidimensional continuum that can be constructed in northern New Jersey today. It is clear that succession (autogenic succession of Tansley, 1926) is progressing from a prevailing oak forest to forests dominated by hem-lock or sugar maple. If succession (including both autogenic and allogenic) could continue for long periods of time in the direction it is now headed, it would almost certainly lead to increasing dominance by sugar maple, and com-plete disappearance of hemlock-dominated communities as well as the ridge communities whose habitats the present cycle of erosion is destroying. In terms of Whittaker's (1951) concept, the "climax pattern" is becoming increasingly homogeneous. But the details of the process have not been the same in the past as they are now nor are they likely to be in the future. Climate and available flora have changed and will continue to do so.

Evaluation of the Continuum Concept as Applied to Northern New Jersey Forests

No other attempt to apply a continuum analysis to the vegetation of any segment of North America has revealed the simplicity and straightforwardness of the now classic presentation of Curtis and McIntosh (1951).

Extensive analysis of their data resulted in an ordination of stands in a uni-dimensional vegetational continuum. Curtis and McIntosh felt that it gave quantitative mathematical expression to Gleason's (1926, 1939) hypothesis of the individualistic nature of plant communities and precise quantitative refutation of Nichol's (1929) concept of discrete communities with definite structure and definable boundaries.

Brown and Curtis (1952) applied this simple unidimensional continuum concept to the upland hardwood forests of northern Wisconsin. Examination of their Table 1 and a comparison of it with Table 2 of Curtis and McIntosh (1951) show the difficulty they encountered in the application of the method of leading dominants to the selection of a new set of "climax adaptation num-bers." The difficulties at the *Tsuga-Acer* end of the table are apparent. They suggest to us not one end point to their series but two mutually antagonistic though not mutually exclusive end points, *Acer saccharum* and *Tsuga cana-densis,* with doubt cast on the linear nature of the continuum. In spite of the relative difficulties of ordination, so successful and straightforward a process in the case of the more southerly stands of Curtis and McIntosh, Brown and Cur-tis clarified the interpretation of the continuum index, stating that "Its main use is in ranking the stands along a gradient, such that those stands which are most similar from the standpoint of their trees are placed close together, while those with greater dissimilarity are more remote from each other" (along a continuum index scale). Their clarification of the nature of the continuum and its use in community description by analogy with the visible light spectrum suggests strongly the equivalence of angstrom units and index numbers on a unilinear continuum for accurate characterization of color and forest type, respectively. They state that, "Recognition of the fact that there is a gradient in forest composition correlated with an observable cline in habitat factors permits the designation of a particular stand or series of stands with any degree of precision requisite to the study."

Succeeding papers by Curtis and co-workers (Gilbert and Curtis, 1953, Curtis, 1955, Tresner, Backus, and Curtis, 1954, Hale, 1955, and Bond, 1957) do not reflect any appreciable modification of the continuum concept until that of Bray and Curtis (1957) whose approach was probably influenced by the findings of McIntosh (1951) in the York Woods.

Although the expression "continuum index" does not appear in their paper, it seems apparent that Bray and Curtis had come to realize that stands of very similar or identical continuum indices might actually be quite diverse in composition. This suggested additional influences acting mostly independently of a main set of influences responsible for the primary linear continuum. In our New Jersey studies we soon concluded that there was little possibility of a unidimensional interpretation of a continuum. To locate factors that might help to account for the diversity of our calculated continuum indices, we turned to the data of Cantlon (1953) on the vegetation of contrasting north and south slopes of Cushetunk Mountain. Cantlon, sampling the vegetation of stands laid out on the contour about 60 m down the 20-degree slope north and south from the 700-ft ridge top, calculated "degrees of vegetative difference" on the two slopes as about 45 for trees and about 75 for saplings. In spite of this considerable diversity, our calculations of continuum indices for the two stands, treating them simply as part of our study, gave 43 for the north slope and 45 for the south slope.

Our findings from Cushetunk led us to the analysis of all available pairs of stands with like continuum indices as reported in Table 3. The tremendous compositional diversity as revealed and particularized in the body of the paper was the strongest factor leading to our rejection of any unidimensional interpretation of the vegetation under study. In New Jersey we lacked a substantial amount of earlier critical work of the sort available to Bray and Curtis (1957) leading to their ordination of the upland forest communities of southern Wisconsin. Forsaking the continuum index and working from Gleason's (1920) coefficient of community, they developed a new and elegant ordination technique which is successful in visualizing the multidimensional variation in the nature of the sampled vegetation and which, furthermore, places some of the controlling environmental factors (e.g., soil moisture, soil reaction) in relationship to the component unidimensional continuum. Their technique involves the distribution of stands on y and z axes in addition to the primary x axis of the unidimensional continuum, resulting in the presentation of a 3-dimensional ordination. Curtis (1959, p. 481 ff.) finally gathered together in one large work the evidence that "major vegetation types are multidimensional in nature and that a unidimensional continuum is an oversimplification of the interrelationships of the stands which constitute the type." Although lacking adequate supporting data that might lead to definite conclusions as to many of the factors responsible for the vegetation of the area, our study of each stand was intensive, involving the accumulation of data for shrubs and herbs (Davidson and Buell, *in press*) as well as trees and saplings. Our data indicate the applicability of a pluridimensional continuum, of the sort constructed by Bray and Curtis, as characterizing the existing forest vegetation of northern New Jersey. The examination of distributions of continuum indices in relationship to other variables (substratum, altitude, exposure, etc.) proved to be a productive part of our analysis, directing attention to various avenues of thought and treatment. Possibly the most interesting of these was the light shed on the importance of successional status in influencing the continuum index, as discussed in the body of the paper. We have concluded that if, in a large group of stands, all factors (e.g., substratum, altitude, slope, etc.) were alike, with the exception of successional status (and secondary factors directly attributable to successional status), the calculated continuum indices would fall along a unidimensional continuum. We believe that much of the vegetational continuum of Curtis and McIntosh in their comparatively simple physiographic setting was an expression of successional status. Our unsuccessful attempt to apply the simple continuum approach has strengthened this opinion and also led us to our most significant conclusions regarding the nature of mature or "climax" vegetation of northern New Jersey. In particular, we have concluded that today's prevailing oak-dominated forest vegetation is largely successional in nature and that, in terms of process, the development is towards a sugar maple-dominated forest.

Literature Cited

Baird, J. 1956. The ecology of the Watchung Reservation, Union County, New Jersey. Dept. of Botany, Rutgers University, New Brunswick, New Jersey. 83 p.

Bond, R. R. 1957. Ecological distribution of breeding birds in the upland forests of southern Wisconsin. Ecol. Monogr. 27: 351–384.

Braun, E. L. 1950. Deciduous forests of eastern North America. Blakiston Co., Philadelphia. 596 p.

Bray, J. R., and J. T. Curtis. 1957. An ordination of the upland forest communities of southern Wisconsin. Ecol. Monogr. 27: 325–349.

Brown, R. T., and J. T. Curtis. 1952. The upland, conifer-hardwood forests of northern Wisconsin. Ecol. Monogr. 22: 217–234.

Buell, M. F., H. F. Buell, and J. A. Small. 1954. Fire in the history of Mettler's Woods. Bull. Torrey Bot. Club 81: 253–255.

Cantlon, J. E. 1953. Vegetation and microclimates on north and south slopes of Cushetunk Mountain, New Jersey. Ecol. Monogr. 23: 241–270.

Clements, F. E. 1936. Nature and structure of the climax. J. Ecol. 24: 252–284.

Cochran, W. G. 1954. Some methods for strengthening the common X^2 tests. Biometrics 10: 417–451.

Collins, S. 1956. The biotic communities of Greenbrook Sanctuary. Palisades Nature Association, Englewood, New Jersey. 112 p.

Cottam, G., and J. T. Curtis. 1956. The use of distance measures in phytosociological sampling. Ecology 37: 451–460.

Cowles, H. C. 1901. The physiographic ecology of Chicago and vicinity. Bot. Gaz. 31: 73–108, 145–182.

Curtis, J. T. 1955. A prairie continuum in Wisconsin. Ecology 36: 558–566.

———. 1959. The vegetation of Wisconsin. Univ. of Wisc. Press, Madison. 657 p.

Curtis, J. T., and R. P. McIntosh. 1951. An upland forest continuum in the prairie-forest border region of Wisconsin. Ecology 32: 476–496.

Davidson, D. W., and M. F. Buell. In press. Shrub and herb continua of upland forests of nothern New Jersey. Amer. Midl. Natur.

Day, G. M. 1953. The Indian as an ecological factor in the northeastern forest. Ecology 34: 329–346.

Fernald, M. L. 1950. Gray's manual of botany. 8th ed. American Book Co., N.Y.

Gilbert, M. L., and J. T. Curtis. 1953. Relation of the understory to the upland forest in the prairie-forest border region of Wisconsin. Wisconsin Acad. Sci., Arts and Lett. 42: 183–195.

Gleason, H. A. 1920. Some applications of the quadrat method. Bull. Torrey Bot. Club 47: 21–33.

———. 1926. The individualistic concept of the plant association. Bull. Torrey Bot. Club 53: 7–26.

———. 1939. The individualistic concept of the plant association. Amer. Midl. Natur. 21: 92–110.

Goodall, D. W. 1963. The continuum and the individualistic association. Vegetation 11: 297–316.

Hale, M. E., Jr. 1955. Phytosociology of corticolous cryptogams in the upland forests of southern Wisconsin. Ecology 36: 45–63.

Hawley, R. C., and A. F. Hawes. 1912. Forestry in New England. John Wiley and Sons, N.Y.

Kulczynski, S. 1937. Zespoly roslin w Pieninach.—Die Pflanzenassociationen der Pieninen. Polon. Acad. Sci. Math. et Lettres, Cl. des Sci. Math. et Nat. Bull. Internatl. ser. B. Suppl. II 1927: 57–203, (n.v.).

Manning, W. E. 1950. A key to the hickories north of Virginia with notes on the two pignuts, Carya glabra and C. ovalis. Rhodora 52: 188–199.

Maycock, P. F., and J. T. Curtis. 1960. The phytosociology of the boreal conifer-hardwood forests of the Great Lakes Region. Ecol. Monogr. 30: 1–35.

McDonough, W. T., and M. F. Buell. 1956. The vegetation of Voorhees State Park, New Jersey. Amer. Midl. Natur. 56: 473–490.

McIntosh, R. P. 1957. The York Woods, a case history of forest succession in southern Wisconsin. Ecology 38: 29–37.

———. 1958. Plant communities. Science 128: 115–120.

Moore, B., H. M. Richards, H. A. Gleason, and A. B. Stout. 1924. Hemlock and its environment. Bull. N.Y. Bot. Gard. 12: 325–350.

Nichols, G. E. 1929. Plant associations and their classification. Proc. Int. Cong. Plant Sci. 1: 629–641.

Niering, W. A. 1953. The past and present vegetation of High Point State Park, New Jersey. Ecol. Monogr. 23: 127–148.

Ohmann, L. F. 1964. Vegetation-topography relationships in New Jersey. Ph.D. thesis. Rutgers Univ., N.J. Univ. Microfilms. Ann Arbor, Mich. 109 p.

Oosting, H. J. 1956. The study of plant communities. W. H. Freeman and Co., San Francisco, Calif. 440 p.

Parmelee, G. W. 1953. The oak upland continuum in southern Michigan. Ph.D. thesis, Michigan State College, E. Lansing, Mich. 279 p.

Pearson, P. R. 1960a. New Jersey limestone vegetation. Ph.D. thesis. Rutgers Univ., N.J. Univ. Microfilms. Ann Arbor, Mich. 96 p.

————. 1960b. Upland forests on the Kittatinny limestone and Franklin marble of northern New Jersey. Bull. N.J. Acad. Sci. 5: 3–19.

————. 1962. Increasing importance of sugar maple on two calcareous formations in New Jersey. Ecology 43: 711–718.

Penfound, W. T. 1945. A study of phytosociological relationships by means of aggregations of colored cards. Ecology 26: 38–57.

Ratcliffe, D. A. 1959. The vegetation of Carneddau, North Wales, 1. Grasslands, heaths, and bogs. J. Ecol. 47: 447–481.

Snedecor, G. W. 1956. Statistical methods. Iowa State Coll. Press, Ames, Iowa. 450 p.

Tansley, A. G. 1926. Succession: the concept and its values. Proc. Int. Cong. Plant Sci. 1: 677–686.

Tresner, H. D., M. P. Backus, and J. T. Curtis. 1954. Soil microfungi in relation to the hardwood forest continuum in southern Wisconsin. Mycologia 46: 314–333.

Vermeule, C. C., A. Hollick, J. B. Smith, and G. Pinchot. 1900. Report on forests in Ann. Rept. State Geologist for 1899. Trenton, N.J. 101 p.

Whittaker, R. H. 1951. A criticism of the plant association and climatic climax concepts. Northwest Sci. 25: 17–31.

Wolfe, J. N., and G. E. Gilbert. 1956. A bioclimatic laboratory in southern Ohio. Ohio J. Sci. 107: 108–120.

Wolfe, J. N., R. T. Wareham, and H. T. Scofield. 1949. Microclimates and macroclimate of Neotoma, a small valley in central Ohio. Ohio Biol. Surv. Bull. 41. 267 p.

Jerry S. Olson

Energy Storage and the Balance of Producers and Decomposers in Ecological Systems

Introduction

The net rate of change in energy or material stored in an ecological system or its parts equals the rate of income minus the rate of loss. These rates may be expressed for various trophic levels (Lindeman, 1942) or species, and also for the accumulated dead organic matter. In forests, both the living and the dead materials accumulate substantial reservoirs of energy, as shown by caloric measurements of Ovington (1961), Ovington and Heitkamp (1960), and others.

The rates of loss from all reservoirs can be expressed conveniently by a parameter k, which equals the fraction of the stored quantity that is lost per (short) unit time, without implying yet whether these fractions are approximately constant or not. Jenny, Gessel, and Bingham (1949) and recently Greenland and Nye (1959) have used such fractional loss rates, as constants, in characterizing the turnover and build-up of dead organic litter and soil humus. A confusing difference in approach and formulas which these papers use can be resolved in the following review of simple mathematical models for litter production and decay in idealized evergreen and deciduous forests. The wide range of decay rates estimated here from data on forests of very contrasting climates helps to account for the great differences in total accumulation of organic carbon on top of mineral soil (horizontal axis of Fig. 1), and in the promptness in approaching their maximum storage capacity for dead organic matter.

Ovington's examples (1961) confirm that a substantial fraction (often one-third to one-half or more) of the energy and carbon annually fixed in forests is contributed to the forest floor as litter fall (mostly leaves). Because of this, and because litterfall is generally related to the quantity of photosynthetic machinery in the system, it is an interesting index of ecosystem productivity. Fig. 1 shows a wide range in litter production, plotted along the vertical axis in terms of grams of carbon per square meter per year. Litter production is "very high," sometimes above 400 g/m^2 in tropical forests of America (Jenny

Reprinted by permission of the author and publisher from *Ecology, 44*: 322–331, 1963.

et al., 1949) and Africa (Greenland and Nye, 1959). It is "medium" or "high," 100–200 or 200–400 g/m², in the northern and southern pine forests of the eastern United States. California mountain forest data (Jenny et al., 1949), when expressed in terms of carbon (using C contents based on Jenny, 1950) show medium to low production (50–200 g/m²). "Very low" litter production, below 50 g/m² carbon, would normally indicate relatively non-productive forest.

The scatter in any one portion of Fig. 1 indicates that the production and storage of dead organic carbon are not closely related. In fact, the diagram as a whole demonstrates an inverse relation. Low storage of carbon in the highly productive tropical forests contrasts with high levels of carbon and energy accumulation in the relatively unproductive cool temperate forests. A major reason for this inverse relation clearly involves rates at which dead organic matter is broken down or incorporated into the mineral soil by organisms. Chemical composition of coniferous litter, as well as low temperature, tends to retard biological activity in the northern or subalpine forests. Under the assumption that the forest floors in the stands here selected may approximate a steady state, one method of estimating the decay parameter k can be made from the ratio of the vertical and horizontal coordinates of each point on Fig. 1; other methods are also indicated below.

Models and Methods

Let X be measured either as ovendry weight, organic carbon, or energy in dead organic matter per square meter of ground surface, and let the income rate, and either the amount or the fraction lost per unit time, be expressed in comparable units. The opening sentence on net rates of change for a discrete interval of time (day or year) Δt can be restated as:

$$\frac{\Delta X}{\Delta t} = \text{income for interval} - \text{loss for interval.} \tag{1}$$

For the model of steady income, L, the instantaneous rate of change is the limit as Δt and ΔX approach zero

$$\frac{dX}{dt} = L - kX \tag{2}$$

The loss rate kX is considered as a product of the amount accumulated (X) and the instantaneous fractional loss rate, k, which will first be considered for the special case of a constant loss rate.

If and when accumulation reaches a steady-state level, X_{ss}, then (by definition of a steady state) the rate of change in equation (2) is 0, so income = loss.

$$L = kX_{\text{steady state}} = kX_{ss} \tag{3}$$

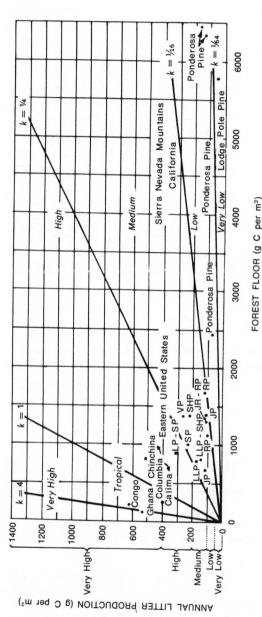

Figure 1

Estimation of decomposition rate factor k for carbon in evergreen forests, from the ratio of annual little production L to (approximately) steady-state accumulation of forest floor X_{ss}. Tropical data for Ghana from Nye (1961) for Congo from Laudelot and Meyer (1954), and for Columbia from Jenny (1950) for mixed forests at 30 m above sea level (Calima and 1630 m (Chinchina). Southern pine forests data adapted from Heyward and Barnette (1936) for *Pinus palustris* (longleaf pine, LLP), *Pinus elliotti* (splash pine, SHP) and mixtures on southeastern U.S. coastal plain; from Metz (1952, 1954) for *Pinus echinata* (shortleaf pine, SP) and its mixtures with *Pinus taeda* (Loblolly pine, LP) on the South Carolina piedmont; from McGinnis (1958) for *Pinus virginiana* (Virginia or scrub pine, VP) in the Appalachian Ridge and Valley province at Oak Ridge, Tennessee. Northern pine forest data from Minnesota adapted from Alway and Zon (1930) for *Pinus banksiana* (jack pine, JP), *Pinus resinosa* (red or Norway pine, RP) and mixtures. Sierra Nevada data from Jenny, Gessel, and Bingham (1949) and Jenny (1950) for *Pinus ponderosa* and *Pinus contorta* (lodgepole pine) at various elevations above sea level.

321

For this case, the rate parameter k can be estimated by the ratio of income to steady-state total, as the ratio of the vertical axis over the horizontal axis of Fig. 1 (slopes of the diagonal lines).

$$k = L/X_{ss} \qquad (4)$$

While equation (4) represents one method of estimating loss rates from harvest of litter and forest floor materials in the field, experimental approaches are also being used for more direct estimates of loss rates (Shanks and Olson, 1961, Olson and Crossley, 1963). Where L and k can be estimated independently of X, then their ratio might be used to predict the steady-state level yet to be accumulated in an ecosystem which has not yet come to a balance of income and loss.

$$X_{ss} = L/k \qquad (5)$$

Decay With No Production

The special case in which $L = 0$ approximates our current experiments (Shanks and Olson, 1961) in which litter is confined in mesh bags and re-measured after loss of differential increments of material, dX. Equation (2) can be rearranged to express these losses as a fraction of the residue X currently remaining.

$$\frac{dX}{X} = - k \, dt \qquad (6)$$

The model for constant fractional weight loss implies (by integration) a constant negative slope, $-k$, on a semilog graph of the amount remaining from an initial quantity X_o at $t = 0$.

$$\text{natural logarithm } (X) = - t + \text{natural logarithm } (X_o) \qquad (7)$$

The fraction remaining is

$$\text{natural log } (\frac{X}{X_o}) = - kt \qquad (8)$$

Statistical estimation of this slope provides a second method for estimating the parameter k.

Taking antilogarithms of both sides of equation (8) gives the fraction remaining as a negative exponential function, like that shown on Fig. 2a.

$$\frac{X}{X_o} = e^{-kt} \qquad (9)$$

For example, after 1 year of biological decay and physical breakdown, the fraction remaining would ideally be $X/X_o = e^{-k}$. A third method for estimating the instantaneous rate of breakdown (really a special case of the second method) makes allowance for the change in weight loss, kX, which is due to changes in X (assuming k constant). Jenny expressed this loss as a fraction of the original total and called it k':

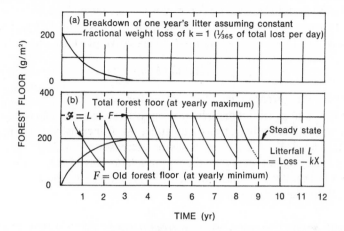

Figure 2

(a) Negative exponential curve for idealized litter decay, assuming weight loss proportional to amount remaining at any one time. (b) Gradually rising exponential curve for accumulation under conditions of steady income and loss, compared with step-wise curve for additions and losses of litter in idealized deciduous ecosystem.

$$k' = \Delta X / X = 1 - X/X_0 = 1 - e^{-kt} \tag{10}$$

From equations (8) to (10), the relation of k' to the instantaneous decay rate k is:

$$k = - \text{natural log } (X/X_o) = - ln(1 - k') \tag{11}$$

Where the time interval is short (e.g., expressed in loss per day), or where the decay is slow even for time units as long as a year, the change in X during the interval is small, k and k' are both small fractions of 1, and there is little numerical difference between them. However, for time spans as long as a year, the k' for litter decay is frequently a large fraction of 1, and k may be equal to 1 (as in Fig. 2)or may exceed 1 (see below). For $k = 1$, $k' = 1 - e^{-1} = 0.632$.

Accumulation With Continuous Litterfall (Case 1)

For the case in which litter is almost steadily falling, at a rate L which the model assumes constant, equation (2) can be rewritten like equation (6) after dividing all terms by k:

$$\frac{dX}{(L/k - X)} = - k \, dt \tag{12}$$

This has an integral like equation (7).

$$ln(L/k - X) = - kt - \text{constant} \qquad (13)$$

For an initial condition with no forest floor (e.g., burned off by ground fire), $X = 0$ at $t = 0$, and the constant in equation (13) is $- ln(L/k)$. The antilog of equation (13) gives the solution—a rising curve like that shown in Fig. 2b.

$$X = (L/k)(1 = e^{-kt}) \qquad (14)$$

This curve is the mirror image of the curve for decay, shown in Fig. 2(a), for the case $k = 1$ in yearly units, which is equivalent to a daily loss of $1/365$ of the total weight remaining at any one time. As k increases or decreases, the steady-state level $X_{ss} = L/k$ decreases or increases accordingly. But there is also a speeding up or delay in the approach to this steady state, which is illustrated in Fig. 3 by the dashed lines (corresponding to solid lines for decay curves with the same value of k).

Accumulation With Discrete Annual Litterfall (Case 2)

Important differences between case 1, for steady fall, and case 2, for fall at the end of the growing season ("idealized deciduous forest") are illustrated by the jagged curve of Fig. 2(b), for the same values of $L = 200 \, g/m^2$ pro-

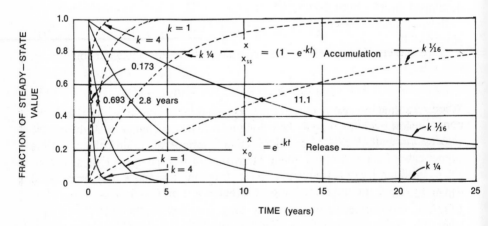

Figure 3

Exponential equations for carbon or energy stored in dead organic matter in a model ecosystem, for four values of $k = 4$, 1, $1/4$, and $1/16$ for very high, high, medium, and low decay rates, respectively. Solid lines for decrease from steady state, assuming production drops from L units per year to 0 at time $t = 0$. Dashed lines for accumulation toward steady state, where production is continuous at L units per year after $t = 0$.

duced per year, and $k = 1$ (or $1/365$ of total lost per day). There is no longer a steady replacement of the litter decomposing between pulses of litterfall, and the remainder of the 200 g after 1 year of decay ($e^{-1} = 0.368$) is less than the amount which had accumulated after either 1 or 2 years of steady fall and decay in case 1. This deficit below the theoretical level for steady accumulation is then made up by the second sudden "autumn" litterfall; but the more rapid loss, kX, again lowers X past the curve given for case 1. Because kX is higher in the first half of each annual decay cycle than in the second half, the steady state of the smooth curve lies a little below the half-way level between the peaks and troughs for the discontinuous case. (Considering intermediate cases, e.g., with quarterly or weekly "installments" of litterfall, would still give a jagged curve with peaks and valleys straddling the rising curve of Fig. 2(b), but with less amplitude between the extremes.)

An equation for the annual peak values J_n which occur right after the nth year's annual fall of litter differs from equation (14) only by the constant $L/k' = T$ for the theoretical limiting value (Olson, 1959a, 1959b):

$$J_n = (L/k')(1 - e^{-kn}) \qquad (15)$$

This is illustrated in Fig. 4, for the value of $k' = 0.25$ (so that $k = 0.288$ from equation (11)). Still lower values for k or k' of course would show slower decay and slower approach to the limiting value for accumulation. The values given are equivalent to the geometric series of Jenny, et al. (1949) which developed directly from the annual increments of L (which they called A).

Between annual events of litterfall in the ideal deciduous model, decay is governed by equations (9) and (10). The value J_n is reduced to a value $F_n = (1 - k')J_n$.

$$F_n = (L(1 - k')/k')(1 - e^{-kn}) \qquad (16)$$

When J approaches an upper limit of $T = 800\ g/m^2$ in Fig. 4, F approaches an upper limit of $0.75T$ or $T - L$, namely $600\ g/m^2$.

After the limiting value T is approached, it is possible to estimate

$$k' = L/T \qquad (17)$$

which equals $A/(F + A)$ in Jenny's terminology, by analogy with equation (4). The ratio of equation (17) may thus be useful in characterizing decay where the deciduous model is a good approximation, and where autumn-peak values can be measured directly, or summed by taking late summer values (F) and adding the litter which falls in the autumn. Even in this case, it is necessary to use equation (11) if it is desired to find actual decay rates k, which can be converted to short time units simply by a change in time scale. In the case of a forest with little or no seasonal alternation, equation (4) can be used, as Greenland and Nye proposed (1959, p. 287) for a direct measure of effective litter decay. It should be noted, however, that the term F_E in their paper refers to the steadily rising curve in Fig. 2(b) (including a *fraction* of the current

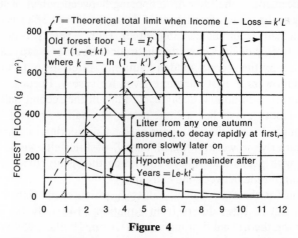

Figure 4

Exponential decay and accumulation curves for ideal-ized deciduous forest, with sudden annual litterfall of $L = 200$ g/m², and annual decomposition $k' = 1 - e^{-k} = 0.25$ of total present at any one time, so $k = 0.288$.

year's litter, and some older material), not strictly material which had been subject to one or more years of decay (*cf.* Jenny et al., 1949).

For both deciduous and coniferous forests, of course, litterfall is actually spread over a period of time. Both the peaks and valleys of the stairstep curve should be rounded off to something like the form shown by the short dotted lines of Fig. 4. Periodic litter inputs that are not discrete are suggested else-where as a better approximation compromising between two extremes of case 1 and case 2 (Neel and Olson, 1962), but the extreme cases suffice for discussion of the illustrative data in the present paper. Other important limitations on the assumption of year-to-year uniformity of L and k are acknowledged as noted below, and can be overcome by elaboration of the mathematics or by the aid of computer techniques (Neel and Olson, 1962, Olson, 1963). However, these objections do not invalidate the basic ideas of the models or the kinds of conclusions drawn by Jenny et al. (1949) and by Greenland and Nye (1959).

Results on Estimating Decomposition Parameters

The estimates of k (from equation (4)) range from high values near $k = 4$ for the African forests, down to about 1 for two forests from Columbia. Pine forests of southeastern United States have values scattering around the line for $k = 0.25$ (1/4), while Minnesota pine forests range down toward the line for $k = 0.0625$ (1/16). Jenny et al. (1949) emphasized the high accumulation of litter in the California profiles and very slow decay parameters, down to 0.009 for lodgepole pine at 3,000 m altitude. Because such a small fraction of any one year's production is spent in decomposition during early stages of forest floor accumulation, storage of organic matter and of energy must continue until the total becomes so large that the product kX gradually approaches the income L and approximates the balance in equation (3). The time required for such an adjustment is considered next.

Durations and Levels of Accumulation

A convenient virtue of the simple exponential model is that the time required to reach halfway to the asymptotic level is the same time as that required for decomposition of half of the accumulated organic matter (Fig. 3). For either equation (9), (14), (15), or (16), this time is given by the solution of $0.5 = e^{-kt}$ for t, which is $-1n(0.5)/k = 0.693/k$. We have an analogy with radioactive half-life, or half-time for accumulation of radioactive materials. Another analogy is with "biological half-time" for either the elimination or the accumulation of materials in organisms or organs. The parameter $0.693/k = T_{0.5}$ may be viewed as a "half-time" for environmental accumulation or decay. Such half-times may be useful descriptive parameters, even in cases where an exponential model is not strictly applicable.

If an exponential model is valid, the time period $3/k$ should be that required for attaining 95% of the final level, while $5/k$ should approximate time needed to reach 99% of the final level. The reciprocal $1/k$ is the time required for decomposition to the fraction $1/e = 0.368$ of the initial level, or accumulation to $1 - 1/e = 0.632$ of the final level (see Fig. 3). This reciprocal can be viewed as the "time constant" for the component of an ecosystem circuit, analogous with that for discharging or charging of a condenser in a simple electrical circuit or in the integrator of an analog computer.

Such numbers are readily obtainable from tables of exponentials or logarithms, and a few have been selected in Tables 1 and 2 to represent the range of values particularly important for organic matter decay for cases 1 and 2 discussed above.

Figs. 5–7 provide illustrations of the great differences in the levels of accumulation and the promptness of equilibration to be expected for various combinations of productivity and decay parameters. Values of k plotted here are for the idealized maximum accumulation immediately following litterfall in a deciduous forest case from Table 2. Comparison with Table 1 suggests that numerically the differences between deciduous and evergreen forests would not be great, especially for values of k or k' below about 0.06 or 0.016 which are shown in Figs. 6 and 7. For values higher than 0.1, numerical differences between k and k' become greater. The sawtooth character of the accumulation curve whose peak values are shown in Fig. 5 ($k' = 0.25$, $k = 0.288$) were already brought out on a larger scale, in Fig. 4.

Table 1

Parameters for Exponential Accumulation of Organic Matter or Energy in Ecosystems with Steady Litterfall Rate (L)

$k = \dfrac{L}{X_{ss}}$	$\dfrac{1}{k} = \dfrac{X_{ss}}{L}$	"Half-time" $\dfrac{0.6931}{k}$	95% time $\dfrac{3}{k}$	Steady-State Level for Production of L Units Per Year L/K			
				$L = 50$	$L = 100$	$L = 200$	$L = 400$
4	0.25	0.173	0.75	12.5	25	50	100
2	0.5	0.346	1.50	25	50	100	200
1	1.0	0.693	3.0	50	100	200	400
0.693	1.442	1.000	4.33	72	144	289	577
0.5	2	1.386	6	100	200	400	800
0.25	4	2.772	12	200	400	800	1,600
0.125	8	5.544	24	400	800	1,600	3,200
0.0625	16	11.09	48	800	1,600	3,200	6,400
0.0312	32	22.21	96	1,600	3,200	6,400	12,800
0.0156	64	44.42	192	3,200	6,400	12,800	25,600
0.01	100	69.31	300	5,000	10,000	20,000	40,000
0.003	333	232.3	1,000	15,000	30,000	60,000	120,000
0.001	1,000	693.1	3,000	50,000	100,000	200,000	400,000

Table 2

Parameters for Seasonal Accumulation and Decay of Organic Litter, with Sudden Litterfall of L *Units, Once Each Year* (*Idealized Deciduous Forest*)

k	$k' = \dfrac{1}{1 - e^{-k}}$	$\dfrac{L + F_{ss}}{L}$	$\dfrac{0.6931}{k}$	$\dfrac{3}{k}$	For $L = 200$		For $L = 400$	
					F_{ss}	F_{ss}	F_{ss}	F_{ss}
4	0.9717	1.010	0.173	0.75	204	4	407	7
2	0.865	1.156	0.346	1.50	231	31	462	62
1	0.632	1.582	0.693	3.00	316	116	632	232
0.693	0.50	2	1.00	4.33	400	200	800	400
0.288	0.25	4	2.41	10.4	800	600	1,600	1,200
0.136	0.125	8	5.19	22.5	1,600	1,400	3,200	2,800
0.0645	0.0625	16	10.7	46.5	3,200	3,000	6,400	6,000
0.0317	0.0312	32	21.8	94.5	6,400	6,200	12,800	12,800
0.0157	0.0156	64	44.0	190.5	12,800	12,600	25,600	25,200
0.0100	0.0100	100	69.3	300	20,000	19,800	40,000	39,600

Discussion

The rate parameter k in part measures the effectiveness of decomposer organisms like fungi, bacteria, and certain animals in breaking down organic materials. Some of this breakdown of litter, accumulated on top of mineral soil, involves leaching and physical transport of materials into the mineral soil, providing income of carbon and energy for soil organic matter. But a

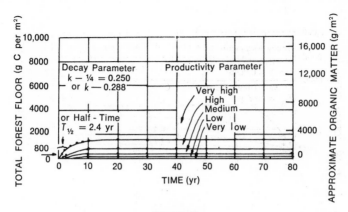

Figure 5

Increase in annual "autumn maximum" of dead organic matter on top of mineral soil for several levels of litter productivity parameter L, for idealized deciduous forest. Medium decay rates, k and k'.

large fraction presumably represents losses of energy from the ecosystem due to respiration of the decomposing organisms. These must be considered in the energy budget of the ecosystem as a whole.

At the 1959 Symposium on "Energy Flow in Ecosystems" at Pennsylvania State University, where this paper was presented, differences between aquatic and terrestrial systems and between the approaches of the workers investigating them were emphasized by several papers. The first two papers by Beyers (1962) and by Wilson illustrated progress and difficulties in the use of several methods aiming at direct measurement of rates of oxygen and CO_2 exchange and C^{14} uptake from which limnologists and oceanographers infer rates of energy flow. In planktonic microcosms decomposition rates and energy turnover are presumably high. But there is nevertheless deposition and accumulation of resistant organic materials in bottom sediments in many environments. This results in a "litter decay" situation and storage of sedimentary carbon somewhat analogous with that considered here for terrestrial systems.

The third paper (see Ovington, 1957, 1961, Ovington and Heitkamp, 1960) illustrated the contrasting approach of terrestrial harvest studies, typically measuring the accumulated net production and calculating average rates of energy flow over increments of time. Ovington estimated that over half of the net production during the development of a 55-year-old pine forest had been released by decomposition. The relative importance of the decomposer pathways of energy flow was even greater in younger forests and herbaceous ecosystems.

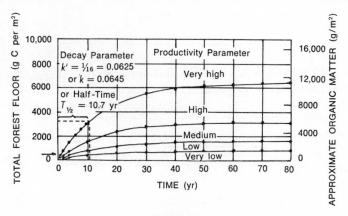

Increase in annual "autumn maximum" of dead
organic matter on top of mineral soil for several levels
of litter productivity parameter L, for idealized deciduous forest. Low decay rates.

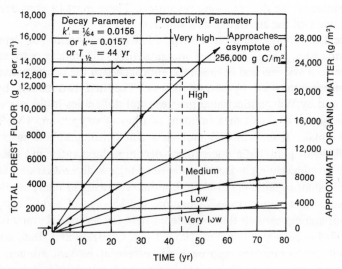

Figure 7

Increase in annual "autumn maximum" of dead
organic matter on top of mineral soil for several
levels of litter productivity parameter L, for idealized
deciduous forest. Very low decay rates. Note great
differences in both the asymptotic accumulation level
and the promptness of attaining this level; also the
similarity of k and k' in Figs. 6 and 7.

Implications for Net Production and Succession

Present illustrations show the wide variation in the period during which the ecosystem as a whole may show a positive net storage (production minus loss) of energy in the form of dead organic matter, unincorporated in mineral soil. Thick humus layers in many northern regions require many decades to develop. Even longer durations will normally be required for equilibration of production and loss of organic matter or humus within the mineral soil. For example, rates of accumulation of soil nitrogen and humus in sand dune soils of approximately known ages indicated values of k near 0.003, so that $3/k$ or about 1,000 years would be needed to attain 95% of the steady-state level (Olson, 1958). Depending on what assumptions are made about contributions of organic matter to the mineral soil from the forest floor and roots (cf. Jenny, 1950, vs. Greenland and Nye, 1959), decomposition rates for soil organic matter in many other soils may show similar lags in accumulation. Even maximum estimates involve only a few percent decay per year, so $3/k$ is of the order of centuries.

Considering the total development of an ecosystem, a "climax" condition in the sense of a steady state, or zero net *community* storage of matter or energy, may not be attained until long after composition and average biomass of many living species has become nearly constant, or begun to oscillate around some average value.

One aspect of natural community development involves the readjustment of all components of an ecosystem toward an asymptotic condition. The condition approached is influenced by a given set of values for the productivity and decay parameters. Some biological developments may be specifically delayed until litter and soil humus have approached near their steady-state values.

A second aspect of developmental succession involves gradual or sudden changes in levels of production or rates of decay, controlled by the presence of new species of plants or animals, and new physical and chemical characteristics of the materials they produce. A typical succession may thus involve alternating episodes of adjustment toward specific levels and fairly sudden shifts when the parameters governing these levels change, as illustrated by E. P. Odum (1960). Slow and sudden changes in soil, which are regulated by parameters for losses of materials from the soil, may both contribute to long-term trends in succession.

As noted earlier (Olson, 1958), quantitative models for changes in community succession and soil development can thereby impart a mathematical significance to Cowles's classic statement (1899): that succession represents a "variable approaching a variable, rather than a constant." The first variable consists of the vector sum of properties describing the state of the ecosystem. The second variable includes the asymptotic condition which is being approached during a given phase of development, and the parameters like L and k which govern the level of this condition. While the first variable may change rapidly at first, then slowly for a while as it approaches a steady state (or oscillates around it), a change in the second variable and the parameters which govern it will bring the whole system into a new period of readjustment.

Modifications of Models

The assumptions of constant production and constant decomposition parameters will accordingly have to be modified to treat many special cases. One change is the allowance for low production during early stages of population development and succession, and a positive feedback to favor higher productivity as growth and development proceed. The result is a sigmoid curve pattern for accumulation of living organic matter, litter, and incorporated humus like the analog computer graphs of Neel and Olson (1962). H. T. Odum's paper (1960) on electrical network analogs did not account for any condition other than the steady state. It could be extended to the accumulations through time by the addition of capacitors into his circuit.*

Some aquatic systems and bogs (Lindeman, 1942) have prolonged accumulation of peat or other biogenic sediments, where decomposition may be even slower than in any of the terrestrial systems. Some important ecosystems may share characteristics of terrestrial and aquatic communities and are modified by import and export of energy and materials by means of water currents, as noted in the papers on salt marshes by Smalley (1960) and Kuenzler (1961) (see also Odum and Smalley, 1959). Their data on invertebrate herbivores and Golley's (1960) on vetebrates also show that a measurable but fairly small fraction of energy flow passes through consumers as compared with that through decomposers, except in systems that are heavily grazed.

Decomposition may be so slow as to require a modification in the model for aquatic systems because of the possible failure to level off at any constant asymptote. If organic matter is essentially removed from access to decomposers during burial in bottom sediments, a given vertical column through the ecosystem extending down through these sediments may show the continued storage of energy in the forms which ultimately contribute to our fossil fuels of peat, coal, petroleum, or oil shale.

A particularly interesting case of the changing parameters mentioned earlier involves the increase in decomposition rate after early stages in community development or succession have passed. This often results in the breakdown of thick forest floor accumulations which commonly occur in first-generation conifer forests in many ecological successions. While lower storage of energy and mineral nutrients may be found in later successional stages (often deciduous or mixed forests), the faster turnover of the nutrient elements may permit the primary productivity of the system to be higher than before. On the other hand, there may be developments of succession which actually represent a

---

* This modification which I suggested to Odum in March 1959 has been made in his later electrical analog network. It introduces a positive feedback by manually charging the production parameter.

degeneration, if the losses of important nutrients or of the favorable physical characteristics of organic humus proceed so rapidly that they cannot be balanced by production.

The equations outlined above are given in terms of deterministic models and are analogous with the differential equations and solutions in physics. Even for physical models (as in radioactive decay, for example) there are chance fluctuations which make these equations only approximations to what happens in reality. We could similarly visualize many complicating chance variables which could make the actual state of any given ecosystem fluctuate around the hypothetical conditions which are here projected on the basis of a simple model. In addition to chance fluctuations, there are important oscillations (besides the abrupt seasonal stops indicated in Fig. 2) which might be superimposed on the simple trends given here, and some of these are covered elsewhere (Neel and Olson, 1962).

These further developments can be handled by direct extension of the simple differential equations and exponential equations used here. They are facilitated by the use of analog computers which perform the integrations electrically or electronically (Olson, 1963). Furthermore, the use of comuputer components aids the connection of many components into a whole electrical or electronic circuit to simulate the trophic structure of the ecosystem. The physical operations simulating integration sidestep many of the complications in the analytical representation of integrals arising when the outputs of some components of the system serve as inputs to the next components (Neel and Olson, 1962, Appendix). While the individual components might follow a simple exponential development controlled by income and loss, as in Figs. 2–7 if their inputs were constant, the various lags in the build-up of inputs to different parts of the system can be allowed for in the behavior of the analog model.

Summary

While some fraction of the solar energy fixed by producing plants is released by respiration of these plants and of animals, much of it is stored in dead organic matter until released by decomposing organisms, at rates which vary greatly from place to place. The general differential equation for the rate of change in energy storage is illustrated by models for build-up and decomposition of organic matter, particularly for litter in deciduous or evergreen forests. Equations of Jenny et al. (1949) and Greenland and Nye (1959) each have a useful place in estimating decay parameters. For the case of steady production and decay, the ratio of annual litter production, L, to the amount accumulated on top of mineral soil in a steady state, X_{ss}, provides estimates of the decomposition parameter k. Estimates range from over 4 in certain tropical forests to less than 0.01 in subalpine forests. Decomposition rates for organic matter within mineral soils may range from near 0.01 to 0.001.

Since it takes a period of about $3/k$ years before storage has attained 95%

of its steady-state level, many ecosystems continue to show a positive net community production for centuries—perhaps long after changes in numbers and biomass of some species are reduced to minor fluctuations around a "climax" composition. On the other hand, the slow change in soil conditions may in some cases facilitate the introduction of new species after some delay during succession. The change in productivity or decomposition parameters controlled by these species may lead in turn to a series of later readjustments in energy storage and release, which modify litter and soil conditions. Modified microenvironments in turn may further alter the succession and "climax."

Literature Cited

Alway, F. J., and R. Zon. 1930. Quantity and nutrient content of pine leaf litter. J. Forestry 28: 715–727.

Beyers, R. 1962. The metabolism of twelve aquatic laboratory microecosystems. Ph.D. Thesis, University of Texas, Austin, Texas. 123 p.

Cowles, H. C. 1899. The ecological relations of the vegetation on the sand dunes of Lake Michigan. Botan. Gaz. 27: 361–391.

Golley, F. B. 1960. Energy dynamics of a food chain of an old-field community. Ecol. Monographs 30: 187–206.

Greenland, D. J., and P. H. Nye. 1959. Increases in the carbon and nitrogen contents of tropical soils under natural fallows. J. Soil Sci. 10: 284–299.

Heyward, Frank, and R. M. Barnette. 1936. Field characteristics and partial chemical analyses of the humus layer of longleaf pine forest soils. Florida Agr. Expt. Sta. Bull. 302, 27 p.

Jenny, Hans. 1950. Causes of the high nitrogen and organic matter content of certain tropical forest soils. Soil Sci. 69: 63–69.

Jenny, Hans, S. P. Gessel, and F. T. Bingham. 1949. Comparative study of decomposition rates of organic matter in temperate and tropical regions. Soil Sci. 68: 419–432.

Kuenzler, E. J. 1961. Structure and energy flow of a mussel population in a Georgia salt marsh. Limnol. Oceanog. 6: 191–204.

Laudelot, H., and J. Meyer. 1954. Les cycles d'elements mineraux et de matiere organique en foret equatoriale congolaise. Trans. 5th Int. Congr. Soil Sci. 2: 267–272.

Lindeman, R. L. 1942. The trophic-dynamic aspect of ecology. Ecology 23: 399–419.

McGinnis, John. 1958. Forest litter and humus types of East Tennessee. M.S. Thesis, University of Tennessee.

Metz, L. J. 1952. Weight and nitrogen and calcium content of the annual litter fall of forests in the South Carolina Piedmont. Soil Sci. Soc. Am. Proc. 16: 38–41.

———. 1954. Forest floor in the Piedmont Region of South Carolina. Soil Sci. Soc. Am. Proc. 18: 335–338.

Neel, R. B., and J. S. Olson. 1962. The use of analog computers for simulating the movement of isotopes in ecological systems. Oak Ridge National Laboratory ORNL-3172.

Nye, P. H. 1961. Organic matter and nutrient cycles under moist tropical forest. Plant and Soil 13: 333–346.

Odum, E. P. 1960. Organic production and turnover in old field succession. Ecology 41: 34–49.

Odum, E. P., and A. E. Smalley. 1959. Comparison of population energy flow of a herbivorous and a deposit-feeding invertebrate in a salt marsh ecosystem. Proc. Natl. Acad. Sci. 45: 617–622.

Odum, H. T. 1960. Ecological potential and analog circuits for the ecosystem. Am. Scientist 48: 1–8.

Olson, J. S. 1958. Rates of succession and soil changes on southern Lake Michigan sand dunes. Botan. Gaz. 119: 125–170.

————. 1959a. Forest studies, p. 41–45. *In* Health Physics Division Annual Progress Report period ending July 31, 1959, Oak Ridge Nat. Lab., ORNL-2806.

————. 1959b. Exponential equations relating productivity, decay, and accumulation of forest litter. IX Internat. Bot. Congr. Proc. 2: 287.

————. 1963. Analog computer models for movement of radionuclides through ecosystems. In Radioecology: Proc. of First National Symposium. Reinhold Publ. Co. (in press). New York.

Olson, J. S., and D. A. Crossley, Jr. 1963. Tracer studies of the breakdown of forest litter. In Radioecology: Proc. of First National Symposium. Reinhold Publ. Co. (in press). New York.

Ovington, J. D. 1957. Dry-matter production by *Pinus sylvestris* L. Ann. Bot. NS 21: 287–314.

————. 1961. Some aspects of energy flow in plantations of *Pinus sylvestris*. Ann. Bot. 25: 12–20.

Ovington, J. D., and D. Heitkamp. 1960. Accumulation of energy in forest plantations in Britain. J. Ecology 48: 639–646.

Shanks, R. E., and J. S. Olson. 1961. First-year breakdown of leaf litter in Southern Appalachian forests. Science 134: 194–195.

Smalley, A. E. 1960. Energy flow of a salt marsh grasshopper population. Ecology 41: 672–677.

Manfred D. Engelmann

Energetics, Terrestrial Field Studies, and Animal Productivity

Introduction

There is currently a feeling among ecologists that their science has reached maturity, and that the concepts and knowledge of this science are destined to shape the future of our burgeoning human population (Sears, 1964; Odum, 1964; Blair, 1964; Cole, 1964; and others). These scientists consider ecology to be a "respectable" science for reasons ranging from the fact that problems of ecology are concerned with practical considerations (such as atomic fallout, overpopulation, pollution, and pesticides) to the fact that the ecologists are using models, both mathematical and verbal, to guide future experiments. In this age of an accelerated pace of human events and immense social pressures, a premium has been placed upon the directed approach and rightly or wrongly scientists are called upon to justify their studies and indicate their importance either to the body of knowledge called science or to human problems, or both. If ecology, then, is to be a part of the new trend and to be in the mainstream of science and human destiny, ecologists must justify their science and elucidate its importance to the human effort.

The goal of this paper is to evaluate the growth and development of terrestrial energetics at this point in its history. The task is by no means a small one. Even though the accumulated literature at present is rather limited, the studies that have been reported are recorded in many different journals covering diverse approaches to ecological research. In this article, the subject of field estimation of productivity will be approached in three ways: first, the historical and theoretical bases which undergird terrestrial productivity studies will be considered; second, the various works in the field will be reviewed, with particular emphasis upon the relationships of the papers to one another and the type of data each yields; finally, the progress of terrestrial energetic studies as a whole will be evaluated and areas wherein critical research is needed will be indicated. I must admit that I face some difficulty performing the task set before me with necessary thoroughness, especially with respect to the final point.

Reprinted by permission of the author and publisher from *Advances in Ecological Research, 3:* 73–115, 1966.

However, I hope that my efforts will give others further insight into the problems in the field and thus enhance its progress.

Three Approaches to Energetic Studies

There are probably three main approaches to the problem of field estimates of animal production. The preceding statement is qualified because the word productivity has various interpretations. Not one of the definitions given in *Webster's Unabridged Dictionary* would suitably characterize the highly specialized nature of "production" as used in the field of energetics. The cattlemen and farmers use the word to mean such measurements as number of head or bushels per acre, the biologist refers to number of individuals born per unit time as "production." Most of the time, the ecologist also employs the latter meaning when constructing life tables or dealing with other aspects of population. However, when the term calorie is considered, the terms production and productivity take on more restricted meanings. The restricted meaning, moreover, was not immediately recognized, but evolved slowly through the 1930's and 1940's. Variations in the use of these terms by different authors are eloquently summarized by Macfadyen, 1963a, pages 160 and 161. His table clearly demonstrates why the term productivity provokes a confused response from "production scientists." To avoid many of the difficulties raised, I wish to sidestep the issue by stating the two definitions of productivity used in this paper. They are: (1) net productivity, the number of calories represented by the new individuals and the increase in weight of the population per unit of time; and, (2) gross productivity, the total number of calories expended by the population in maintenance, i.e. respiration, plus the calories represented by numbers produced and increase in population weight or biomass. In referring to the three main sources of productivity information, then, I am specifically referring to that portion of the literature which is concerned with caloric values and transfers.

The first major source of information on energetics of natural communities has its origins in physiological studies dating from the investigations of Lavoisier in the late 18th century. They emphasize the homeostatic mechanisms of the organism, the investigator exploring the individual's response to an environmental stress. Some aspect of the animal's metabolic rate is measured during the various stress situations. When respiration rate or heat production is used as the measure of response of the animal to stress, the data are potentially useful in an energetics analysis. The stress studies themselves, however, are usually not sufficient for energetics analysis because field data on numbers or biomass are lacking. The studies of the physiological ecologist (or the ecological physiologist) are concerned primarily with the individual and form a tremendous and diverse reservoir of information, useful in making field estimates.

The second major source of information on energetics of natural communities comes from analysis of maintenance energy by what I refer to as the

"Bornebusch" approach, which is based on the assessment of three key parameters—numbers of individuals, biomass, and oxygen consumption. When these parameters are known for different populations in the field or for different communities, the resulting data can then be used to compare the impact of the different populations on the community or the relative amounts of energy flow through the different communities. The key factor in a Bornebusch type study is comparison of the total metabolism of different populations as reflected by respiration rates. Respiration rates can be a sound means of comparing populations, because in most animals about 70% of the assimilated calories are used for maintenance and thus show up as respiration. From the community point of view, all of the calories captured as radiant energy will eventually be dissipated as heat via respiration (exceptions are peat bogs and rapidly buried organic deposits). On the other hand, population or community analysis using species diversity or numbers presents great problems. Here we are comparing unlike elements and more or less objectively making them equivalent, i.e., a species as a unit. The Bornebusch approach utilizes units which are common to all animals and plants, i.e. mass and respiratory metabolism. Thus, the comparisons are less subjective.

The third approach to this subject of energetics of natural communities comes from the trophic-dynamic or Lindeman school of community metabolism. The guiding principle in this type of study is the Lindeman (1942) model. It consists of a flow diagram of energy made up of the following components: λ_x, the energy coming into a trophic or feeding level of the system in the form of food or sunlight; Λ_x, the energy found in the bodies of individuals which make up the trophic level, i.e. the standing crop energy; R_x, the energy lost to the trophic level in respiration; D_x, the energy lost to the trophic level by way of the decomposers; and λ_{x+1}, the energy lost to the trophic level from consumption by the next trophic level (see diagram). The flow diagram is in turn based upon several laws and assumptions. They are as follows: (1) the laws of thermodynamics hold for plants and animals; (2) plants and animals can be grouped together into trophic levels according to their feeding habits; (3) there are at least three trophic levels (there may be more) which are: (a) producers (green plants); (b) herbivores (animals feeding upon the green plants); and (c) carnivores (animals feeding upon the herbivores); and (4) the system is in equilibrium; and (5) calories are the basic units of the trophic scheme. From these assumptions, it can be deduced that: (1) each succeeding trophic level will have fewer calories than the preceding one, and (2) that there is a finite number of trophic levels. In a steady state condition, λ_x, will equal the sum of $R_x + D_x + \lambda_{x+1}$. For increasing or decreasing populations, λ_x will equal $R_x + D_x + \lambda_{x+1} + \Delta\Lambda_x$, where $\Delta\Lambda_x$ is the increase or decrease in energy of the standing crop. However, the Lindeman model is not designed to handle situations of imbalance because of the equilibrium assumption.

A very important point should be emphasized here, one that is most apt to cause confusion when discussing the Lindeman model. A body is made up of both matter and energy. The energetics approach is concerned only with

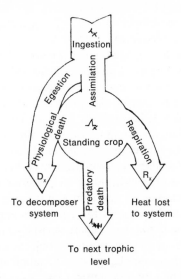

Ingestion

Assimilation

Egestion

Physiological death

Standing crop

Respiration

D_x

Predatory death

R_x

To decomposer system

Heat lost to system

To next trophic level

Figure 1

Schematic representation of the Lindeman model. The drawing depicts a single trophic level with the energy flow indicated by the arrows. For a complete representation of the trophic levels of an "old-field" community see Engelmann, 1961, p. 235.

energy, not the matter. The matter is recycled through the biosphere, being used again and again through successive ages. Energy is not recycled by the biosphere. Each time organisms transfer potential energy from one trophic level to the next, a portion of the energy is lost in the transfer, never to be regained by the system. Thus, when we speak of standing crop, we are concerned not with the matter this represents but with the amount of energy necessary to hold that matter together.

The trophic dynamic approach to the problem, then, is concerned primarily with food relationships (i.e. the food of the community), the assignment of populations to food levels, and the total energy flow through an area or community. A complete analysis of this kind results in an energy balance sheet for the community and therefore should give a number of internal checks on the consistency of the various estimates of energies. If a model is to be a useful guide to further research, it must have particular characteristics which result in logical deductions and predictions. Three important criteria for judging whether a model will result in useful information are as follows: (1) the internal consistency of the model; (2) the number of important testable hypotheses resulting from the model; and (3) the relevance of the model to existing concepts and hypotheses. How does the Lindeman model hold up under these criteria? Slobodkin (1962) has indicated that Lindeman's model is more or less internally consistent and leads to testable hypotheses. This model immediately raises three testable questions, which are: (1) What is the maximum number of food links in an area? (2) Is there a characteristic ratio between the calories contained in one trophic level and the calories contained in the succeeding level? and (3) Are there any consistencies between the ratios of the productivity of a species and that of its predators?

Criterion three mentioned above (the clarification and integration of existing concepts and hypotheses) seems also to be met at this stage of our knowledge by Lindeman's model. It fits logically with the concept of community. If the community is real, then energy flow within community boundaries will be much greater than across community boundaries. Therefore, the tool for more certainly delimiting and defining communities may be within the ecologist's grasp. It is very likely that the Lindeman model or some modification of it will give us a better understanding of the community concept. Other ecological concepts can be reevaluated by use of the energetics approach. For example, the subjectively determined, dominant, characteristic, influential, conspicuous, and rare species categories can be given a more objective basis using energetics criteria. A species with a large number of slow metabolizing individuals may be less important to the community than another species with fewer metabolically or reproductively active individuals. Finally, the Lindeman model depends heavily upon natural history observations, life tables, metabolic data, phenology, physiology, and, in short, the majority of the factual information accumulated from natural communities over the years. This model, though imperfect, can give a new dimension to the old concepts in ecology. There are, of course, other models in the ecological literature which are designed to define and characterize elements of certain ecological concepts (e.g. MacArthur, 1960; Hairston, 1959; Hairston et al., 1960; Patten, 1959; et cetera). All of these are of value in our present stage of knowledge. Some models may eventually have greater significance than do those based on energetics. Others may contribute much to the Lindeman model. Of course all of them are subject to a great deal of debate, and the resolution of the debate will come from a conclusive experiment or observation. As has been pointed out by Slobodkin (1962) and will be underlined again in this paper—the paucity of the data in the field of energetics at this time emphasizes the need for research rather than discourse.

Historical Considerations

At first glance there is a parallel between the spread of the study of energetics in ecology and the evolution of the vertebrates. Both had their origins in fresh water and then spread to the sea, but only with reluctance did they clamber to the land. It required 20 years from the beginning of the productivity studies to the enunciation of the guiding principles of those studies and it required another 20 years for those studies to spread to terrestrial situations.

Although the work of Birge and Juday laid down the beginnings of productivity studies in 1922 and the trophic dynamic approach was proposed by Lindeman in 1942, the first major work on terrestrial systems did not appear in the literature until 1960 when Golley published a *Microtus* food chain analysis in the Lindeman tradition. The limnologists and oceanographers during the forties and fifties produced numerous works on freshwater and marine habitats.

The terrestrial biologists were not completely inactive during this period, for Bornebusch (1930) did his classical study on beech forests in Denmark. He paid attention not only to the number of individuals in each species but also to their weights and respiratory rates. It was apparent to Bornebusch that the different rates of metabolism of the different species populations could alter their importance to the community. His methods, however, were not utilized by others working on natural communities and his work remains a solitary landmark in the literature. To be sure, the engine-like nature of the living organism was elucidated by Lavoisier in 1777 and many workers through the years turned their attention to the bioenergetics of animals. All of these works, however, were concerned with single individuals of either man or domestic species (Atwater and Benedict, 1903; Armsby, 1903; Brody, 1945).

Ecologists of the 1940's and 1950's presumably had the techniques and information available to carry out energetic studies on terrestrial communities. Why were not these studies carried out earlier? There is no certain answer to this question, but part of the explanation lies in the different characteristics of the two major environments (terrestrial versus aquatic), as well as in the elements of human whim and communication. The aquatic environment is easily definable with rather clear-cut boundaries. The majority of the physical components of the liquid environment can be measured by simple chemical tests. The portions of an aquatic environment stay relatively constant during the diel cycle and have a limited range of variation during the annual cycle. Last and by no means least, most aquatic environments have a biota which is taxonomically well defined and not tremendously complex. On the other hand, the terrestrial situation is very complex. For example, moisture variation from day to day and place to place has a tremendous influence on the biota of an area and poses a formidable measurement problem for the investigator. Moisture can precipitate in an area in the form of rain, snow, sleet, or dew, and can be lost in the area as run-off or evaporation. A single aspect of the moisture content of the air can be recorded as relative humidity, vapor pressure, saturation deficit, absolute humidity, specific humidity, and mixing ratio (Platt and Griffiths, 1964). The obvious variability of the physical terrestrial environment is one of the deterrents to a complete energetics study.

The biological elements of this environment further complicate the matter. Many of the taxa important to terrestrial communities are poorly known. It has been stated in the literature that there are about 650,000 species of described insects in the world (Metcalf and Flint, 1939), and it is estimated that 2,500,000 species exist at this time. The insects are an important component of every terrestrial community, both from the standpoint of numbers and of activity. Thus, almost half the species present in the natural community are not as yet recognized by science. Taxonomically, the insects are well known when compared to some other taxa such as mites or nematodes. Furthermore, the number of species present in any single area may be great. Evans (1964), for example, reported 1700 species captured from the herb strata of an "old field" in Michigan. Two hundred and sixty of these species occur commonly and were believed to represent the resident fauna of that field. Hairston (1959) and Hairston and Byers (1954) recorded 271 species of arthropods found in the soil of the same "old field." For this 15-acre field in southern Michigan then, nearly 2000 species of arthropods have been recorded, of which about 320 are part of the normal resident fauna. The task of keeping the species categories separated during energetics analysis is formidable.

The problems which made terrestrial communities less suitable for energetics studies in the 1940's are still present. The need for making such studies is becoming more evident and more urgent, and thus these pioneer studies set forth the first crude guides to the methods necessary for such an endeavor and yield data which begin to define the limits of the problem.

To make a complete energetics analysis we must have estimates on ingestion rates, assimilation rates, egestion rates, respiration rates, growth rates, death rates, numbers and biomass, and the calories represented by these figures. None of these parameters is directly measurable in the laboratory or field but must be calculated from several kinds of data. Paradoxically, a good portion of the data necessary for field estimates must come from laboratory studies.

If energetics studies are to be properly evaluated, it is essential to understand the general procedures of obtaining the relevant data. Measurement of ingestion rates requires knowledge of the amount of food the animal consumes during a certain time period and the caloric value of the food consumed. If the amount ingested cannot be measured directly in the field, estimates must be made from ingestion data on animals in enclosures or in culture cages.

Direct measurements of assimilation rate must be done in the laboratory, but this parameter can be estimated from an equation when ingestion and egestion rates are known. It should be noted that every rate estimated from an equation eliminates one of the internal checks inherent in the Lindeman system. The calories egested are not important to the particular population or trophic level which "produce" them, but the feces are important for the decomposer system since they make up part of the energy source of the decomposers. Energetically, feces contribute no calories to the population for performing work and require only that the organism expend energy to move them through the digestive tract. The animals which can move great quantities of non-utilizable material through the digestive tract with small amounts of energy would of course have some adaptive advantage, but present methods used in energetics studies are not sufficiently refined to answer such questions.

The respiration rate represents the maintenance portion of the energy budget, that portion of the assimilated food necessary to keep the organism together and functioning. Respiration can be estimated by measuring either oxygen consumption or carbon dioxide production. There are numerous devices which measure oxygen uptake, but they generally fall into three major types: the constant pressure, constant volume, and differential (Dixon, 1952). The most widely used apparatus in tissue culture study is the constant volume type represented by the Warburg respirometer. Yet in most of the energetics studies at present, some form of a constant pressure apparatus is employed. The major exception to this statement is found where very small organisms (mites, collembola, etc.) are concerned, and then the Cartesian diver apparatus (a constant volume type) is used. Several studies employ some method of estimating respiration rate by CO_2 production. This usually involves capturing the CO_2 in a standard basic solution, thus converting the base to a salt and then titrating the remaining base with an acid standard. It must be kept in mind that in energetics studies the number of units of O_2 respired is not so important to know as the number of calories represented by this respiration, because it is an estimate of the amount of heat the population loses in the process of maintenance. Conceivably, it should be possible to measure the heat production directly via calorimetry in the field. However, at present the technique required for direct field calorimetry has not yet been attempted.

Growth rates are measured either in the field or in the laboratory where the animals are kept in cages or cultures. Each approach presents problems. In the laboratory, growth rates can be measured very accurately, but the conditions under which the animals are kept are not those of the field. Field studies, on the other hand, have the advantage of natural surroundings, normal activities, and usual diets, but present the problem of measuring and keeping track of the growth rates of particular individuals. Still another approach to the measurement of growth rates is that of deducing them from the numbers of individuals found in various size categories during successive field samplings. This approach is particularly useful for the meiofauna and the microfauna where marking, release, and recapture techniques have not yet been worked out.

Data on death rates are obtained in the same way as are data on growth rates. Cage or culture studies, however, yield only data on deaths resulting from physiological limitations, and the survival rate is higher than that found in field populations due to the absence of predation.

The most reasonable approach at this time seems to be the construction of a life table (Allee *et al.*, 1949, page 265) from laboratory or enclosure data, and the adjustment of this table to field conditions. One of the most complete life tables we have for an animal other than man is that of the human louse, *Pediculus humanus* (Evans and Smith, 1952), yet no one has yet seen fit to work out the energetics of this animal. Complete life table data are very hard to obtain, but yield estimates of standing crop and turnover rates, these being far superior to the estimates derived from simple field counts.

The entire field estimate depends ultimately upon the estimate of the numbers of individuals present in the area. A large amount of literature has accumulated concerning the many and varied techniques for sampling populations. The techniques vary with the type of terrain and the kind of animal being sampled. Dice (1952) and Macfadyen (1963a) among others have written good general chapters on sampling techniques. Each investigator, however, has his own modification of some existing technique made necessary by the kinds of animals and the terrain encountered as well as by the time, materials, and money available to him. Several other estimates (e.g. total numbers of individuals present during a period of time, biomass, standing crop, age and/or size classifications, and total respiration per annum) are derived directly from the number of organisms counted in the field sampling program. Thus, it is important that these counts be as accurate as possible. When field data on numbers are not accurate, as in the case of Bornebusch (Birch and Clark, 1953), the study loses a good deal of its usefulness.

As previously stated, numbers of individuals, *per se,* are not useful to the energetics analysis and, thus, conversion must be made to energy units. The information necessary for the conversion is: (1) the weight of each individual and (2) the calories represented by the weight. Weight or biomass, then, is the intermediate step between numbers and calories. Under certain circumstances, weights are assigned from graphs or equations relating some aspect of size to weight. Dry weight or live weight may be used, but dry weight is preferable because it eliminates the possible variation in water content of the individual. The weighted material must then be burned in a calorimeter to obtain the equivalent calories.

Lists of energy values for various animals and plants have been compiled by Golley (1961) and Slobodkin and Richman (1961). Average values derived from such lists are often used where direct calorimetry cannot be undertaken by the investigator. Aside from the techniques necessary for making energy estimates, there are also several ratios or relationships which are useful in comparing different species, populations, or communities. Three such ratios appear to be important to the studies of energetics of terrestrial animals. The first relationship is more or less characteristic of the individual, the efficiency of digestion. The efficiency of digestion can be calculated also for a population and, thus, can be used in a broader sense; however, it is ultimately based upon each individual's ability to consume and assimilate food. The ratio is defined as follows: the efficiency of digestion is equal to the number of calories assimilated divided by the number of calories ingested. This ratio is important because food consumption in the field is difficult to measure directly. If the investigator has information on either the amount of ingested material or the growth plus the maintenance amounts, then the formula for digestive efficiency can give him some estimate of the food ingested during the period of time in question.

The second ratio of importance to energetics studies is the relationship between metabolic rate and weight of the animal. This is used also as a predictive tool in an effort to estimate respiratory rate or metabolic rate when only the weight of the animal is known. The general formula for this relationship is:

$M = aW^b$, where M represents metabolic rate, W is the weight of the individual, and a and b are constants. The value obtained for the constant b in a set of experiments can be used to compare the metabolism of two animals. Theoretically, a and b should be constant, and b should be equal to 0.67. However, this is not actually the case, and the formula for the weight metabolism relationship becomes a comparative as well as a predictive tool.

The third ratio is one characteristic of the Lindeman or trophic efficiency model. When this ratio was first proposed by Lindeman (1942) he called it "progressive efficiency" and defined it as λ_n divided by λ_{n-1} times 100, where λ_n was the number of calories ingested by the organisms feeding on Λ_{n-1}, and λ_{n-1} is the number of calories ingested by Λ_{n-1}. Hutchinson (Lindeman, 1942) called this the "true productivity" of the energy level. Slobodkin (1960), recognizing the confusion surrounding this important ratio, renamed it "ecological efficiency." Patten (1959), in his paper on cybernetics and energetics, renamed this same ratio the "efficiency of transfer of ingested energy"; Davis and Golley (1963) called it "utilization efficiency"; while Wiegert (1964), pleading for uniformity in nomenclature and for names which outline the important features of the efficiency ratios, introduced the title of "gross efficiency of yield divided by ingestion." The term "ecological efficiency" seems to me to be the most convenient and the least ambiguous and I shall use it when discussing the ratio of the number of calories removed by the predators (λ_n) divided by the number of calories ingested by the prey (λ_{n-1}) times 100. Note that the ecological efficiency does not compare gross productivity of two successive levels, but rather compares the ingestion rates of the two successive levels. Ecological efficiency, then, is an important ratio when one community is compared with another, as well as when two trophic levels are compared. The ratio is primarily important to the Lindeman model rather than to any practical applications by man. There are other comparisons in the form of efficiency ratios, made by the trophic analysis (Patten, 1959). It may be that through increasing knowledge one or more of these ratios will become more important to the ecologist studying the energetics of ecosystems as well as to the production manager. However, at this stage, the three relationships listed above seem to be the most important; discussion will be confined to them. Using the approaches and ratios listed above as a framework, we can now look at the research in the field in an effort to: (1) understand what has been done or attempted to date; (2) view data thus far accumulated on net and gross productivity in terrestrial communities and (3) evaluate the information in terms of theoretical and practical objectives.

Physiological Studies Which Yield Energetics Information

I have set a rather arbitrary limitation on my discussion of the physiological literature. I will consider chiefly papers which either have used another author's field data, made estimates of field energies, or have provided physiological data used by other researchers in making field estimates.

Several studies have reported oxygen consumption at various temperatures: for a spider, *Lycosa pseudoannulata* (Itô, 1964), the collared lizard *Crotaphytus collaris* (Dawson and Templeton, 1963), crossbills, *Loxia curvirostra sitkensis* and *L. l. leucoptera* (Dawson and Tordoff, 1964), the eastern cardinal, *Richmondena cardinalis* (Dawson, 1958), the English sparrow, *Passer d. domesticus* (Kendeigh, 1944 and 1949) and *Emberiza* (Wallgren, 1954) and several rodents including *Zapus, Eutainias, Microtus,* and *Glaucomys* (Morrison and Ryser, 1951), *Dipodomys* and *Citellus* (Dawson, 1955). Other studies deal with food consumption in relationship to temperature (e.g. Sealander, 1952) or with food utilization and digestion (e.g. Waldbauer, 1964; Gere, 1956a, b; Van der Drift, 1958). Still others have done notable works compiling great areas of knowledge, such as the books or chapters by Brody (1945), King and Farner (1961).

Several of the papers are worth particular note. Itô (1964) is one of the few whose writing concerned some aspects of the energetics of a predator. Using a microchemical technique for carbon dioxide production, Itô was able to estimate energy utilization of the spider which averaged about 35.81 g cal/g (live weight)/day, or about 150.94 g cal/g (dry weight)/day. Using these data and making assumptions on assimilation, he estimated that the spider required 73 g cal/g (live weight)/day in food to maintain itself. This study has most of the elements necessary for a field estimate and lacks only data on numbers present in a natural habitat.

The book by Brody, *Bioenergetics and Growth,* deserves special mention because of its importance as a standard reference on energetics. This work is concerned with domesticated farm animals and thus is useful in calculating farm productivities. However, many of the chapters are of a general nature and contain a wealth of information concerning such vital subjects as energetics and energy units; energetic efficiencies of growth and work processes; nutrition, the principle of diminishing increments in efficiency; homeostasis and organismic theories; methods in animal calorimetry; and the energetic efficiencies of muscular work. For the most part, the book discusses such aspects as the processes of growth and metabolism. Marshall's *Biology and Comparative Physiology of the Birds,* Vol. II, contains much information on energetics. The chapter on energy metabolism, thermo-regulation, and body temperature contains information on calorimetry, metabolic rates, energy metabolism and the variation in energy metabolism. The chapters on flight, long distance orientation, behavior, and bird populations also contain information which is potentially useful in making field energy estimates.

The study undertaken by West (1960) on the tree sparrow, *Spizella arborea,* met all but one of the requirements of a complete field productivity study; field data are lacking on numbers of individuals. West's primary concerns were: (1) the number of calories necessary to support the birds in their environment; (2) the caloric burden of migration and incubation. Food consumed and excrement produced (West used this term to mean egestion plus excretion) by the birds was measured both in the laboratory and in outdoor cages at

Churchill, Manitoba, Canada (the birds' breeding range) and at Urbana, Illinois, U.S.A. (the wintering range). Values averaged around 4.4 kg cal for the food and 3.7 kg cal for the feces. The energy consumption of the birds varied with the ambient temperature from 34.23 kcal/bird/day (1.64 kcal/g/day) at −30° C to 10.77 kcal/bird/day (0.49 kcal/g/day) at 30° C. Day length also caused variation in calorie requirements and caloric consumption. From these and other data West constructed a series of equations and a graph for the annual energy budget of an adult bird. The equation which related gross energy intake of the bird to temperature was $GE = 25.89$ kcal/bird/day—$0.254\ T°$ C. The equation which represented metabolizable energy with relationship to temperature was $ME = 19.05$ kcal/bird/day—$0.167\ T°$ C. Each bird required roughly 7460 kg cal each year to live, migrate and reproduce in the wild. West had no figures on the area necessary to provide these calories and, thus, no productivity figures per unit area for the population were given.

The last paper of a primarily physiological nature I wish to discuss is that of Pearson (1960) which has many elements of the Bornebusch approach although emphasizing the homeostatic mechanisms of the harvest mice. Pearson considered oxygen consumption and its relationshipship to ambient temperature. The effects of nest, insulation of hair, huddling and exercise upon metabolism are investigated. Finally, Pearson turned to the bioenergetics of the mice and using data from several sources, calculated the oxygen consumption for an average mouse during an average June day and an average December day in California. He calculated energy estimates for the mice, assuming both diurnal and nocturnal activity patterns. These values equalled 1370 cc and 1782 cc of oxygen respectively, averaging 1576 cc of oxygen per day and were equal to 7.6 kcal/mouse/day for the nocturnal pattern. Using population data from another investigator, Pearson estimated that the mouse population dissipated on an average 91 kcal/day/acre which is about ½ to 1% of the daily energy stored by the plants on that acre. If Pearson's average daily estimate were used to calculate an annual respiration sum, it would equal 8.741 kcal/m²/ann. The final question in Pearson's paper concerned the cost of nocturnal activity of the mouse *Reithrodontomys megalotis*. Pearson estimated that nocturnal activity costs 420 g cal/day or the energy contained in three and one-half grains of wheat. This, then, is the price a mouse must pay to keep away from hawks and other diurnal predators.

Comparison of these papers as a group with respect to their productivity significance is a difficult task, for the papers do not approach the problem of metabolism in the same manner. The data were inconclusive, in most cases, due to the lack of information about population size and structure, lack of data on the temperature of the environment, and lack of information on the natural diet. We can compare respiration ratios (Table 1), but this information will lead only to statements about the metabolic intensity of each species. Even the estimates of the annual population respiration totals by Pearson were unsatisfactory, for although we have estimates of the maintenance requirements of the mouse, we have no estimates of the calories produced in the form of new

Table 1

Comparison of Respiration Rates of Several Wild Animals

Oxygen Consumed g cal/g animal/day	Temperature of Exp.	Common Name of Animal	Author	
150.94	29° C	Spider	Itô	1964
950 to 731	Dec. to June	Mouse	Pearson	1960
1640 to 490	−30° to +30° C	Sparrow	West	1960

tissue. The value of the papers just discussed lies rather in the potential value of the data for field ecologists rather than in their direct contribution to the energetics field.

Studies Concerned Primarily with Maintenance Metabolism of Populations in the Environment

I describe the studies discussed under this heading as the "Bornebusch school," although most have gone one step further than Bornebusch in that they calculated the calories burned by the population rather than just the oxygen consumed by it. This approach can be employed at one of three different levels of organization: (1) the species population, (2) the higher taxon (e.g. order and class), and (3) the community. The work of Pearson (1960) could be considered under the Bornebusch approach as well as under the physiological approach, for the final portion of his paper deals with maintenance metabolism of the field population. Others dealing with maintenance metabolism of species populations in the field are McNab (1963), Nielsen (1961), O'Connor (1963), and Phillipson (1962). Berthet (1963) attacked the problem at the taxon level while Bornebusch (1930) and Macfadyen (1963a, b) dealt with the community.

McNab's (1963) paper dealt with three species of the field mouse *Peromyscus*. Starting with the physical and physiological elements which influence the metabolism of a mouse, McNab derived a series of formulae which eventually described the metabolic requirements of the mouse for a 24-h period. Using these formulae and information about environnmental temperature, size of animals, and numbers of individuals present in a tract of chaparral near Berkeley, California, and assuming 60% assimilation, McNab came to the following conclusions about the mouse populations. (1) Homiotherms have little energy available for work other than homeostasis. (2) The amount of energy for activity has an inverse relationship with body weight. (3) Mouse populations consume only 2–5% of the primary productivity of the chaparral. *P. maniculatas* was estimated to consume 14 kcal/day in June. Of the 14 kcals, it assimilated 8.37 kcal/day. The total mouse population of the three species of *Peromyscus* on the 26 acres of chaparral (32 *P. maniculatus,* 22 *P. truei,* and 13 *P. californicus*) during a typical June day consumed 24 kcal/acre. During a typical February day they dissipated 59 kcal/acre in respiration and consumed 100 kcal/acre/day in food. Using another set of data on grassland,

McNab estimated the "mice" (*Reithrodontonmys, Peromyscus,* and *Microtus*) required 203 kcal/acre/day in summer and, thus, consumed 338 kcal/acre/day. McNab commented upon the estimates of Odum *et al.* (1962), noting that their 2.5 activity factor was arbitrary and too high, and recalculated the energy flow of the "old field" mice to 19.8 kcal/acre/day—a value which represented only 1.8 to 3.6% of the seeds producted on the old field.

Nielsen (1961) also deals with the respiratory metabolism of field populations and adheres to the Bornebusch pattern in that oxygen consumption was estimated, but, the values were not converted to caloric equivalents. Nielsen obtained data on respiration rate of enchytraeid worms via Cartesian diver in the laboratory. Using field information, he calculated respiratory values for field populations of both enchytraeids and nematodes. He took into consideration (1) environmental temperature, (2) activity, (3) oxygen tension, (4) drought or moisture content of the soil, and (5) mean body weight, in making the field estimate (see Table 2). If we make the assumption that the RQ of the

Table 2

The Numbers of Individuals and Calories Respired by the Enchytraeid and Nematode Worms in a Permanent Pasture in Denmark.
Data from Nielsen, 1961

Taxon	Station	No. of Individuals $\times 10^3/m^2$	Respiration Total Litres of $0^2/m^2/yr$	Calories Released Yearly via Respiration kcal/m^2/yr[†]
Enchytraeidae	1	44	7	33.6
	4	30	10	48.0
	18	74	32	153.6
Nematoda	1	1×10^4	43–63	206.4–302.4
	4	5×10^3	31–46	148.8–220.8
	18	1×10^4	71	340.8

† Calculated by the present author using 4.8 kcal/L conversion factor.

animals is 0.85 (an average RQ for a mixed diet), then each litre of oxygen will yield 4.8 kcal of heat.

Using the respiration figures and making some assumptions about the nature of assimilated food of the nematodes, Nielsen estimated that these animals required 800 kg of bacteria (live weight) and 320 kg of plant root cells (live weight) to satisfy the respiratory requirements indicated by his calculations. The diet of enchytraeids was assumed to be bacteria and the amount required to maintain the enchytraeids was estimated at 300–400 kg (live weight). Nielsen pointed out succinctly that knowledge of numbers of individuals alone is not sufficient to allow judgment of population. Data on the enchytraeids indicated that the site with the smallest numbers of individuals per meter square did not have the lowest respiratory metabolism. Presumably, then, the animals at "station 4" had a greater impact upon the environment than did those at "station 1." However, the consumption of energy for body maintenance is not the sole influence an animal can have upon its environment.

O'Connor (1963) studied three species of enchytraeid worms from English coniferous soils, obtaining information on (1) mean monthly population density in the field, (2) the numbers of individuals in each size category, (3) monthly age structure of the population as well as weights of the size categories, and (4) mean monthly field temperatures. From these data, he estimated that 14.33×10^4 worms/m² will weigh 10.794 g (dry weight), and respire 149.5 kcal. O'Connor also pointed out that the number of individuals alone can be unreliable as an indication of the importance of a species. In Table 3 we see the relative rank each species holds with respect to a particu-

Table 3

The Relative Rank Held by Three Species of Enchytraeidae when Compared with one another. Original Data from O'Connor, 1963

Species	Numbers/m²	Biomass	Individual Respiration	Total Calories Population Dissipates Annually
Hemihenlea cambrensis	First	First	Second	Second
Achaeta eiseni	Second	Third	Third	Third
Cognettia cognettii	Third	Second	First	First

lar characteristic; first rank representing the largest value and the third rank representing the smallest value. *Cognettia* is the third in numbers present in the field when compared to the others, but first in the annual dissipation of calories. O'Connor compared his data obtained from the Douglas fir forest with the data Neilsen obtained from pasture soil. The figures from "Station 18" of Neilsen's study yielded about the same values as O'Connor's, both populations releasing about 150 kcal/m²/year. The physical factors of the two sites (Wales versus Denmark), were similar.

Phillipson (1962) dealt with the populations of *Mitopus morio* and *Oligolophus tridens* (Phalangiidae). Using a continuously recording, constant pressure respirometer which automatically replaced the oxygen used, Phillipson obtained respiration values for all stages of the two species of harvestmen which showed that the day-night respiration rates of the animals differed as well as did daily respiration totals. Using a series of independent observations on food consumption and respiration requirements, he concluded that the animals were not utilizing the components of their diet (i.e. fat, proteins, and carbohydrates) in the same proportions as they occur in the food. Uniform absorption is widely assumed in energetic studies, but Phillipson contended that there is differential absorption especially by the immature stages of the animals. Employing field data and biomass estimates from other studies, Phillipson estimated that the phalangids free from 1 34 to 1.47 kcal/m² of ground layer in an English deciduous woods in a year. The daily respiration rates of the phalangids agreed closely with those of the lycosid spider (Table 4). However, though the harvestmen showed a decreasing respiration per unit size with increasing weight (a common relationship in animals), data on lycosids did not follow that pattern. The respiration rate of the lycosid was

Table 4

Comparison of Respiration Rates of Several Predatory Arthropods.
Data from Phillipson, 1962 and Itô, 1964

Species	Cal Respired/ g dry wt/day	Live Wt Individuals (mg)
Mitopus morio	85–95	3.7–56.1
Oligolophus tridens	120–130	3.1–17.3
Lycosa pseudoannulata	150.9	1–150

measured at 29° C, while those of the harvestmen were measured at 16° C. If we assume a Q^{10} of two, then the lycosids respired about 56 cal/g/day (dry weight). This is the expected value for an animal of that size (note Table 4 gives live weights for size comparison rather than dry weights). Phillipson's paper is important because of the conclusions drawn about differential assimilation of food and the information gained on energy utilization by arthropod predators.

The study by Berthet (1963), also concerned with soil arthropods, was centered on herbivores or generalized feeders. He dealt with all the species of a particular taxon (the Oribatei) found in the soil layers of the Meedael Forest, Belgium. The animals were removed from the forest soil to the laboratory, where their respiratory rate was measured in a Cartesian diver respirometer. The respiratory rates were measured at 15°, 10°, 5°, and 0° C, respectively, during successive two-hour intervals. The respiration rate of the 16 oribatid species was related to temperature according to the equation $Y = a + bX$, where Y is the log to the base 10 of the oxygen consumed $\times 10^{-3}$ ml; X is the temperature; and "a" and "b" are constants, "b" being one-tenth the antilog of the Q^{10} value. Values of the Q^{10} ranged from 2.6 to 5.6 and averaged 3.9 for the 16 species tested at these temperatures. The relationship between daily oxygen consumption, weight of the individuals, and temperature was described by the formula $Y = 18.059 + 0.7 \overset{\bullet}{W} - 0.487 Z$, where Y equals the log 10 of the oxygen consumed $\times 10^{-3}$ ml/individual/day, W equals log 10 rate of the individuals in μg, Z equals 1×10^4 divided by the temperature in degrees A. Using these formulae, data on numbers and biomass of the oribatid mites, and data on the annual temperature fluctuation of the forest soil, Berthet estimated that the oribatids respired a total of 4.488 L (oxygen)/m²/annum. (See Table 5.)

Table 5

The Numbers, Biomass, Respiration and Calorie Requirements of Oribatid
Mites Found in Belgium Forest Soil. Original Data from Berthet, 1963

Taxon	No. of Individuals $\times 10^3/m^2$	Biomass gm/m²	Oxygen Consumption L/m²/yr	Calories Released kcal/m²/yr[†]
Oribatei (46 spp)	133.6	5.377	4.488	21.54

† Assuming 4.8 kcal/L Oxygen consumed.

Berthet, like Nielsen, did not calculate the caloric equivalents for the respiration figures. If we convert by the factor of 4.8 kcal/L oxygen, we find that 21.54 kcal were released by the population in one m² during a year.

The two authors who studied the problem of maintenance metabolism on the community level of organization were Bornebusch (1930) and Macfadyen (1963a, b). Bornebusch confined his calculations to the areas he sampled, while Macfadyen, in an effort to point out some norm or pattern of energy utilization, analyzed the data of other workers as well as his own.

The analysis of the five Danish forest soils is summarized in Table 6. It has been claimed by various authors (Birch and Clark, 1953; Macfadyen, 1963b) that the density figures given by Bornebusch were low and, thus, that all of his calculations were deficient. This contention was supported by a comparison with the figures of Van der Drift (1951) on beech forest soils in the Netherlands. Even though comparison of Bornebusch's figures with those of other authors was thus difficult, the significance of his conclusions is not altered. The efficiency of his extraction technique was probably the same for each of his sites and, therefore, the same magnitude of error was present in all of his calculations, thus, the data had comparative values. Bornebusch's observations include the following: (1) The slower the decomposition of the humus, the greater were the numbers of arthropods present and the lower was their total weight. (2) The weight of the forest soil fauna was a more reliable index to their activity than was the number of individuals. (See Table 6.) The best

Table 6

Density, Biomass, and Respiration of the Fauna Found in Five Forest Soils. Data from Bornebusch, 1930

Soil Type	Mean Density		Mean Biomass		Respiration 13° C	
	#/m²	Rank	g/m²	Rank	mg O₂/hr/m²	Rank
Oak Mull	2,978	5	76.81	1	17.74	1
Beech Mull #5	4,424	4	37.76	2	11.51	3
Beech #4, raw humus	14,163	1	24.02	3	12.08	2
Spruce Mull	10,790	3	10.72	4	6.74	5
Spruce, raw humus	11,938	2	9.84	5	7.09	4

index, however, was the oxygen consumption rate of the fauna. (3) Large earthworms were most important in rich mull soils, mixing and aerating the top layers. (4) In raw humus where earthworms are sparse, arthropods initiated the breakdown of the material to be decomposed. Bornebusch concluded with a statement which underlines the importance of the soil fauna to the soil building process, and he called the attention of the forester to this fauna and directed him to take heed of soil organisms, a directive which has, on the whole, been disregarded or has passed unnoticed.

Macfadyen employed the maintenance metabolism of populations as a comparative tool, but his scope was much broader and his figures admittedly more approximate than those of other authors. The purpose of a study such as Macfadyen's is creation of a framework, admittedly imperfect, in an effort either to reveal some pattern or principle which will be useful as a predictive tool, or to give a basis of organization which, as new data accumulate, may be modified into another more precise framework. In his book *Animal Ecology* (1963a, page 234), Macfadyen set forth the framework of a hypothetical grassland soil community, indicating the approximate relationship each taxonomic component should have to this community. In the grassland soil, bacteria were more numerous and harvestmen were the least numerous. Plants (bacteria and fungi) accounted for 1400 g/m² of the soil biota, while animals accounted for only 225.9 g. In terms of metabolic activity, nematodes were the most important animal group, followed by earthworms, enchytraeids, and collembola.

In Doeksen and Van der Drift (1963), Macfadyen sets forth a more comprehensive framework, comparing different communities (pages 8, 9) as well as components within the communities. He used data from several authors in the compilation of this table. The table contained data from both forest (coniferous and deciduous) and grassland communities.

In Table 7 are listed the percentage of animals comprising each major trophic group as given by Macfadyen and the rank each group held with equivalent trophic groups of the other communities. I have used these data to compute a rough carnivore-herbivore ratio and several generalizations emerge: (1) There is a rather constant percentage (20 to 33%) of herbivores—this category includes animals which reside in the soil and feed upon algae and roots of green plants but not upon bacteria and fungi. (2) There is an inverse relationship between the percentages of predators and large decomposers (sig. at the 5% level using Spearman rank correlation (Siegel, 1956, page 202)). (3) It would appear that there is an inverse relationship between the percentages of large decomposers and small decomposers; however, the r_s equals 0.5, which is not significant. Most of the deviation comes from a single observation (Spruce, R. H. (6). If this item were removed, the relationship between large and small decomposers would attain statistical significance at the 5% level ($r_s = 0.69$), but since we have no justification for eleminating the data on the Spruce, R. H. (6) community, the relationship remains doubtful.

It is also important to note that in Macfadyen's data the predator-herbivore ratio was not constant and did not seem to correlate either directly or inversely with an other element of the community.

Macfadyen (1963b) points out that, although the various taxonomic components vary considerably from community to community, the total picture of metabolism remains remarkably constant (although in view of the adjustments and assumptions made, the figures thus derived must be considered as tentative). From information on bacterial respiration and field experiments with soil respiration, Macfadyen estimated that animal respiration represented from 10 to 20% of the total soil metabolism. He concluded that the soil fauna is important in its "catalytic" activity and control of the energy passing through the decomposition cycle.

Table 7

The Comparison of Percent or Rank of Annual Caloric Dissipation and Predator-Herbivore Ratio of Different Trophic Groups Found in Nine Natural Communities on the British Isles and the European Continent. Data from Macfadyen, 1963b

Community	1 Grass-land	2 Lime-stone Grass	3 Juncus Moor	4 Oak Mull	5 Beech R H	6 Beech Mull (15)	7 Beech Mull (4)	8 Spruce Mull (1)	9 Spruce R H (6)
Herbivore Rank	8	7	3	4	9	6	2	5	1
Herbivore %	22.29	25.65	31.77	30.85	20.36	27.25	32.08	28.36	32.91
Large Decomposer Rank	4	1	8	2	5	3	6	7	9
L. Decomposer %	27.36	55.54	1.21	33.49	8.42	31.24	3.46	3.3	0.54
Small Decomposer Rank	4	9	1	6	2	8	3	5	7
S. Decomposer %	39.32	17.38	64.18	29.87	46.06	23.92	45.41	36.48	29.12
Predator Rank	6	9	8	7	3	5	4	2	1
Predator %	10.95	1.38	2.85	5.79	25.15	17.58	19.05	31.86	37.43
Rank Total kcal/yr	1	2	4	7	9	5	3	8	6
Ratio carnivore/herbivore	0.1232	0.0140	0.0293	0.0614	0.3360	0.2133	0.2353	0.4675	0.5981

When the studies on maintenance metabolism are reviewed as a group, at least three salient points emerge. First, annual maintenance metabolism is a better indication of the impact of a population or group on an area than are numbers or biomass. However, it was pointed out by Phillipson, Macfadyen, and O'Connor that respiratory metabolism rates alone do not represent the full impact of the population. The eating habits, efficiency of digestion, and rate of reproduction can have marked effect upon the community—effects which are not indicated in the Bornebusch type of analysis. Finally, it is of interest to note that the majority of the investigations were on soil animals or soil communities. This could be due either to tradition or to the fact that the soil provides many species and complex relationships readily accessible in small areas. The added fact that this system plays an important role in the economy of man probably also lends impetus to the pursuit of soil study.

Studies Which Emphasize the Trophic Scheme Analysis of Communities

This last group of studies gives us our best figures on animal productivity in natural communities. These studies are concerned not only with estimates of maintenance energies, but also with the incorporation of calories into new protoplasm. These growth calories can either fall prey to another trophic level, or increase the biomass of the population. The capacity of the population to produce these surplus calories determines the ultimate structure of the community as well as the usefulness of that community to man. With regard to this last point, we must bear in mind that the net productivity of a natural population is not equivalent to its yield useful to man. If man were to utilize the complete net production of a population, he would have to assume the role of predator and decomposer for the entire population. Man begins to approach this relationship with his domestic animals, but the natural community presents a different situation.

Investigators utilizing the trophic dynamic approach at the population level were: Golley and Gentry (1964), Odum and Smalley (1959), Odum et al. (1962), Petrides and Swank (1965), Smalley (1960), and Wiegert (1964). Only one author (Golley, 1960) has approached the subject of field energetics from the standpoint of energy flow through a food chain, while two investigators (Englemann, 1961; Teal, 1962) have attempted some kind of analysis at the community level. Three of the papers reported data on homiotherms (Golley, 1960; Odum et al., 1962; Petrides and Swank, 1965), while the remainder dealt with poikilotherms, particularly insects. Most of the investigators used field data to create complete energy budgets.

Trophic Dynamic Analysis of the Salt Marsh Ecotone

Smalley (1960), working on the insects of a salt marsh, has provided basic information utilized by other authors. His data for the grasshopper, *Orcheli-*

mum fidicinium, were used in his own 1960 paper, the paper by Odum and Smalley (1959) and the paper by Teal (1962). His basic sampling tool was a sweep net, standardized against captures in a square meter cage placed randomly on the sampling area. With these tools, Smalley could collect data on numbers of individuals, and size categories of individuals. Weights were assigned to the size categories by weighing representative individuals from each size category. A simple constant pressure respirometer was used to measure respiration rates. Observations on caged individuals were used in making estimates of egestion rates. Calorific values for various biological materials were determined in a Parr bomb calorimeter. Ingestion was figured as the sum of respiration, "production" and defecation. "Production" in this case then referred to net production which included estimates of new nymphs produced and numbers of individuals lost to the population through death. Estimates were lacking on numbers of eggs produced by the population. Smalley calculated that a biomass equivalent to 10.8 kcal/m² respired 18.6 kcal of oxygen annually. Gross production by the population equaled 29.4 kcal/m²/year. Gross production by the population equaled 29.4 kcal/m²/year. Assimilation efficiency averaged 27.4% and ranged from 20.8 to 35.4%. Smalley estimated that the grasshoppers ingested 107 kcal of the 5200 kcal produced annually on each square meter of the marsh. The grasshoppers consumed only 2% of the net amount produced by the flora available to them.

It is of interest that the net productivity of this population was estimated entirely from the data on calories lost to the population via death. This population, as in the case of many insects, overwintered in the egg stage and, thus, the adults died off at the end of the season, their bodies going directly to the decomposer system. The net production estimate of the grasshopper, however, was still short, for Smalley did not have data on the number of deaths for every stage in the life cycle.

The paper by Odum and Smalley (1959) summarized energetics data for grasshopper and snail populations living in the salt marsh on Sapelo Island off the coast of Georgia. The data for this study were collected my Smalley. The authors calculated that the grasshopper, *Orchelimum,* ingested 48 kcal/m²/year of *Spartina* grass. Thirty-six percent of the food ingested was assimilated. The gross production of the grasshopper was 28 kcal/m²/year. The snail (*Littorina*) feeding upon the decaying grass stems and algae, etc., was 45% efficient in assimilating its food and yielded a gross productivity of 290 kcal/m²/year. No ingestion figure was given for the snail. Since the organism was 45% efficient in assimilating food, it must have egested 55% of the material, or 354 kcal/m²/year. Thus, the *Littorina* population ingested annually a total of 644 kcal/m². *Littorina* used only 14% of its assimilated energy for production of new individuals, while the grasshopper utilized 37% of its energy in reproduction. These figures can give us a minimal estimate of net productivity in the two species, but losses due to death were not stated in this paper. Net production in the grasshopper was 10.4 kcal/m²/year, and in the snail, 40.6 kcal/m²/year. The major point Odum and Smalley made was that even though numbers of individuals and biomass varied in the salt marsh "community" the energy flow through the population remained relatively constant.

It is also worth noting the difference between the figures used by Odum and Smalley (1959) and those used by Smalley (1960). First, there was a 1.4 kcal/m²/year difference in the figures on gross productivity in the two papers. Secondly, Odum and Smalley used an assimilation figure of 36%, resulting in an estimate of 77.77 kcal/m² ingested annually, while Smalley set the assimilation rate at 27.4 and the ingestion rate at 107 kcal/m²/year. In the first case, the maximum assimilation rate was used. In the second assimilation was an average rate. Thus, the first paper compared the average efficiency of the animal, while the second compared the maximum efficiency.

The salt marsh is not typically a terrestrial community but is rather an ecotone. The fact that typically marine populations as well as terrestrial populations can be found at times in the same square meter plot tends to complicate analysis of this type of habitat. Allowances must also be made in the analysis for immigration and emigration of materials and population, particularly if the inflow and outflow of energy is not equal.

Teal (1962) attempted an analysis of the energetics of the salt marsh community. He employed data from several sources in making his estimates. A number of assumptions were used to give estimates where data were lacking. He stated production equalled 0.25 to 0.3 respiration; energy degradation was equal under anaerobic and aerobic conditions; the raccoons had an assimilation equal to that of the Clapper rails; spiders and carnivorous birds took the same proportion of the prey as did the mud crabs, rails, and raccoons which preyed upon detritus algae feeders. Some of these assumptions were supported by logic or circumstantial evidence; others, such at the last two listed, were not.

The energy flow through the salt marsh system was summarized by Teal as follows: Input as light 6×10^5 kcal/m²/year, loss in photosynthesis 563,620 kcal/m²/year, gross production of the producers 36,380 kcal/m²/year, respiration by the producers 28,175 kcal/m²/year, net production of the producers 8205 kcal/m²/year, bacterial respiration 3890 kcal/m²/year, primary consumer respiration 596 kcal/m²/year, secondary consumer respiration 48 kcal/m²/year.

The total energy released by the consumers equaled 4534 kcal/m²/year or 55% of the net production of the producers, leaving 3671 kcal/m²/year to be exported by tides and other losses. This "community" contained a great number of marine and freshwater species. If we confined attention to terrestrial animals then his data on the grasshopper, *Orchelimum,* the plant bug, *Prokelisia,* and the nematodes should be considered. The data on the grasshopper were those of Smalley (1960). The gross productivity of 29.4 kcal/m² was used by Teal. A gross productivity figure of 275 kcal/m²/year was reported for an average standing crop of 70 kcal/m² for *Prokelisia,* the plant bug. Teal calculated that the nematodes respired 64 kcal/m²/year, and he assumed production in the marsh to be 21 kcal/m²/year or 25% of the respiration rate. Teal did not calculate ecological efficiencies for the various trophic levels, although he did report efficiences for the utilization of the *Spartina* standing crop by the insects (4.6%). If we use the formula by Engelmann (1961) which is correctly reported by Slobodkin (1962, p. 98), an ecological efficiency of 6.8 can be obtained for the herbivore-carnivore trophic levels. Teal's paper is important because it deals with an ecotone. The work suffers because it relied too heavily upon assumptions and was not sufficiently comprehensive.

Trophic Dynamic Analysis of "Old Field" Communities

The second group of papers to be discussed center on the "old field" habitat. Studies have been made under the very different climatic conditions of southern Michigan and Georgia.

Golley and Gentry (1964) studied the bioenergetics of the southern harvester ant, *Pogonomyrmex badius* in South Carolina. They located ant hills in the "old field" study area, labeled individuals radioactively with P^{32} to estimate the numbers of animals in each hill by mark—release—and recapture methods. Ant hills were excavated to ascertain the numbers of all stages present, and respiration measurements were made on the various stages. Counts indicated that there were 0.0027 hills/m^2 and that each hill contained from 4000 to 6000 individuals. From data on numbers present and respiration studies, it was calculated that 14.2–47.7 kcal/m^2/year were lost by the population in respiration. Using the numbers of young found in the hills, plus supplementary data, Golley and Gentry estimated that the ants produced 0.09 kcal/m^2 in new individuals each year. The authors did not make an estimate of calories lost to the population through death. The total estimates for *P. badius* were: net productivity 0.09 kcal/m^2/year; gross productivity 14.29 to 47.79 kcal/m^2/year. Golley and Gentry reported that the ant was primarily a gramnivore and that the field produced 22 kcal/m^2/year in seeds. The ant, then, consumed the equivalent of 64 to 213% of the seed crop each year. Since the field also supported other gramnivores (mice and sparrows), the authors concluded that other foods must have been used by the ants in addition to seed. The authors noted that the ant consumed more energy than either the sparrow (4 kcal/m^2/150 days) or the mouse (7–17 kcal/m^2/year) population associated with it in the "old fields."

Because of the division of labor within the colony, the marking technique was not successful for estimating the total number of individuals in the hill. Data for net production were also difficult to evaluate, because the authors took the top birth production figures rather than averages; yet they had no estimate for deaths of adults or young during their life span. Net production, in this case, requires estimates for both parameters because most of the individuals lived more than one year. The important point is, however, that maintenance metabolism required 99.6% of the total assimilated energy. No estimate of ingestion was attempted and, therefore, we have no information on the total number of calories consumed annually by the population. The data presented by Golley and Gentry indicated that, in the "old field," the harvester ant was an important herbivore converting most of its assimilated energy into maintenance and very little energy into net production.

Odum *et al.* (1962) worked in the abandoned fields ("old fields") associated with the Savannah River Plant of the U.S. Atomic Energy Commission, Georgia. The authors concentrated on two grasshopper species (*Melanoplus femur-rubrum,* and *M. biliteratus*), the tree cricket (*Oeconthus nigricornis*), a mouse (*Peromyscus polionotus*), and a sparrow (*Passerculus sandwichensis*). The mice were live-trapped, the sparrows captured with mist nets, and the Orthoptera were captured with sweep nets and in cages after the procedures originated by Smalley. Caloric equivalents were obtained by Parr bomb calorimetry. Metabolism was measured both in terms of caged animals and by respirometry.

The field energy was assumed to be twice maintenance energy (an assumption questioned by McNab, 1963). The authors estimated that gross production of the sparrow was 3.6 kcal/m^2/year. However, since southern Georgia is the wintering range for these birds, there was virtually no net production (0.04 kcal/m^2/year). Gross production for the mouse was 6.7 kcal/m^2/year, with average net production at only 0.12 kcal/m^2/year. Gross production for the Orthoptera was 25.6 kcal/m^2/year and net production was 4.0 kcal/m^2/year. Once the authors had determined the total amount of each food consumed, they could find out how much of the standing crop of green plants the herbivores utilized. The gramnivorous birds and mice used from 10% to 50% of the seeds consumed, whereas the herbivorous Orthoptera utilized only 2% to 7% of the plant foliage. Golley and Gentry estimated that the ant, *P. badius,* consumed the equivalent of 64% to 213% of the seed crop on these same fields. Thus it would appear that from 74% to 263% of the seed crop produced on each m^2 was used by these three species during the year. This can only imply that either the seed crop was underestimated or the animal utilization overestimated, or both.

Analysis of droppings of vesper and field sparrows in Michigan showed that during the spring and early summer before a seed crop was produced, these animals were carnivores. Even during the fall, the birds continued to include insects in their diet along with seeds (personal communication, F. C. Evans). McNab (1963) believed that the food utilization data on the mouse (Odum *et al.,* 1962) were too high. Golley and Gentry (1964) recognized the fact that *P. badius* must have been using foods other than seeds. Thus, these calculations on seed utilization demonstrate that studies on energetics require careful observations on feeding habits, as well as careful measurements of metabolic and reproductive processes.

It is of interest to compare data from Wiegert's very careful study (1964) on the spittle bug *Philaenus spumarius* of "old fields" with the data previously discussed from the salt marsh and the southern "old field." Wiegert also used the aforementioned sweep net and cage method to measure the spittle bug population. He reported the confidence limits for his samples. Respiration rates were measured on all stages of the animals; the caloric values of these rates were determined; also feeding habits and migratory patterns were studied. A great deal of Wiegert's study was devoted to the feeding efficiency of the various stages of the spittle bug. He found that the immature individuals were 30% to 58% efficient (average 36%) in assimilating nutriment from the plant sap, while the adults were 71%–80% efficient (average 76%) on the same material. However, when it came to listing the productivity for the "old field," Wiegert ran into difficulty. A population must be able to produce a minimum number of new individuals, if it is to maintain itself from year to year. The *Philaenus* population could not do this on the "old field." Wiegert calculated the intrinsic rate of natural increase of this population on the "old field" to be −5.8 to −6.0. The continued presence of the spittle bug population on the "old field" was supported by immigration of new individuals from surrounding alfalfa fields. Thus, the net production of *P. spumarius* ranged from 0.048 to 0.096 kcal/m²/year and the gross productivity ranged from 0.582 to 1.167 kcal/m²/year. Immigration contributed from 0.516 to 1.138 additional kcal annually to each square meter of the "old field" in the form of immigrants which later failed to survive. In contrast, a small alfalfa field produced (net) 15.125 kcal/m² of animals. Gross productivity amounted to 38.565 kcal/m²/year. When the alfalfa in this field was cut, and the quantity of primary producers drastically reduced, thereafter the spittle bug adults moved out of these fields into other areas which could support them. Thus, although the "old field" was able to provide sustenance for a certain number of adults, there was not energy sufficient to maintain the population on a permanent basis. Ninety to ninety-five percent of the adult animals dying on the "old field" were immigrants. Wiegert was able to calculate the ecological efficiency (gross efficiency of yield/ingestion) by assuming "instantaneous predation." The figures he obtained ranged from 0.8%–17.4%.

Wiegert's paper is significant, not only because it is an example of careful analysis, but because it dealt with a species in the two extremes of its total habitat range. The gross and net productivities in the alfalfa field exceeded most other productivities for arthropods reported in the literature (save that of *P. badius,* Golley and Gentry, 1964). Yet, in the "old field" the spittle bugs could not survive. Wiegert's study pointed again to the inadequacy of the Lindeman model in a situation of imbalance.

Another study made of this "old field" of the E. S. George Reserve was concerned with the soil arthropods (Engelmann, 1961). The study used the author's results and data collected previously by Hairston and Byers (1954). The mite population was estimated from monthly soil samples processed in Tullgren funnels. Individuals of each species were weighed on a quartz helix balance, and the numbers and weight data were used to estimate biomass. Data on respiration rates measured with a simple constant-pressure respirometer were used in conjunction with biomass information to calculate total maintenance metabolism. Radiotracer experiments gave figures on ingestion. Soil organisms were cultured in the laboratory and studied to gain information on life span, ingestion and egestion, and birth rate. Information from cultures and field data provided a basis for making assumptions on survival. From these data a complete energy balance sheet was constructed for the Oribatei.

The study approached the problem of energetics at two levels: first at a lower level, or taxon, concentrating upon the Oribatei; on a second level all of the soil arthropods were included. The analysis of data on oribatids resulted in estimates as follows: a standing crop of 0.27 kcal on an average square meter of "old field"; ingested 10.248 kcal; assimilated 2.058 kcal; respired 1.965 kcal, and lost through mortality 0.43 kcal each year.

These data and preserved materials of Hairston and Byers (1954) were used to estimate the ecological efficiency of the carnivores with respect to the herbivores. Knowledge of respiration estimates and assimilation efficiency for both herbivores and carnivores made possible calculations of efficiency values. The most reasonable ecological efficiencies ranged from 8% to 30% with 16.9% the most probable value. The production on this field was very low when compared with the area sampled by Berthet, for example. Nematodes and rotifers were scarce in the poor, well-drained field soil. The combined respiration of these organisms yielded about $0.36 \text{ kcal}/m^2/\text{year}$.

This study had two positive aspects from the standpoint of energetics. First, the work represented an attempt to analyze total flow of energy through the soil. Second, all of the data in the oribatid balance sheet were a product of separate observations; none of the figures were derived from equations. The study had several inadequacies which could affect the significance of the results. Taxonomic identification was the greatest deficiency. Secondly, there was a problem of questionable efficiency of the Tullgren extractor, particularly when used on dry summer samples. Finally, temperatures of microhabitats were not known. I am now acquiring additional new information which may increase the figures for net and gross productivity of the Oribatei.

Let us move to another study of an "old field" habitat. The subject of a paper by Golley (1960) was the food chain involving the bluegrass-vole-least weasel. Golley obtained data on abundance, age structure, respiration, assimilation, and egestion rates of the vole *Microtus*. The least weasel (*Mustella*) data were largely based upon assumptions, the majority of them reasonable. Good information was obtained on the food of the mouse which was Kentucky bluegrass (*Poa pratensis*). Golley calculated that a standing crop of 0.021–0.553 kcal of mouse on 1 m^2 would release 17 kcal in respiration and produce 0.517 kcal in young each year. As was the case in Wiegert's study, it was difficult to balance the ledger because of caloric transport. The mice were able to maintain themselves in the area, although Golley found evidence of both immigration and emigration. An estimated 1.35 $\text{kcal}/m^2/\text{year}$ of mice moved into the area, a quantity almost twice that accounted for by net production. Thus, on the portion of the "old field" studied, the number of deaths was higher than the number of individuals produced on that area. The gross productivity of the *Microtus* population was 17.517 $\text{kcal}/m^2/\text{year}$. *Mustella,* the least weasel, had a net productivity of 0.013 $\text{kcal}/m^2/\text{year}$ and a gross productivity of 5.564 $\text{kcal}/m^2/\text{year}$. *Microtus* used 1.6% of the total net production of the

Kentucky bluegrass, while *Mustella* consumed 31% of the net production of the *Microtus* population. Though not calculated by Golley, ecological efficiencies for the weasel and mouse would be 2.3%. This percentage represented only a portion of predation, as the weasel was not the only predator on the mouse population.

Most of Golley's figures seemed to be reasonable. An analysis of the food chain is a very fruitful approach to the energetics problem. He did, however, get an unexpectedly high estimate for the assimilation rate of *Microtus* (90%). Most other herbivores assimilate from 65% to 75% of their food (Brody [1945, p. 80], McNab [1963], Pearson [1960]). If the rate cited by Golley truly reflects the ability of the animal to absorb food, rather than an experimental error, then, unlike most other animals, *Microtus* had a great advantage in being able to utilize most of the food it consumed.

Trophic Studies in a Savannah Community

Last to be reviewed in this paper is an energetics study done on the African Savannah and concerned with the largest land animal, the African Elephant. Petrides and Swank (1965) studied a population of *Loxodonta africana* in 28.5 square miles (7381.5 hectares) of Queen Elizabeth National Park, Uganda. They counted the individuals in the total population and classified them according to sex and age. Their age distribution was as follows: 14.6% calves, 24.3% immatures, 14.4% sub-adults, and 46.7% adults. Growth rate data came from other sources and were chiefly based on measurements of captive elephants in zoos. From these data a growth curve was plotted which fitted the size of the wild individuals. The authors then created a life table, using growth rates and population structure. They estimated that 70% of the calves survived the 1st year. Their survival rate then jumped to 80% in the 2nd year and was 95% by puberty in the 14th year. After the beginning adult years when the survival rate was 98%, it began to drop again. An average elephant fixed as new protoplasm 165.6×10^3 kcal/year, but since there were only 5.37 elephants per square mile, net production amounted to only 0.34 kcal/m²/year.

The physiological data of Benedict (1936) on elephants were used to calculate maintenance metabolism and rate of ingestion. Petrides and Swank established that for the elephant an average standing crop of 7.1 kcal on 1 m² respired 23 kcal and consumed 71.6 kcal of food annually. Gross productivity was 23.34 kcal/m²/year, while net productivity was only 0.34 kcal/m²/year. The elephant used 9.6% of the total browse available.

Petrides and Swank compared the productivity of the African elephant to that of the mouse, white-tailed deer, and cattle. They found that the elephant maintained a tremendous biomass on a relatively coarse diet. Assimilation was poor (44%) when compared with that of other mammals, and growth rate was slow; however, net production of the African elephant was 40% that of good beef cattle. The authors also pointed out that the elephant changed conditions in the Savannah by such activities as digging water holes and pushing down trees, making areas habitable for other game. The authors went on to suggest how herds could be managed so as to give maximum benefit to man and other animals.

The paper by Petrides and Swank is significant in that it demonstrates how physiological data can be applied to field data and good energetics estimates thereby obtained. The paper also demonstrated how energetics data could be useful in practical application. Some of the figures given by Petrides and Swank may be questioned because only a few observations were represented, but allowing for the paucity of observations, this remains a stimulating and valuable study.

There are not enough trophic efficiency studies as yet to give a clear picture of either the structures of communities or the validity of the Lindeman model. Yet, the data thus far gathered suggest several interesting trends or hypotheses at the population level which could guide future research. The values determined for several population parameters in various energetics studies have been listed in Table 8. If net production and maintenance metabolism are analyzed by using Spearman rank correlation, there is indicated a relationship, significant at the 5% level. Yet, when all the data are plotted on a graph (Fig. 2), only a slight indication of a regression is shown. If, however, the points are separated with respect to the degree of temperature regulation, data for poikilotherms reflect a rather clear-cut trend. One point on the graph, representing information on the harvest ant, *P. badius,* is far removed from those of other poikilotherms, the rest falling along a line described by the following formula: $\text{Log } R = 62 + 0.86 \text{ Log } p.$ (*"R"* represents the number of k calories respired by the population found per m^2/year and *"p"* represents the net productivity in $kcal/m^2$/year.) Slobodkin (1960) pointed out that in *Daphnia* after the maintenance requirement was met, the remaining calories went into reproduction, a fact borne out by this graph. If the data on *P. badius* are included in the regression, 0.62 becomes one and the slope changes to 0.55. There is, however, at least one good biological reason for considering the ant to be an exception to the usual pattern of energetics found in most animals; namely, the workers and soldiers are sterile. Although there were 4000 to 6000 individuals in a colony, only two were capable of reproducing. One would expect that, when compared with respiratory metabolism, productivity in ants would be low. From the point of view of energetics, the ant colony is inefficient, burning a disproportionate amount of energy to produce so little; yet, ants seem to be very successful in the world today. It is of interest to note that the point on Fig. 2 representing data for the ant falls among the group of points representing the data for homiotherms.

The homiotherms, too, apparently burn a disproportionate amount of energy for what is produced in the way of new protoplasm, at least by standards of poikilotherm production. Yet, the homiotherms are also very successful today.

Table 8

*Productivity, Maintenance Metabolism, Percent Utilization, and Ecological
Efficiency of Different Animals Found in Various Communities.
Data Compiled from Several Authors*

Taxon	Prod in kcal/m²/yr		Maintenance Metabolism in kcal/m²/yr	% Utilization of Net Production Food	Ecological Efficiency	Habitat	Authority
	Net	Gross					
Invertebrates							
1. *Littorina* sp.	40.6	290	249.4	—	—	Salt marsh	Odum and Smalley, 1959
2. Nematodes	21.0	85	64.0	—	6.8	Salt marsh	Teal, 1962
3. *Orchelimum fidicinum*	10.8	29.4	18.6	2	—	Salt marsh	Smalley, 1960
4. *Prokelisia* sp.	—	275.0	—	4.6	6.8	Salt marsh	Teal, 1962
5. Orthoptera (3 spp.)	4.0	25.6	21.6	2–7	—	Old Field	Odum *et al.*, 1962
6. *Philaenus spumarius*	0.048–0.096	0.582–1.167	0.778†	—	—	Old Field	Wiegert, 1964
7. *P. spumarius*	15.125	38.565	23.44	—	0.8–17.4	Alfalfa field	Wiegert, 1964
8. *Pogonomyrmex badius*	0.09	14.29–47.79	31.03†	64–213	—	Old Field	Golley and Gentry, 1964
9. Oribatei	0.43	2.008	1.578	—	8–30	Old Field	Engelmann, 1961
Vertebrates							
10. *Passerculus*	0.04	3.6	3.56	10–50	—	Old Field	Odum *et al.*, 1962
11. *Microtus*	0.517	17.517	17.00	1.6	2.3 ‡	Old Field	Golley, 1960
12. *Peromyscus*	0.12	6.7	6.58	10–50	—	Old Field	Odum *et al.*, 1962
13. *Loxodonta africana*	0.34	23.34	23.00	9.6	—	Savannah	Petrides and Swank, 1965
14. *Mustela*	0.013	5.564	5.551	31.0	2.3 ‡	Old Field	Golley, 1960

† Average.

‡ Single species.

364

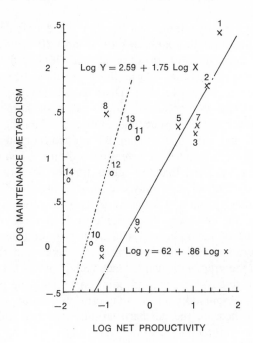

LOG NET PRODUCTIVITY

Figure 2

The relationship between maintenance metabolism and net productivity. The points represented by "x's" are poikilotherms and the "o's" are homiotherms. The solid line represents the poikilotherm regression while the dotted line represents homiotherm regression. The numbers associated with each point correspond to the identification numbers in the left-hand column in Table 8.

The five points representing the birds and mammals fall along a regression line described by the following formula: Log $R = 2.59 + 1.75$ Log $p;$ "R" and "p" having been previously defined. The regressions for homiotherms and poikilotherms converge, but it is difficult to say that the closely grouped points for the homiotherms represent the true slope of the line. Points Nos. 10 and 14 have a greater effect on the regression than do the other three. It is conceivable that the slope of the line is actually nearer that of the poikilotherm data. More information is needed on the energetics of homiotherms.

If we generalize from these data, we come to a rather startling conclusion. First, the biological world is divided into two separate realms with reference to energetics: the thermoregulators and the nonregulators. Second, the nonregulators are more efficient producers than are the thermoregulators. If this were the whole story, mammals and birds could not compete with the rest of the animal kingdom, and beef farmers would be raising grasshoppers for meat.

The key to this apparently paradoxical situation is the assimilation efficiency of the organisms concerned. Poikilotherms are at most 30% efficient in digesting food whereas most homiotherms are around 70% efficient. Thus, the poikilotherm has to consume more calories if it is to gain sufficient nutrition for the maintenance and reproductive tasks. Does the efficiency of digestion and assimilation compensate the organism for the cost of homiothermy? This question has no answer at the present time. However, when the five situations (two homiotherms, and three poikilotherms) are considered wherein total calories ingested are known and if they were plotted on a graph similar to Fig. 1, the new plot would suggest that the curves for poikilotherms and homiotherms approach one another, and may even merge broadly. Thus, it would appear that poikilothermy and homiothermy are two answers to the same problems of existence in the environment. It would be interesting to know where data for populations of heliotherms (such as lizards and snakes) and the "variable homiotherms" (such as the sloths, opossums, and the true hibernators) will fall on the graphs of maintenance metabolism—net production.

The studies seem to suggest a second point concerning the productivity of various populations. Populations in the southern latitudes appear to be more productive than do those in the northern latitudes. Such a difference seems reasonable, because warmer temperatures and longer growing seasons make possible greater productivity.

Still a third additional hypothesis suggested by these data is that populations have greater productivity in simpler situations (such as pioneer communities). Thus, the salt marsh populations are more productive than are those of the southern "old field" which in turn are more productive than are those of the northern "old field." In a like manner, the population studied in the northern alfalfa field far exceed the production of the same populations found on the northern "old field." We must remember that here productivity of single populations within different communities is under discussion rather than productivity of a community.

The trends suggested in these studies seem to support our present ideas about population size within communities (i.e. that pioneer communities are made up of a few large populations while climax communities are made up of numerous relatively small populations).

Finally, the data on ecological efficiency and on efficiency of use indicate that each population utilizes only a small portion of the available calories (the one exception being the use of seeds on the southern "old field"). The most frequently reported figures on food utilization were: 2% for herbivores and 30% for carnivores. When considering ecological efficiency of a trophic level (i.e. the soil arthropods) the maximum efficiency is only 30% and the remaining 70% then goes into other energy pathways. Thus, it is obvious that the energy fixed by the plants "cascades" into a number of energy "sumps" before it is completely dissipated through respiration.

Projection

I stated in the introduction that many ecologists feel their science has come of age. Odum (1964) in particular points to energetics as the new ecology. If energetics is indeed the new ecology, what guiding principles and predictive models have been developed to guide future inquiry and to aid the energetics ecologist to answer the crucial practical questions of the day? We must admit that, thus far, the Lindeman model has been the major guiding principle in energetics. We must also state that this model has been very little tested and practically unchanged since its inception over 20 years ago. If it is to be useful, a model for a community must apply to all situations. Since this paper is primarily concerned with terrestrial communities, let us consider the information contributed by the terrestrial ecologists in the light of the Lindeman model.

First, only three terrestrial communities have been studied thus far and none has been analyzed completely. Second, none of these studies was able either to support or refute the Lindeman model, since populations, not trophic levels, were studied. Third, the data in the studies were all tentative, since the magnitude of the errors involved in the computations cannot be analyzed. The proponents of the Lindeman model are further hindered by other problems, inherent in the nature of the model: (1) many animals do not fit into a single trophic level, but their food habits, fall into two or more levels; (2) situations of imbalance are common in all communities although they are usually reduced in the climax community. The model must be modified to take these problems into account. Ours may be the age of ecology, but it appears that energetics has not yet come of age.

If the study of energetics is to mature in "its era," energetics ecologists must make a concerted effort to sample more communities with the Lindeman model in mind. Research should be aimed at analysis of food chains and food webs. Such studies would serve not only to document the metabolism of the populations concerned, but also to test hypotheses concerning energy transfers and biomass ratios between trophic levels. Only in this way can the true relationship between reality and the model be found.

It seems to me that the second area ripe for study is delimitation of communities. To date, no natural area has been investigated to see whether energy units can define or locate the boundaries of a community, and to find out whether the energy boundaries, if detectable, correspond with other observable signs, interpreted as community boundaries.

Finally, at this point, some relationship is indicated between net productivity and maintenance metabolism (see Fig. 2). It is important to remember that the relationship ($\text{Log } Rp = 0.62 + 0.86 \text{ Log } p$) was obtained from data provided by 5 different authors, working on several species of animals and using markedly different techniques to make energetic estimates. The majority of the points on Fig. 1 represent single species populations. Point 7, however, represents all of the oribatid mites in the "old field" soil (Engelmann, 1961). While working with the plot, I questioned the position of point 7, for it represents data from about eighteen species. Yet this point lies near a regression line derived mostly from points representing single species data. I used the new formula to check further the position of the oribatid data on Fig. 2 as well as to make a preliminary check on the plausibility of this formula. In my original analysis (Engelmann. 1961) the productivity estimates came from two independent sources, one based on egg production in three species of mites (particularly *Oppia nova* and *Scherloribates levigatus*) in cultures, and the other from the deduced death rate of the adult population. This net production figure, then, was not compiled from individual production rates for each population. By using the net productivity formula for poikilotherms listed above, I was able to calculate from the annual respiratory metabolism the net production for each species of oribatid found on the "old field" (Table 9). The im-

Table 9

Net Reproduction of Oribatid Mites Calculated from the Maintenance-Net Reproduction Formula. Respiration Data from Engelmann, 1961

Species Number†	Species Name	Net Productivity in g cal/m²/yr
101	*Tectocepheus velatus* (Mich.)	86.0
102	*Scherloribates pallidulus*	39.3
103	*Camisia* sp.	25.0‡
105	Immature	—
108a	*Oppia nova*	32.4
108c	*Cultroribula* sp. (*divergens*)	9.5
108d	*Suctobelba* sp.	4.4
108e	*Oppia minutissima*	0.6
109	*Rhysotritia ardua*	28.1
110	*Peloribates curtipilus*	27.4
111	*Allogalumna alatum*	17.5
112a	Immature	—
112b	Immature	—
113	Adult Oppidae	1.1
114	*Trhypochthonius* sp. (*tectorum*)	69.5
115	*Belba* sp.	0.5
116	Immature	—
117	*Thyrisoma ovata*	14.5
118	Immature	—
119	Immature	—
120	*Liochthonius perpusillus* and *Brachychthonius jugatus*	17.2‡
121	*Zygoribatula rostrata*	27.6
126	Tarsonomid	13.5‡
128	Tarsonomid	14.3‡
	Total	428.4

† Identification system used by Engelmann, 1961.
‡ Assumed 1/3 population productive.

mature individuals were not reproducing and thus were not included in the calculation. Certain other populations (marked with asterisks) were not originally separated into groups of adults and young, because all stages were readily identified as belonging to the same species. Thus, I arbitrarily assumed that one-third of the population were adults, capable of reproduction, and two-thirds were immatures. The total net productivity as calculated by the net productivity equation for poikilotherms (using the above-mentioned omissions and assumptions) was 428 cal/m²/yr while the net productivity calculated by oviposition data and turnover rate was 430 cal. If no assumption were made about the mixed populations (*), the total would have been 568.3 cal/m²/yr. In the first case the agreement would be phenomenal and in the second instance there would still be reasonable agreement. Thus, I feel that the new equation has great potential, but should be more fully tested.

If we are concerned with predicting net productivity of a community, we cannot use the simple equation for respiration and net productivity. As more data on species respiration are added, the calculations deviate further from the true figure, e.g., if we take the total respiration data from Macfadyen's (1963b) Grassland No. 1 and use it in the equation, net productivity is estimated at 650 kcal/m²/yr. If the productivity is then calculated for each trophic level and taxon listed, an estimate of only 470.7 kcal/m²/yr results (some 27% lower than the estimate based upon total annual respiration). But, the taxa listed by Macfadyen were not species. Rather they were orders and phyla and thus we could predict that net productivity of the entire community is still less than the estimate made using taxon analysis.

If the poikilotherm net productivity curve is valid, then the net productivity of this portion of an animal community could be calculated, where the annual respiration is known. The formula would be

$$\text{Log } p = \frac{\sum_{N}^{1} \text{Log } Rp - 0.62}{0.86}$$

where N is the total number of poikilothermic species in the community, P, net productivity in calories and Rp, annual respiration in calories. It follows that estimation of net productivity should be possible, if the average respiration $(\overline{Rp})$ and the total number of species present in the community are known, by using the formula:

$$\text{Log } p = \frac{N \text{ Log } \overline{Rp} - 0.62}{0.83}$$

When testing this formula on Macfadyen's (1963b) community data and my own oribatid data (Engelmann, 1961, Table 4, p. 226), I found that the average respiration consistently gave an estimate which was 8 to 12% lower than net productivity calculated from the respiration of each individual species. The formula for calculating community net productivity, using average respiration rate would then become:

$$\text{Log } p = \frac{N \text{ Log } Rp - 0.62}{0.83} + 0.1 \left(\frac{\text{Log } \overline{Rp} - 0.62}{0.83} \right)$$

which is not very satisfying.

Finally, if we are to calculate the total net productivity of an entire animal community, we must include a term for the homiotherms. The homiotherm regression in Fig. 2 does not show a significant correlation with the points on the figure. If we assume, however, that the regression line fits, then the equation for total net productivity of the community would be:

$$\text{Log } p = \frac{\sum\limits_{N}^{1} \text{Log } Rp - 0.62 + \sum\limits_{N1}^{1} \text{Log } Rh - 2.59}{2.61}$$

where N equals the total number of poikilothermic species, N^1 equals total number of homiothermic species, Rp = annual respiration (in kcal) of poikilotherms, and Rh = annual respiration (in kcal) of homiotherms. If, however, the homiotherm slope is actually that of the poikilotherms, then the constant in the homiotherm portion of the equation would be 1.7 and the divisor would be changed to 1.72.

These equations, if valid, will be useful tools for the further analysis of communities, inasmuch as the respiration of a species is relatively easy to measure.

Finally, it is reasonable to hypothesize that a relationship exists between total caloric ingestion and net productivity. It is also probable that the relationship of calories ingested and net productivity at the community level, though simpler, is not so accurate as the relationships of respiration and net productivity.

In summary, then, we have taken a brief look at the growth of the principles of energetics as applied to field populations. At the start, studies were concerned mainly with the physics of combustion by animals. Subsequently the science grew and fragmented into three lines of attack. The physiological studies provide a potential reservoir of information. The maintenance metabolism studies provide comparisons at the population and community levels which emphasize the intensity of the energy flow. The trophic-dynamic studies yield a model and data on net productivity. From a close examination of the field as a whole, one can say that the study of energetics (particularly terrestrial) is still in its developing stage—not yet in any sense so mature as is sometimes proposed. Yet, the Lindeman model, and maintenance metabolism studies, are providing guidelines for field investigations. Such studies are, in turn, yielding data necessary for further speculation, prediction, and model refinement. Even though methods are still crude, new principles are beginning to emerge, and this discipline shows great promise.

I wish to express my gratitude to Dr. John A. Wallwork (Westfield College, London, England) and Dr. Tyler Woolley (Colorado State University) for the identifications of the Oribatei, to Dr. George Petrides (Michigan State University) for making the manuscript of his paper available, to Dr. D. Strawbridge and Mr. W. Weist (Michigan State University) for their discussions on mathematical aspects of the work, to the National Science Foundation for funds supporting a portion of the mite research reported in this paper. I am particularly grateful to my wife, Patricia, for her patient help with the manuscript.

References

Allee, W. C., Emerson, A. E., Park, O., Park, T. and Schmidt, K. P. (1949). "Principles of Animal Ecology." Philadelphia: Saunders.

Armsby, H. P. (1903). "Principles of Animal Nutrition." New York.

Atwater, W. O. and Benedict, F. G. (1903). "The Metabolism of Matter and Energy in the Human Body." U.S. Department of Agriculture Bulletin 136.

Benedict, F. G. (1936). "Physiology of the Elephant," Washington: Carnegie Institute, Publ. 474.

Berthet, P. (1963). Mésure de la consommation d'oxygène des Oribatides (Acariens) de la litière des forêts. *In* "Soil Organisms," 18–31.

Birch, L. C. and Clarke, P. D. (1953). *Quart. Rev. Biol.* 28: 13–36. Forest soil as an ecological community with special reference to the fauna.

Birge, E. A. and Juday, C. (1922). *Bull. Wisconsin Geol. Nat. Hist. Surv.* 64: 1–222. The inland lakes of Wisconsin. The plankton. Part I. Its quantity and chemical composition.

Blair, W. F. (1964). *Bio. Sci.* 14: 17–19. The case for ecology.

Bornebusch, C. H. (1930). "The Fauna of The Forest Soil." Copenhagen.

Brody, Samuel. (1945). "Bioenergetics and Growth, with Special Reference to the Efficiency Complex in Domestic Animals." New York: Reinhold. Reprinted (1964). New York: Hafner.

Cole, L. C. (1964). *Bio. Sci.* 14: 30–32. The impending emergence of ecological thought.

Davis, D. E. and Golley, F. B. (1963). "Principles in Mammalogy." New York: Reinhold.

Dawson, W. R. (1955). *J. Mammal.* 36: 543–553. The relation of oxygen consumption to temperature in desert rodents.

Dawson, W. R. (1958). *Physiol. Zool.* 31: 37–48. Relation of oxygen consumption and evaporative water loss to temperature in the cardinal.

Dawson, W. R. and Templeton, J. R. (1963). *Physiol. Zool.* 36: 219–236. Physiological responses to temperature in the lizard *Crotaphytus collaris*.

Dawson, W. R. and Tordoff, H. B. (1964). *Auk,* 81: 26–35. Relation of oxygen consumption to temperature in red and white-winged crossbills.

Dice, L. R. (1952). "Natural Communities." Ann Arbor: University of Michigan Press.

Dixon, M. (1952). "Manometric Methods." London: Cambridge University Press.

Doeksen, J. and Van der Drift, J. (eds.) (1963). "Soil Organisms," Amsterdam, Netherlands: North Holland Pub. Co.

Engelmann, M. D. (1961). *Ecol. Monogr.* 31: 221–238. Reprinted in Hazen (1964). 332–349. The role of soil arthropods in the energetics of an old-field community.

Evans, F. C. (1964). *Bull. Ecol. Soc. Amer.* 45, 95. Seasonal changes in composition of an insect community.

Evans, F. C. and Smith, F. E. (1952). *Amer. Nat.* 86: 299–310. The intrinsic rate of natural increase for the human louse, *Pediculus humanus* L.

Gere, G. (1956a). *Acta Biol. Hung.* 6: 258–271. The examination of the feeding biology and the humificative function of Diplopoda and Isopoda.

Gere, G. (1956b). *Opus. Zool.* 1: 29–32. Investigations concerning energy turn-over of *Hyphantria cunea* Drury caterpillars.

Golley, F. B. (1960). *Ecol. Monogr.* 30, 187–206. Energy Dynamics of a food chain of an old-field community.

Golley, F. B. (1961). *Ecology,* 42: 581–584. Energy values of ecological materials.

Golley, F. B. and Gentry, J. D. (1964). *Ecology,* 45: 217–225. Bioenergetics of the southern harvest ant, *Pogonomyrmex badius.*

Hairston, N. G. (1959). *Ecology,* 40(3): 404–416. Reprinted in Hazen (1964), 319–331. Species abundance and community organization.

Hairston, N. G. and Byers, G. W. (1954). *Contr. Lab. Vert. Biol. Univ. Mich.* 64: 1–37. A study in community ecology: The soil arthropods in a field in southern Michigan.

Hairston, N. G., Smith, F. E. and Slobodkin, L. B. (1960). *Amer. Nat.* 94: 421–425. Reprinted in Hazen (1964), 288–292. Community structure, population control, and competition.

Hazen, W. E. (ed.). (1964). "Readings in Population and Community Ecology," Philadelphia: Saunders.

Itô, Y. (1964). *Res. Population Ecol.* 6: 13–21. Preliminary studies on the respiratory energy loss of a spider, *Lycosa pseudoannulata.*

Kendeigh, S. C. (1944). *J. exp. Zool.* 96: 1–16. Effect of air temperature on rate of energy metabolism in the English sparrow.

Kendeigh, S. C. (1964). *Auk,* 66: 113–127. Effect of temperature and season on energy resources of the English sparrow.

King, J. R. and Farner, D. S. (1961). *In* Marshall (1961), 215–288. Energy metabolism, thermoregulation, and body temperature.

Lavoisier, A. L. (1777). *Mem. Acad. Sci.,* p. 185. Experiences sur la respiration des animaux et sur la changements qui arrivent a'l'air en passant par leur poumons.

Lindeman, R. L. (1942). *Ecology,* 23: 399–418. Reprinted in Hazen (1964). 206–225. The trophic-dynamic aspect of ecology.

MacArthur, R. H. (1960). *Amer. Nat.* 94: 25–36. Reprinted in Hazen (1964). 307–318. On the relative abundance of species.

Macfadyen, A. (1963a). "Animal Ecology, Aims and Methods." London: Pitman.

Macfadyen, A. (1963b). *In* "Soil Organisms," 3–17. The contribution of the micro-fauna to total soil metabolism.

Marshall, A. J. (ed.). (1961). "Biology and Comparative Physiology of Birds, Vol. II." New York: Academic Press.

McNab, B. K. (1963). *Ecology,* 44: 521–532. A model of the energy budget of a wild mouse.

Metcalf, C. L. and Flint, W. P. (1939). "Destructive and Useful Insects," New York: McGraw-Hill.

Morrison, P. R. and Ryer, G. A. (1951). *Fed. Proc.* 10(1): Part I. Temperature and metabolism in some Wisconsin mammals.

Nielsen, C. O. (1961). *Oikos,* 12: 17–35. Respiratory metabolism of some populations of enchytraeid worms and free living nematods.

O'Connor, F. B. (1963). *In* "Soil Organisms," 32–48. Oxygen consumption and population metabolism of some populations of Enchytraeidae from North Wales.

Odum, E. P. (1964). *Bio. Sci.* 14: 14–16. The new ecology.

Odum, E. P. and Smalley, A. E. (1959). *Proc. Nat. Acad. Sci., Wash.* 45: 617–622. Comparison of population energy flow of a herbiverous and a deposit-feeding invertebrate in a salt marsh ecosystem.

Odum, E. P., Connell, C. E. and Davenport, L. B. (1962). *Ecology,* 43: 88–96. Population energy flow of three primary consumer components of old-field ecosystems.

Pattern, B. C. (1959). *Ecology,* 40: 221–231. An introduction to the cybernetics of the ecosystem: the trophic-dynamic aspect.

Pearson, O. P. (1960). *Physiol. Zool.* 33: 152–160. The oxygen consumption and bioenergetics of harvest mice.

Petrides, G. A. and Swank, W. G. (1965). Estimating the productivity and energy relations of an African elephant population. *Proceed. 9th International Grasslands Congress,* São Paulo, Brazil.

Phillipson, J. (1962). *Oikos,* 13: 311–322. Respirometry and study of energy turnover in natural systems with particular reference to the harvest spider.

Platt, R. B. and Griffiths, J. (1964). "Environmental Measurement and Interpretation." New York: Reinhold.

Sealander, J. A. Jr. (1952). *J. Mamm.* 33: 206–218. Food consumption in *Peromyscus* in relation to air temperature and previous thermal experience.

Sears, P. B. (1964). *Bio. Sci.* 14: 11–13. Ecology—a subversive subject.

Siegel, S. (1956). "Nonparametric Statistics for Behavioral Science." New York: McGraw-Hill.

Slobodkin, B. L. (1960). *Amer. Nat.* 94: 213–236. Ecological energy relationships at the population level.

Slobodkin, B. L. (1962). *In* "Advances in Ecological Research, Vol. 1" (J. B. Cragg, ed.), pp. 69–101. London: Academic Press. Energy in animal ecology.

Slobodkin, B. L. and Richman, S. (1961). *Nature, Lond.* 191: 299. Calories/gm. in species of animals.

Smalley, A. E. (1960). *Ecology.* 41: 672–677. Energy flow of a salt marsh grasshopper population.

Teal, J. M. (1962). *Ecology,* 43: 614–624. Energy flow in the salt marsh ecosystem of Georgia.

Van der Drift, J. (1951). "Analysis of the Animal Community in a Beech Forest Floor," Wageningen.

Van der Drift, J. (1958). The role of the soil fauna in the decomposition of forest litter. 15th Intern. Congress Zool., London, Sect. 4, paper 3, 357–360.

Waldbauer, G. P. (1964). *Ent. Exper. Appli.* 7: 253–269. Consumption, digestion and utilization of solanaceous and non-solanaceous plants by larvae of the tobacco hornworm, *Protoparce sexta* (Johan.) (Lepidoptera: Sphingidae).

Wallgren, H. (1954). *Acta Zool. Fenn.* 84: 1–110. Energy metabolism of two species of the genus *Emberiza* as correlated with distribution and migration.

West, G. (1960). *Auk,* 77: 306–329. Seasonal variation in the energy balance of the tree sparrow in relation to migration.

Wiegert, R. G. (1964). *Ecol. Monogr.* 34: 217–241. Population energetics of meadow spittle bugs (*Philaenus spurmarius* L.) as affected by migration and habitat.

R. Margalef

On Certain Unifying Principles in Ecology

Structure of the Ecosystem

Ecosystems have a structure, in the sense that they are composed of different parts or elements, and these are arranged in a definite pattern. The interrelations between the constituent elements are the basis of the structure. Of course, it is possible to recognize and measure different degrees of structure. One measure would be the number of parameters needed for describing a certain situation.

More specifically, ecosystems formed by a greater number of species allow for a higher number of specific relations in food webs, parasitism, etc. These require a longer description, to express an equivalent degree of knowledge. Considering the ecosystem in terms of individuals distributed in different species is only one of several possibilities; we can think of it also in relation to chemical compounds or biochemical systems. For example, assimilatory pigments provide a very concrete and useful botanical approach. A similar concept of structure can be applied even to the environment. Consider, for instance, the kinds and proportions of organic substances produced by organisms and present in aquatic ecosystems.

The main point is that the "real" structure of an ecosystem is a property that remains out of reach, but this complete structure is reflected in many aspects of the ecosystem that can be subjected to observation: in the distribution of individuals into species, in the pattern of the food net, in the distribution of total assimilatory pigments in kinds of pigments, and so on.

Structure, in general, becomes more complex, more rich, as time passes; structure is linked to history. For a quantitative measure of structure it seems convenient to select a name that suggests this historical character, for instance, maturity. In general, we may speak of a more complex ecosystem as a more mature ecosystem. The term maturity suggests a trend, and moreover maintains a contact with the traditional dynamic approach in the study of natural communities, which has always been a source of inspiration.

Maturity, then, is a quality that increases with time in any undisturbed ecosystem. Field ecologists use many criteria to estimate the maturity of an esosystem, without the need of assessing its precise place in an actual succes-

Reprinted by permission of the author and publisher from *The American Naturalist, 97:* 357–374, 1963.

sion. Empirical knowledge of succession leads one to consider as more mature the ecosystems that are more complex; that is, composed of a great number of elements, with long food chains, and with relations between species well defined or more specialized. Strictly stenophagous animals, parasites, all sorts of very precise symbiotic or defensive relations, are commoner in mature ecosystems. Furthermore, situations are more predictable, the average life of individuals is longer, the number of produced offspring lower, and internal organization of the ecosystem turns random disturbances into quasiregular rhythms. Leaving aside for the moment the aspects of turnover and rhythms to be dealt with later, we can focus now on the structure and how it can be expressed quantitatively.

Practical situations impose severe limitations on theoretical possibilities. Theoretically, it would be possible to compute a diversity index, expressing the distributions of individuals into species in the whole ecosystem. This is most conveniently done by determining the average number of bits per individual (Margalef, 1957), but under conditions that are common in natural communities any other diversity index will be applicable. Unfortunately, nobody has even attempted to undertake a complete census of the whole community. Thus, we are forced to compute our diversity through samples of the community, selected by the use of certain technical implements (plankton nets, traps, light to attract insects) or by taxonomical criteria (diversity of birds, of insects, of copepods, of dinoflagellates). Nevertheless, there is evidence that the more inclusive structure is reflected in the composition of these selected parts, arbitrarily chosen by the taxonomic relation of components or by mechanical procedure, but always measured in the same way. Sampling has to be organized very critically. One has to remember, for instance, that samples including small organisms taken at random usually show a lower degree of organization and maturity than samples of bigger animals with definite spatial pattern of distribution, and with forms of behavior utilized by man in their capture. Samples that include organisms belonging to superior trophic levels may represent a higher maturity than samples with a more predominant representation of primary producers.

On the other hand, one can rely on the congruence between estimates of maturity obtained at different levels. There is a good correlation between the diversity in the distribution of individuals into species, and in the diversity of plant pigments in the plankton (Margalef, 1961b). MacArthur (1961) has found a good correlation between bird species diversity, plant species diversity and diversity in the mass distribution of foliage of plants in different strata. A glimpse at the fish market in any place of the world gives an idea of species diversity in the exploited fishery, and in general, biotic diversity of plankton in the same places varies accordingly.

There is no doubt that we can get numbers expressing the structure of ecosystems. If used properly, these numbers permit comparisons. We can tell which system, of two being confronted, is more complex and mature. This can be done either with neighboring ecosystems or with completely independent and distant ecosystems. The handling of diversity data poses certain problems, mostly concerned with the spectrum of diversity in relation to space, but these questions have been discussed elsewhere (Margalef, 1957, 1961a, 1961b) and moreover are not relevant to the present discussion.

The Ecosystem in Relation to Energy and Mass

The ecosystem has different complementary aspects: If we consider the elements and the relations between the elements, we have the structure, whereas in considering matter and energy, we have to deal with metric properties which are perhaps easier to express. The ecosystem is formed by a certain amount of matter (biomass) and there is a budget of matter and energy.

For the moment, let us consider an ecosystem in a steady state, with a material output equal to the material input. Here we need to consider only two quantities: the matter present, or biomass, in the ecosystem, always to be expressed in the same form (total weight, dry weight); and the potential energy necessary for maintenance in the ecosystem, amounting to total respiration and other losses. Both quantities can be considered in every ecosystem and simply equated to primary production (P) and biomass (B); both concepts are of common usage in ecology. Their relation (P/B) can be stated as flow of energy per unit biomass; it is the turnover rate of Cushing, Humphrey, Banse and Laevastu (1958) and the productivity index under natural light conditions of Strickland (1960). Note that it is convenient always to take the total biomass including that of the animals. The dimensions of the ratio P/B are L^2T^{-3}, when P is expressed as power; and T^{-1} as simple turnover. The dimensional quotient $L^{-2}T^2$ represents the amount of biomass necessary to carry a given quantity of potential energy and may change from ecosystem to ecosystem.

What is important is the empirical relation between structure and energy flow per unit biomass. More mature ecosystems, with a richer structure, have a lower primary production per unit biomass. This has been observed in laboratory cultures and all the scattered data found in the literature that seem relevant in this connection, mostly on pelagic communities, point towards the same conclusion or, at least, do not contradict it. The ratio P/B is taken as the ratio expressed by *primary production/total biomass,* including all elements of the ecosystem, such as the consumers, etc. In ecosystems of higher maturity there is a more complete use of food, there is a greater proportion of animals, and energy cascades through a more considerable number of steps. This is true in aquatic ecosystems, but in terrestrial ecosystems a somewhat paradoxical situation arises owing to a certain exaggerated dominance of vegetation. On the other hand, the great number of possible kinds of relations in a mature ecosystem allows a higher efficiency in every relation. If these relations are considered as communication channels, less noise comes into them.

There is another way to look at the relations between energy flow per unit biomass and structure, based on an experiment that can be introduced in every ecology course. We start with an old aquarium harboring a mixed population. We can measure diversity in the distribution of individuals into species, and in the distribution of pigments; also we measure total biomass and primary production. The results are criteria for attributing to the system, a certain quantitative expression of rather high maturity. Then we lead the ecosystem to a state of lower maturity: the more effective way of doing this is to stir the contents of the aquarium and pour into it some nutritive solution. We get a bloom of plankton and the state of lower maturity is reflected both in a decreased diversity at all levels, and in an increased ratio—*primary production/biomass*. Of course, the relation—*biomass of plants/biomass of animals*—changes to the benefit of plants. This simple experiment has a counterpart in terrestrial ecology: plowing a field and putting manure into it, and this is one of the oldest experiments in ecology.

If we want to follow the experiment, we leave the aquarium containing our "rejuvenated" population alone. As time goes on the ratio expressed by *primary production/total biomass* drops, both by increase of biomass and by reduction of primary production. Diversity increases at every level. Maturity increases. This is succession.

Perhaps the most instructive period in the experiment is when maturity decreases rapidly. Why does diversity decrease, as energy flow per unit biomass becomes higher and higher? At this moment, the system is suddenly able to produce a great power output, but only if there is not too much concern for efficiency (Odum and Pinkerston, 1955). Certain pigments capable of rapid synthesis and occupying a key position in photosynthesis (for example, chlorophyll A) increase much more than others. Pigment diversity drops. Similarly, species with the highest maximal rate of potential increase become advantageously dominant, and diversity drops. We are always confronted with a fall in species diversity in similar situations involving utilization of a sudden burst of potential productivity, for example, in a plankton bloom, in a polluted river, or in a cultivated field.

It seems safe to assume that maturity has a double measure: In its structural aspect, it can be measured in terms of diversity or of complexity over a certain number of levels. In the aspects relating to matter and energy, it can be measured as primary production per unit of total biomass. The connections between complementary aspects and measures require theoretical consideration.

The ratio—*primary production/total biomass* has not been selected for theoretical considerations, but simply because it is easily at hand. But the true meaning of biomass, if we think over this expression, has to be construed as something that is the keeper of organization, something that is proportional to the influence that an actual ecosystem can exert on future events. If this influence over the future is simply equated with dry weight or any other usual expression of biomass, one foresees inaccuracies. In fact, the same amount of dry weight may have a different influence on future developments according to how it is organized. Moreover, elements that actually are not counted as parts of biomass, such as dead wood, burrows, and the like, are elements of organization, since they exert a certain influence on the future development of the ecosystem. From a general theoretical standpoint, it would be advisable to replace the ratio *primary production/total biomass* by a more sophisticated ratio; turning to the converse (B/P), it could be defined as the amount of information that can be maintained with a definite spending of potential energy. Here information is taken in the sense of something at which life has arrived through a series of decisions, and that influences, in one or another sense, future events. The ratio P/B may be considered also as metabolism per unit biomass. The rate of change of average community metabolism is always negative along succession.

The ideas developed so far can be summarized as follows. An ecosystem that has a complex structure, rich in information, needs a lower amount of energy for maintaining such structure. If we consider the interrelations between the elements of an ecosystem as communication channels, we can state that such channels function on the average more effectively, with a lower noise level, if they are multiple and diverse, linking elements not subjected to great changes. Then, loss of energy is lower, and the energy necessary for preventing decay of the whole ecosystem amounts relatively to less. This seems to be one of the basic principles of ecology, probably recognized tacitly by most writers, although rarely put in an explicit way.

Succession and Fluctuations

Any ecosystem not subjected to strong disturbances coming from outside, changes in a progressive and directional way. We say that the ecosystem becomes more mature. The two most noticeable changes accompanying this process are the increase of complexity of structure and the decrease of the energy flow per unit biomass. This theoretical background leads us to accept a sort of natural selection in the possible rearrangements of the ecosystem: Links between the elements of an ecosystem can be substituted by other links that work with a higher efficiency, requiring a change in the elements and often an increase in the number of elements and connections. The new situation now has an excess of potential energy. This can be used in developing the ecosystem further, for instance, by adding biomass after driving more matter into the system. A more complex state, with a reduced waste of energy, allows maintenance of the same biomass with a lower supply of energy—or a higher biomass with the same supply of energy—and replaces automatically any previous state.

The only limit set to this progressive change is interference from the physical environment. Succession can build history only when the environment is stable. In the case of a changing environment, the selected ecosystem will be composed of species with a high reproductive rate and lower special requirements. Such an ecosystem is less diverse and less complex; the energy flow per unit biomass remains relatively high. There is another situation where an ecosystem cannot increase maturity: when there is a constant loss of individuals by diffusion, sedimentation or exploitation by the action of external agents. In such situations, something is exported which otherwise could be used in increasing organization.

The study of succession does not include all relations of ecosystems with time. In a more refined consideration of concepts, diversity may be represented as the width of a communication channel, apt to carry along time a certain amount of organization or of information at the selected level. This sets limitations, of course. An ecosystem with a low biotic diversity cannot carry a high degree of true organization. But a highly diversified community has the capacity for carrying a high amount of organization or information. This does not signify that the potential amount is always actually carried. The difference can be illustrated by comparing a planktonic community with a bottom community over rocky substratum. Both communities may have similar diversities, but the organization based on such diversity can be carried more effectively along time in the benthic community. Here, spatial distribution of individuals belonging to different species (pattern) is preserved, and with it most of the relations existing between such individuals. If we determine the pattern of such a community at a time a, and then at a subsequent time b, and so on, we discover that transitions from one state to the next follow a notable regularity; the pattern's deterministic component is more important than its random component. In other words, diversity effectively measures information that is carried along with time. In the case of the plankton community, the matrix describing the transition probabilities between successive states can be recognized as possessing a deterministic part and a random part; but here the second part is more important than in the benthos: think only of the turbulence of water, carrying organisms and influencing contacts between organisms of different species. In this situation, the channel width is not effectively used because of turbulence—a random element of the environment.

Perhaps the following analogy may clarify the difference under discussion: Let us imagine the structure of a community in terms of a message, written in a language with a number of symbols equal to the number of species, and where individual symbols stand for individuals. A benthic community would be more like a real text written with this language; a planktonic community would be rather comparable with an imaginary text in which letters were not fixed, but are subjected to a certain sort of thermic agitation that makes them change places over and over again, so that the amount of information actually carried would be reduced. The conclusion is that in any estimate of maturity, not only diversity, but also predictability of change with time has to be considered. Ordinarily both characters are correlated. Less mature ecosystems not only have a lower diversity, but in them transition between successive states includes a higher amount of uncertainty. And more diverse ecosystems have, in general, more predictable future states. In other words, in more mature ecosystems the future situation is more dependent on the present than it is on inputs coming from outside. Homeostatis is higher. On the other hand, future states in less mature ecosystems are heavily influenced by external inputs, by changes in the physical environment.

Let us consider any structure formed by interconnected elements, like a nervous net, an automaton, or an ecosystem, and subjected to inputs (changes in the physical environment, as stimuli) and giving off outputs (reaction on the environment, population waves, migrations, rhythms of activity and so on). Internal organization of such a system can turn random inputs or disturbances into much more regular outputs or rhythms. Cole (1951) and Palmgren (1949), among other ecologists, have discussed the possibility that "regular" cycles in populations may originate by the interaction of random inputs, for example, relative strength of year classes, as related to random changes in climatic factors or to alteration in the structure of the existing unispecific population and of the whole ecosystem in which the population is integrated. The properties associated with the structure of the ecosystem define the operations to do with the random inputs, and give more or less regular output patterns. Analogously, a crystalline body converts a random X-ray input into a regular diffraction pattern. It may be pertinent for the ecologists to remember here the importance of general theories on automata and nerve nets, and the theory of storage (Moran, 1959), and the recent developments on random theory (Wiener, 1958; see also Barlow, 1961).

In general, the expected differences in the character of fluctuations in less mature and more mature communities would be as follows. In less mature communities, environmental fluctuations are strong and able to stop the trend to increase maturity at a certain level. Maturity does not increase because abiotic fluctuations are too strong, and homeostatis is difficult to attain in a poorly organized, often a pioneer community. In a more stable environment, succession proceeds and maturity increases; now we have to expect rhythms that are more regular, more independent of environment and often endogenous. Anticipatory power has survival value and is the expression of a complex system, able to produce very efficient homeostatic mechanisms. Up to a certain level, these homeostatic mechanisms can protect the system from disruption due to external agents. Maturity is self-preserving.

Fluctuations of unispecific populations can be considered on the same background. Large fluctuations in populations are to be expected in less mature ecosystems: a rapid increase of numbers of a plant or an animal is possible only in a system that works with low efficiency, the subsequent drop in the number of individuals means either a great mortality and consumption by other organisms, or dispersal or migration out of the ecosystem, in any case a strong flow or export of potential energy. In this sense strong fluctuations in plankton populations represent a heavy export towards other communities, for instance, towards the benthos. Planktonic communities retain always a less mature character than benthic communities, and it is to be expected, in good agreement with observation, that fluctuations in planktonic populations are of shorter period and wider ranges.

Fluctuations of an ecosystem often may be considered as fluctuations in the degree of maturity around an average maturity. At certain periods of the year the ecosystem is less mature than at other times. Such changes could be considered as true successions, starting again and again. In the plankton, for instance, the period of vertical mixing of water corresponds to a less mature aspect of the whole ecosystem and can be taken as the starting point of a succession of phytoplankton. In other elements of pelagic life, changes are simple fluctuations, rather than true successions.

The necessary energy to disrupt an ecosystem probably maintains certain relations with the attained maturity. Anything that keeps an ecosystem oscillating, retains it in a state of low maturity. Often it is the environment, as in the case of successions of phytoplankton. At other times it is an active exploitation from outside that forces a repeated reconstruction and an output of work reconcilable only with less mature states. Because it is of practical value, I want to state again that fluctuations in less mature systems are more related to environmental changes, to abiotic factors; but fluctuations in more mature ecosystems are more dependent on internal conditions of equilibrium, that is, on biotic factors.

Fluctuations in the populations are, of course, accompanied by fluctuations in the biotically controlled properties of environment. For instance, strong yearly fluctuations in the phosphate content of water are linked to less mature and strongly fluctuating plankton populations. They are related also to essentially exploitable fish populations, as Cushing remarked, that is, to fish populations capable of great changes in numbers and, thus, capable of supporting human extraction. In the more mature ecosystems, with damped fluctuations, the supply of nutrients in the environment is kept constantly at a low level, as in tropical forests.

Extensive Systems with Local Differences in the Value of Maturity

We can measure a global property of ecosystems—named maturity for convenience—in different ways: in terms of structure and in terms of energy flow per unit biomass. Applying these criteria in the analysis of the parts of any extensive system, it is possible to estimate maturity in the different points, and map the values, say, of species diversity, of pigment diversity, of primary production per unit of total biomass. As is to be expected, the different maps so prepared are congruent (Margalef, 1961b; Herrera, Margalef and Vives, in press) and, in general, it is possible to trace surfaces linking all the points that have a similar degree of maturity. Every one of such surfaces is a boundary between a subsystem of lower maturity and a subsystem of higher maturity. We can repeat such maps at different times, in order to study succession and changes in the general pattern of distribution of maturity.

As is well known, succession and spatial heterogeneity are strongly linked (Margalef, 1958). Heterogeneity often originates because succession proceeds at different speeds according to the location, and it is a common experience of ecologists that enclaves or spots with a lower maturity—immersed in more mature systems—are related to some local disturbance (strong mixing by underwater springs in the sea, presence of bare rock in terrestrial vegetation, etc.). These exclude, at least for the moment, a further progress in the succession. Every reader will remember sketches in treatises on ecology depicting the vegetation girdles around a senescent lake and showing differences in maturity, that is, in the stage reached in succession if we assume a general trend towards increasing maturity. Maps depicting the distribution of biotic diversity, and of the ratio D_{430}/D_{665} (optical densities at the stated wavelengths of acetone extracts) in plankton populations, are of the same kind. This ratio is a simplified expression of the diversity of pigments. The distribution of the values of the ratio *primary production/respiration,* used by H. T. Odum, may have a similar meaning.

Let us explore what happens along a surface of equal maturity. Remember that at one side we have a subsystem of lower maturity, with a high production per unit biomass, with less strong links between species, subject to wider fluctuations and to an easy dispersal of the elements. At the other side we find a subsystem with a greater biomass for the same energy flow, with well organized relations over elements more strongly localized.

If maturity increases in the less mature system, especially at the proximity of the boundary (which is to be expected from succession) the surface of equal maturity moves towards the less mature subsystem. This is probably accompanied by a flow of energy going the converse way. This means that matter (biomass and non-living matter) goes in both directions, since both coupled subsystems are actually open, but the content of potential energy of such matter is, on the average, higher in the matter going the way of increasing maturity than in the matter going the way of decreasing maturity. The subsystem with a lower maturity maintains a higher ratio between primary production and total present biomass, because it actually loses biomass, in going across the border to the more mature coupled subsystems.

Let us remember that succession is simply the exchange of an excess available energy in the present, for a future increase of biomass. An ecosystem in its present state is less mature and has an excess production that goes to the future and helps reorganize the ecosystem in a more mature form. If there is no available excess production or it is drained out of the system, succession proceeds no further. We will find no difficulty in applying the same type of relation, not to successive states of the same system, but to adjoining systems. What the one does in excess (production) is put in use by the other. There is a transfer, or an exchange, between energy and what can be called an "organizing influence."

It seems important to stress that the different degrees of maturity of two coupled subsystems can be, and have to be, estimated through the study of structure and turnover of every subsystem, with total independence of the eventual existence and direction of any exchange between both subsystems. In other words, it is not necessary to find out that there is a certain exchange between subsystems, in order to label automatically as the less mature the subsystem that exports, and as the more mature the importing subsystem.

The discussion of some concrete examples will permit the development of these ideas, and the proper consideration of changing properties along the boundary. Intensity of exchange between subsystems of different maturity may be quite different.

Plankton, in general, is a less mature system than the benthos. All the required qualifications are there: lower species diversity, lower pigment diversity (lower ratio D_{340}/D_{665}), more uncertainty in defining the relations between successive states and higher primary production per unit of total biomass. In the coupling of plankton and benthos, a net transfer of energy exists from plankton to benthos; it can be said that the plankton, in part, feeds the benthos. Such exchange is due to the combination of several effects. There is a major passive factor: sedimentation of plankton. There are other, biotic, factors, such as the existence of benthonic filter-feeders that actively attract the plankton, pumping production from plankton to benthos. There are also benthonic animals that produce planktonic larvae. Later these larvae become adults and return to the benthonic environment. In general, potential energy going towards the benthos in the form of the settling larvae is higher than potential energy going the opposite way in the form of reproductive cells or hatched larvae.

It is worthwhile to discuss further the relative and the combined importance of these effects. An active exploitation by the more mature system may prevent the progressive development of a coupled subsystem, keeping it in a state of low maturity. As an example, we may cite the heavy passive loss resulting from the sedimentation of plankton. The fact is that the presence of bottom filter-feeding animals in an aquarium drives the free-floating population into a state of lower maturity. Also, animals harboring symbiotic algae probably maintain them in a state of lower maturity, through active absorption of organic compounds. Looking for an analogy in human affairs we may compare such a coupling to colonialism: a master country, taking out the product of an underdeveloped country, impedes its economic progress; that is, its maturity.

The steepness of the gradient between a more mature and a less mature subsystem depends not only on active exploitation, but also on other characteristics. Light is a basic factor in plankton production and is more intense above. Furthermore, sedimentation leads a part of the produced biomass down. It is thus natural to expect that surface planktonic populations will be, in general, less mature than populations living at greater depths. The contrast may be enhanced at the level of pycnoclines; the steepness of gradients is particularly sharp where there is a reduced rate of diffusion or exchange. In such a case, the intensity of exchange between coupled subsystems is clearly related to environmental variables.

The ideas developed in the present section are easily testable by coupling two culture vessels containing populations of different maturity. One culture can be maintained in a situation of lower maturity by being continuously stirred. In this one we will have a bloom of small cells. In the other container, we observe, in most replications of the experience, a notable development of swimming organisms, a heavy growth over the walls and a more important proportion of animal life. This is a simple school experiment, but it illustrates how net energy-flow goes from the less towards the more mature, that is, towards the unstirred subsystem. This experiment can be performed by placing the containers side by side, at the same level, with a connecting tube; also in tall, stratified vessels, where it proves that sedimentation in plankton is one of the multiple mechanisms of transfer.

If we want to consider a comparable example in terrestrial ecology, perhaps we could take the boundary between a forest and a place with open and low vegetation. The boundary should have a tendency to be displaced towards the open land; it is expected that there will be more animals in the forest getting food from grassland, than animals in the grassland getting food in the forest.

Contraction and Expansion of the Ecosystem

In vagrant communities, like plankton, subsidiary problems appear. Here we must choose, as reference, between a system of coordinates fixed in space or a set of coordinates moving with the populations or with the water masses. When transport is accompanied by deformation, if trajectories are not parallel and have different speeds, problems become increasingly complex. There is a possibility that some of these problems are not without analogies in physics.

Expansion of ecosystems in space is frequently associated with individual trajectories at random, and means a reduction in maturity. In contracting communities, movements are often organized and lead to an increase of maturity, or at least of diversity per unit space.

These processes are perhaps not absolutely general, but may be followed easily in laboratory cultures placed in appropriate experimental conditions. Take, for instance, cultures in a liquid medium placed in containers separated by a glass filter-barrier, with the possibility of pumping medium across the porous wall. We can obtain, at will, the usual drop of diversity and increase in the primary production per unit biomass in the subculture towards which we pump the fluid. Another good example, this one in nature, is afforded by the behavior and distribution of plankton in a system formed by alternating convergences and divergences, or convection cells. The divergences harbor less mature and expanding populations, with many diatoms, low diversity, etc., while in the convergences are found communities of a more mature character; they are contracting because flagellates keep moving or swimming upwards to become concentrated above. The whole structure behaves as the coupling of less mature (divergence) with more mature (convergence) subsystems, with the expected net transfer of production from the divergences to the convergences.

Sedimentation of passive plankton is another illustration of the same general model, where transport is directed downwards. In the upper layers, plankton becomes diluted or dispersed and in the lower levels it is concentrated. The continuous drain of a part of the surface plankton needs to be countered by an excess production and does not allow a great increase in organization. For this reason, plankton remains less mature in the upper levels and other effects (exploitation, active movements) may make this vertical difference more conspicuous, or change it otherwise.

Other similar models, where the horizontal dimensions are more important, can be constructed to represent populations in estuaries (both normal or positive, and hypersaline or negative) and also to represent running waters in general, in which the increase in maturity is always downstream (Margalef, 1960).

One need is for the mathematical tools necessary to compute the movements, or the relative displacements, of elements in an ecosystem in terms of any suitable measure of structure. If this is achieved, the way is open for adding the effects of transport and succession, expressing the results as changes in maturity. Such a possibility would be useful in dealing with planktonic communities.

The Partition of Unispecific Populations Moving Freely Across Ecosystems with Local Differences in Maturity

Any unispecific population that expands over a wide range has local differences in the demographic structure, even when internal flow of individuals is important. Any portion of the population with a higher proportion of young individuals (suggesting a lower average life span, and a higher mortality) means a higher energy-flow per unit of biomass. By an obvious analogy, the population can be said to have a less mature demographic structure. In the places where such populations exist, fluctuations are shorter and the range in change of biomass is wider.

Broadly speaking, there is a spatial correspondence between the localization of the less mature portion of a unispecific population and the less mature parts of the whole system. Good examples are furnished by benthic animals that send larvae and young to the less mature and superficial waters, and by migrating birds breeding in the less mature ecosystems of temperate latitudes. Animals tend to spend their adult lives in the more mature systems, but to reproduce in the less mature ones and send larvae or reproductive elements into them.

Monte Lloyd, in a personal communication discussing this point, expressed its meaning very clearly: "I tend to see this as a reflection of a previous evolutionary history: it has always been an advantage to reproduce on less mature ecosystems, since these are maintaining themselves less efficiently, and energy needed for growth is more readily available. Competition for it is less severe. Those individuals that developed behavior patterns which led them to reproduce in less mature systems have left behind more offspring. They have been selected for. The adults, which live in more mature ecosystems, send their young outside to less mature systems to gather energy (growth) and bring it back. Here, certainly is a 'directive influence' emanating from the more mature ecosystems."

In the Mediterranean coasts of east Spain a very good example has been worked out. From the mouth of the Ebro River towards the south, there is a gradient of increasing maturity in the planktonic ecosystem. It is well reflected in diversity indices, pigment composition and other properties. There is an important breeding area of sardine in the less mature part of the system, and the demographical structure of the fish populations changes gradually as maturity of the ecosystem in which they are incorporated increases (data of M. Gomez Larraneta and co-workers). Human exploitation, if restricted geographically, leads to a local decrease of maturity, both of the general ecosystem and in the demographical structure of the selectively exploited species.

Many other examples could be found in insects that breed in aquatic environments but have adult forms that are integrated into terrestrial ecosystems, or in fish that breed in inundation waters.

The fish that migrate between sea water and fresh water offer a special subject for meditation. Eels breed in the sea and spend their adult life in fresh water; in salmon the converse is true. How can this be made consistent with our theory that requires animals to breed always in the less mature part of the available systems? Eels develop in the marine pelagic environment, one of the least mature of marine ecosystems. Adult eels belong to the bottom of lowland fresh water, a relatively mature system. Salmon breed in the upper stretches of streams, one of the less mature freshwater ecosystems. Adult salmon, on the contrary, belong to a more mature system in the marine littoral.

A similar parallelism or adjustment between demographic or age structure and general maturity of the ecosystem is observed not only across space, but also along time. Planktonic animals with a regular reproductive cycle breed when the whole mixed population is in a less mature state, after a pulse of primary production, and when an important surplus of food is available. In this moment the demographic structure of the species under consideration is in a state of very low "maturity."

Temperature and Maturity

A higher temperature induces a higher flow of energy (increased respiration) per unit biomass; organisms are also smaller and have a shorter life span. These changes, observed in the populations of a species at different temperatures, leads us to predict a certain relation between high temperature and low maturity. This parallelism seems to be reinforced by other coincidences.

An ecosystem has chances of survival with different degrees of organization, that is, with higher or with lower maturity. But the general trend is towards an increase of maturity. The reasons for this may have to do with certain principles of thermodynamics. Something similar happens in temperature relationships. There are organisms well adapted to high temperature and to low temperature, but the more common trend in evolution seems to be towards the production of organisms better fit for a lower temperature—bigger size, longer life, and so on (Margalef, 1955). Here is a suggestion, also, of the operation of very general physical principles.

But the ecological picture is rather diverse. At present and in our planet, the most mature ecosystems, the coral reef in the sea, the tropical forest on land, are restricted to warmer environments. In my opinion this is not related to temperature, but to stability of environment. A stable environment, warm or cold, allows the increase of maturity up to a level much higher than a fluctuating environment, cold or warm. Coral reefs are a good example of very mature ecosystems limited to areas of great stability, rather than to areas of a definite temperature as is generally believed. They are lacking in many tropical waters where yearly fluctuations in phosphate content, for instance, are important. Indeed, in such areas with fluctuating conditions (northeast of Venezuela, for instance), we have important pulses of phytoplankton, accompanied by a heavy development of clupeids, all indicators of much less mature ecosystems.

Maturity and Evolution

A related problem that I have discussed elsewhere (Margalef, 1958, 1959) is the relation between pattern (rhythm and mode) of evolution and maturity of the ecosystem in which the species evolves.

In less mature ecosystems or in less mature trophic levels of any ecosystem, we expect species to be short-lived, easily dispersed, able to colonize with rapidity virgin areas, able to leave numerous offspring and, of course, characterized by high ratio *energy flow/biomass*. Phenotypes may be plastic, cyclomorphosis or temporary variation is common, and genetic compatibility between separate and distant populations is rarely lost. They are euryoic, competition is for dominance and evolution may be rapid. They are opportunistic species, subjected to a dynamic type of selection, often for prolificness.

In more mature ecosystems or in more mature areas of their structure, the selected species are of rather long life, with limited but well protected offspring, and with more restricted possibilities of dispersion accompanied by isolation in small breeding units. The species are very well integrated in the respective ecosystems from the standpoint of biochemistry, nutritional needs, behavior, and so on. They have well developed territorial instincts, endogenous rhythms, etc. Development is often canalized and morphological stability is high, but genetic differences between the diverse breeding units are common. Competition between closely related forms may become limited. Success is linked to efficiency and manifested in a stabilizing type of selection.

No wonder evolution in less mature ecosystems, implying a higher flow of energy per unit biomass, is more expensive and by this very fact can be more creative or, at least, go faster.

Another point in the relation between maturity and evolution is worth to recall. By the fact of succession, conditions of equilibrium in every ecosystem are slowly shifting towards characteristics of increased maturity, and the evolution of species is "sucked" towards a better adjustment to conditions of ever-increasing maturity. In the slow process of evolution, so well manifested in the fossil record of phylogenetic series, we can expect many series demonstrating an adjustment to conditions of increasing maturity of ecosystems.

Utility of a Synthetic Approach

Most of what has been discussed can be summarized in two very simple principles:

1. The relative amount of energy necessary for maintaining an ecosystem is related to the degree of structure or organization of this ecosystem. Less energy is necessary for a more complex ecosystem, and the natural trend in succession is towards a decreasing flow of energy per unit of biomass and towards increasing organization. Briefly stated the trend is towards increasing maturity.

2. When two systems of different maturity meet along a boundary that allows an exchange, energy (production) flows towards the more mature subsystem, and the boundary or surface of equal maturity shows a trend to move in an opposite direction to such energy flow.

These general principles clarify many ecological interactions and processes and allow quantitative formulation. They can be used or tested in predicting changes induced by human action. Exploitation is like inflicting a wound upon a heterogeneous organic structure: some tissues or subsystems (more mature) do not regenerate; other (less mature) do and these supply the basis for a further eventual increase of maturity. Maintained exploitation keeps the maturity of the exploited system constantly low. Exploited natural communities come to have a higher primary production per unit biomass, a lower species diversity and, presumably, a lower ratio D_{430}/D_{665}. More energy goes into fluctuations such as those represented by exploited populations or by populations that are integrated into exploited ecosystems. For example, pests have fluctuations with a wider range and shorter periodicity than similar populations that are integrated into more mature, eventually unexploited, ecosystems. Extremely mature ecosystems, such as tropical forests, are unable to go back and are totally disrupted by human exploitation. The examples furnished by fisheries are illustrative: very productive fisheries belong to ecosystems of low maturity, with a fluctuating supply of inorganic nutrients and with notable pulses in plankton production. The less the maturity, the more important the "abiotic" control of populations. Human activity decreases maturity and can enhance fluctuations. The notable exclusion between coral reefs and a heavy production of clupeids in tropical waters has been cited and it is possible to hypothesize that pollution and other alterations along tropical coasts may destroy very mature ecosystems, and then fisheries can become more important than at present. Radiation increase can be expected to act destructively to accumulated information (that is, to biomass) but with no effect on potential energy flow; radiation, then, must reduce the maturity of ecosystems, in part by selective destruction of the more mature elements of the ecosystem. Thus, a great increase in radiation may mean a new push given to an already lagging evolution.

Most of the same principles can be applied to human organizations. Taking as criteria the diversification of skills and jobs (diversity), or the relative flow of potential energy, it is possible to map the "maturity" of states and continents in the ecological sense of organization. Energy flow goes from less mature (rural) areas to more mature (urban) areas. The urban centers represent localized elements that have accumulated high amounts of information, fed on the production of neighboring subsystems, and have exerted a directive action. Very old systems can survive with a small flow of energy, and like their ecological counterparts can break down as a consequence of a minor environmental change. It is possible to deal objectively and quantitatively with big and complex structures, if one never forgets the complementary aspects of energy as related to matter, and structure.

Summary

An attempt is made to provide some unifying principles in ecology. The structure of ecosystems is considered in relation to various components, with emphasis on the characteristics of maturity as measured by diversity data and other determinable features, including primary production (P) and biomass (B). Ecosystems with complex structure and containing a high amount of information can be maintained with a relatively lower expenditure of energy. Oscillations, introduced for example by environmental changes or outside exploration, tend to retain an ecosystem in a state of lower maturity. Where succession is occurring, involving exchange of an excess of available energy for a future increase in biomass, the relations encountered may be applied not only to successive states in the same system, but to adjoining or coupled subsystems. Steepness of the gradient between subsystems is shown to depend on several factors subject to quantitative determination and the relation between these subsystems can be imitated by simple experiment. When ecosystems contract or expand there are corresponding increases or decreases of maturity.

Factors affecting the maturity of ecosystems and of special interest are the movement of species. These suggest a spatial correspondence between the juvenile or immature portion of an unspecific population and the less mature parts of ecosystems available for habitation.

Maturity is related to evolution in a way that permits generalization concerning the type of organisms to be found in ecosystems of more or less maturity and stability. As evolution proceeds, there is a trend toward adjustment to maturity.

The concepts that emerge may be applied to human social systems. Two principles become evident: The energy required to maintain an ecosystem is inversely related to complexity, with the natural trend toward decreasing flow of energy per unit biomass; that is, increased maturity. Secondly, in adjacent systems there is a flow of energy toward the more mature system and an opposite movement in the boundary or surface of equal maturity.

Literature Cited

Barlow, J. S., 1960, Contributed discussion to biological clocks. Cold Spring Harbor Symp. Quant. Biol. 25: 54–55.

Cole, L. C., 1951, Population cycles and random oscillations. J. Wildlife Management 15: 233–252.

Cushing, D. H., 1959, On the nature of production in the sea. Fisheries Invest., Ministry Agr. Fisheries (London) Ser. 2, 22(6): 1–40.

Cushing, D. H., G. F. Humphrey, K. Banse and T. Laevastu, 1958, Report of the committee on terms and equivalents. Rappt. Process. Verbaux Reunions Consul. Perm. Intern. Exploration Mer. 144: 15–16.

Herrera, J., R. Margalef and F. Vives, 1963, Hidrografiia y plancton del area costera entre la desembocadura del Ebro y Castellon (Mediterraneo occidental) de junio de 1960 a junio de 1961. Invest. Pesquera (in press).

MacArthur, R. H., and J. W. MacArthur, 1961, On bird species diversity. Ecology 42: 594–596.

Margalef, R., 1955, Temperatura, dimenssiones y evolucion. Publ. Inst. Biol. Apl. (Barcelona) 19: 13–94.

————, 1957, La teoria de la informacion en ecologia. Mem. real Acad. Cienc. Art. Barcelona 32(13): 373–449.

————, 1958a, Mode of evolution of species in relation to their places in ecological succession. XV Intern. Congress Zool. X(17). 3 pp.

————, 1958b, Temporal succession and spatial heterogeneity in phytoplankton. pp. 323–349. In Perspectives in marine biology. Univ. Calif. Press.

————, 1959, Ecologia, biogeografia y evolucion. Rev. Univ. Madrid 8: 221–273.

————, 1960, Ideas for a synthetic approach to the ecology of running waters. Intern. Rev. ges. Hydrobiol. 45: 133–153.

————, 1961a, Communication of structure in planktonic populations. Limnol. Oceanogr. 6: 124–128.

————, 1961b, Correlations entre certains caracteres synthetiques des populations de phytoplancton. Hydrobiologia 18: 155–164.

————, 1962, Modelos fisicos simplificados de poblaciones de organismos. Mem. real Acad. Cienc. Art. Barcelona 34(5): 83–146.

Moran, P. A. P., 1959, The theory of storage. Methuen & Co., London, 111 pp.

Odum, H. T., and Ch. M. Hoskin, 1958, Comparative studies on the metabolism of marine waters. Publ. Inst. Marine Sci (Port Aransas, Texas) 5: 16–46.

Odum, H. T., and R. Pinkerton, 1955, Time's speed regulator: The optimum efficiency for maximum power output in physical and biological systems. Am. Scientist 43: 331–343.

Palmgren, P., 1949, Some remarks on the short-term fluctuations in the numbers of northern birds and mammals. Oikos 1: 114–141.

Strickland, J. D. H., 1960, Measuring the production of marine phytoplankton. Bull. Fisheries Res. Board Can. 122: 1–172.

Wiener, N., 1958, Nonlinear problems in random theory. John Wiley & Sons, New York. 131 pp.